THE REPRODUCTION OF COLOUR

The Reproduction of Colour

by

R. W. G. HUNT

Ph.D. · D.I.C. · A.R.C.S. · F.R.P.S. · F.R.S.A.

Research Laboratories, Kodak Ltd., Harrow

With a Foreword by

PROFESSOR W. D. WRIGHT · D.Sc. · A.R.C.S. · D.I.C.

Head of the Applied Optics Section Imperial College
of Science & Technology, South Kensington, London

JOHN WILEY & SONS, INC.

First Published 1957
Reprinted (revised) 1961
Second Edition 1967
© Copyright 1967 by Fountain Press
46–47 Chancery Lane, London W.C.2

Printed in Great Britain by
Headley Brothers Ltd., 109 Kingsway, London, W.C.2
and Ashford, Kent

Foreword

THE development of colour photography, colour television, and colour printing demands a very wide and deep understanding of the facts of colour mixture and colour perception. These methods of colour reproduction all have many interesting technical problems to solve, while physiologically, the processes in the eye and the brain exercise their own subtle influences on the visual appearance of a colour reproduction. Moreover, the final assessment of a colour picture calls for aesthetic as well as scientific appraisal.

Evidently, then, a book on the reproduction of colour requires a broad outlook on the part of the author, and Dr. Hunt, with his understanding of the basic theory, his experience of commercial production, and his own contributions to fundamental research, is very well qualified to give a balanced and comprehensive account of the subject. This he has undoubtedly succeeded in doing, and in view of his original work on colour adaptation and the visual response, his comments on the subjective aspects of colour reproduction will command particular respect. However much we may regret that the requirements of a colour reproduction cannot be expressed in precise colorimetric terms, we have to recognize that engineering concepts alone are not enough.

The publication of this book will give much pleasure to Dr. Hunt's colleagues and friends, and especially to those who have had the privilege of listening to him present a paper or deliver a lecture, for the orderly presentation of his material and the clarity of his thought on such occasions deserve, and will now reach, a much wider audience. For myself, I regard it as an honour to have been invited to write this Foreword and by undertaking such an agreeable task to continue my association with Dr. Hunt, which dates from the time when he was a student at the Imperial College, and has included our co-operation in a series of courses at the college on the Fundamentals of Colour Reproduction.

Applied Optics Section,   W. D. WRIGHT
Imperial College of Science and Technology,
London

5

Contents

7

Chapter 8

Chapter 9

PART TWO

COLOUR PHOTOGRAPHY

Chapter 10

9

Chapter 13

Chapter 14

Chapter 15

PART THREE

COLOUR TELEVISION

Chapter 16

THE TRANSMISSION OF COLOUR TELEVISION SIGNALS

Chapter 17

CAMERAS FOR COLOUR TELEVISION

APPENDICES

COLOUR PLATES

Preface

WHEN, during the first half of the nineteenth century, a small band of indefatigable enthusiasts strove to 'fix the images of Nature', their purpose was to fix the colours as well as the tones in their pictures, and it would no doubt have seemed to them like an idle tale if some prophet had revealed that photography was to know a hundred years of black-and-white before colour began to intrude in any measure. Yet such is the case, and this in spite of a number of early milestones which held out great promise. As early as 1810, Seebeck and others knew that if a spectrum was allowed to fall on moist silver-chloride paper many of its colours were recorded, although not with any degree of permanence. In 1853 Prof. Robert Hunt published the third edition of his *Photography*, which contained a whole chapter 'on the possibility of producing photographs in their natural colours'; and he described seeing a number of 'Heliochromes' which were, he wrote, 'perfectly coloured; . . . but the colours soon faded, and it does not appear as yet that any successful mode of fixing the colours has been discovered'. By 1890, however, Prof. Gabrielle Lippmann, of Paris, had not only perfected the technique of 'fixing' these colours (by the same methods as are used in black-and-white photography) but had also much improved the process in other ways and Lippmann colour photographs of very high quality, even by present-day standards, were produced.

Seebeck and Lippmann, however, are not the forerunners of colour photography as we know it today. That honour belongs to the British physicist James Clerk Maxwell, for it was he who in his famous Friday Evening Discourse at the Royal Institution on May 17, 1861, demonstrated for the first time *trichromatic* colour photography. By reducing the number of variables to *three*, Maxwell laid foundations upon which practically all modern colour photography rests.

It was, therefore, a great honour for me when I was asked to give a course of four lectures on 'The Reproduction of Colour' in the very same lecture theatre at the Royal Institution that Maxwell had used nearly a century before when delivering his famous discourse. These four lectures were delivered at the Royal Institution towards the end of 1953, and in an expanded form were repeated, with the assistance of my colleague Mr. J. A. Carter, at the Kodak Research Laboratories in 1954, and issued in written form as duplicated notes. I am indebted to another colleague, Mr. L. S. Thompson, for suggesting to the Fountain Press that they might like to publish these notes in book form.

The object of the book can be stated quite simply. The fundamental principles of colour reproduction, whether by photography, television, or printing, are presented, in the hopes that all those engaged in producing, selling, buying or using colour pictures will be able to see the nature of the problems they encounter. It is hoped that those who want a general statement on colour reproduction will find it in the first part, and those a more detailed discussion of any one application in which they are particularly interested, in one or more of the later parts.

It is quite certain that this book could never have been written without the help that I have received from many colleagues and friends. I would like particularly to thank Prof. W. D. Wright of Imperial College, London, for having introduced me to the fascinating subject of Colour Physics in so able and enjoyable a way, and for having taught me so much of what I know. I am also most grateful to all my Kodak colleagues whose friendly advice and guidance has been so useful: Mr. E. R. Davies first suggested to me the advantages of the $\rho\gamma\beta$ approach outlined in Chapter 2 and both he and Mr. A. Marriage have given invaluable assistance over the years. Others of my colleagues to whom my thanks are due include the late Dr. H. Baines, Mr. J. A. Carter, Dr. A. Batley, Dr. D. A. Spencer, and Mr. T. D. Sanders, all of Kodak Limited, also Mr. R. M. Evans, Dr. D. L. MacAdam, and Dr. W. T. Hanson of the Eastman Kodak Company. In the more specialized chapters towards the end of the book I have had expert assistance from those much more knowledgeable than myself. Mr. M. Hepher, Mr. F. Pollak of Kodak Limited, and Mr. J. A. C. Yule of the Eastman Kodak Company, gave much help in Chapter 21, and Mr. P. S. Carnt contributed very substantially towards the chapters on colour television; others who have helped me with these chapters include Mr. G. F. C. Selby-Lowndes of Kodak Limited, Mr. L. C. Jesty, and Mr. N. R. Phelp.

The prominence of Kodak materials and processes in the photographic sections springs naturally from the fact that the information available to me concerning other manufacturers' products was much more limited; there is no desire to minimize in any way the very real contributions made by the rest of the photographic industry to the development and execution of colour photography as we know it today.

I am very grateful to the editor of the English edition of *Leica Fotografie* for permission to quote extensively from my three articles on Colour Reproduction which appeared in that Journal during 1953. I am also grateful to the Physical Society for permission to reproduce Fig. 7.9, to the Optical Society of America for permission to reproduce Figs. 7.13 and 22.1, and to the Bell Telephone Laboratories for permission to reproduce Fig. 16.4. Finally, my best thanks are due to my father who has made many helpful suggestions.

The reproduction of colour is a fascinating subject; it involves physiology, psychology, physics, chemistry, and technology; it presents complexities which seem well nigh unfathomable; it involves a wide variety of industrial enterprises; yet its climax is an event of the utmost commonplace, looking at pictures.

Preface to the Second Edition

THE ten years which have elapsed between the publication of the first and second editions of *The Reproduction of Colour* have seen tremendous advances in the subject. In photography, the colour transparency, by virtue of its excellent quality and modest price, is now used on a vast scale by the amateur snap-shotter, as well as by the more serious photographer; the colour reflection print is rapidly displacing its black-and-white forerunner as the medium for 'snaps'; professional motion pictures in colour are commonplace; and colour still-photography is widely used for portrait, medical, fashion and commercial uses. Colour television, after a slow start in the U.S.A., is now firmly established there, and services have already begun, or are about to be launched, in many other countries. Colour reproduction in printing has also increased steadily in volume, and progress of outstanding technical interest has been made in equipment.

This abundance of activity has made it desirable to expand the treatment given to the practical means employed in colour reproduction, and it has there-fore become logical to re-arrange the material into Part 1, dealing with Funda-mentals, Part 2 with Colour Photography, Part 3 with Colour Television, and Part 4 with Colour Printing. It is believed that the rearrangement will facilitate the use of the book for reference purposes, but the general reader who wants a broad understanding of the subject without too much detail is advised to omit Chapters 7, 8, 9, 13, 14, 15, and 19, and possibly also Chapter 6, at the first reading.

So much new material has been added, and so many revisions and rearrangements made, that the material has been completely reset. However, those who were kind enough to express their appreciation of the general approach used in the first edition will find that this is still retained in Part 1 of the present edition.

Once again I have been most fortunate in having the assistance of many friends and colleagues and I would like to thank especially Mr. J. A. Carter, Dr. R. A. Jeffreys, Mr. I. T. Pitt, Mr. F. Pollak, and Mr. E. W. H. Selwyn, of Kodak Limited, and Mr. M. C. Goddard, Mr. J. E. Pinney, Dr. P. W. Vittum, and Mr. D. M. Zwick, of the Eastman Kodak Company; and Mr. W. N. Sproson of the B.B.C. Research Centre, who very kindly gave assistance in the preparation of the Chapters on colour television. I am also once more very grateful to my father, Col. F. R. W. Hunt, for help in preparing the index, for proof reading, and for making many helpful suggestions.

In a field which is developing as rapidly as colour reproduction, it is salutary to remember that human colour vision apparently remains remarkably constant over the centuries. For William Benson (in his *Principles of the Science of Colour*, published by Chapman & Hall in 1868) translates Aristotle, in his *Meteorologica* **3**, **2**, in the following words: 'The colours of the rainbow are those which, almost alone, painters cannot make. For they compound some colours: but scarlet, green, and violet are not produced by mixture, and these are the colours of the rainbow.' Colour reproduction in the fourth century before Christ apparently suffered from the same basic limitation as it does today!

PART ONE

FUNDAMENTALS

CHAPTER 1

Physical Colour Reproduction

1. Introduction – *2.* The spectrum – *3.* The micro-dispersion method of colour photography – *4.* The Lippmann method – *5.* Use of identical dyes

1.1 Introduction

THREE hundred years ago, a physics student at Cambridge University would have been told that

> White is that which discharges a copious light equally clear in every direction. Black is that which does not emit light at all or which does it very sparingly. Red is that which emits a light more clear than usual, but interrupted by shady interstices. Blue is that which discharges a rarefied light, as in bodies which consist of white and black particles arranged alternatively. . . . The blue colour of the sea arises from the whiteness of the salt it contains mixed with the blackness of the pure water in which the salt is dissolved (Houston, 1923)[1].

No wonder that Pope wrote:

> 'Nature and Nature's Laws lay hid in night
> God said "Let Newton be!" and all was light.'

In 1666 Newton laid the foundation-stone of colour science, when he discovered that white sunlight was composed of a mixture of all the colours of the spectrum, and this discovery is also the natural starting point to a consideration of the fundamentals of colour reproduction.

1.2 The spectrum

Suppose we are taking a colour photograph of a street in daylight. All the light falling on the street comes from the sun, either directly when the sky is clear, or after diffusion by clouds if the sky is overcast, or after scattering in the atmosphere if there is blue sky. Since sunlight is a mixture of all the colours of the spectrum, our street scene is being illuminated by such a mixture, and some of the components of this mixture will be revealed by certain natural objects. Foliage contains a dye called chlorophyll which has the property of absorbing

---

[1] References will be found at the end of each Chapter, and, in the text, are identified by the author's name and the year of publication of the work referred to.

reddish and bluish light, but transmits greenish light; hence when foliage is illuminated by daylight it suppresses the reddish and bluish components thereof so that only the greenish components are seen by the eye, and we say that the foliage looks green. Similarly, if the street contains a greengrocer's shop and tomatoes are displayed, the tomatoes look red, because they absorb most of the violet, blue, green, and yellow components of the daylight, and reflect mainly the reddish components. It is thus clear that both the quality of the illuminant and the nature of the objects contribute towards the colour seen. If we return to the street after dark, and find that it is lit by sodium lamps, we shall find that the leaves and the tomatoes now look black because the illuminant contains only yellow light and this is absorbed by the foliage and tomatoes; there being no green light for the foliage to reflect, and no red light for the tomatoes to reflect, these colours cannot be seen.

However, the sodium lamp is very exceptional as far as its colour is concerned, and most sources of light are similar to the sun in that they are composed of a mixture of all the colours of the spectrum. This is true of gas-lamps, electric filament lamps, carbon-arcs, flash-bulbs, and most fluorescent lamps. This being so, the extent to which an object reflects the different colours of the spectrum provides a very useful measure of its colour properties.

So far we have only spoken loosely of reddish, or bluish, or yellow light without defining exactly to which part of the spectrum it belongs. Since all light has wave-like properties, and light in different parts of the spectrum corresponds to waves of different length, it is convenient to define each spectral colour by the wavelength of its light. The wavelengths are all extremely short and convenient units of measurement are: the micron (μ) which is equal to one thousandth of a millimetre, the milli-micron (mμ) which is one thousandth of a micron or, which is the same thing, the nano-metre (nm) which is one thousand-millionth (10^{-9}) of a metre, and the Ångström (Å) which is one ten-thousandth of a micron. In the rest of this book we shall mostly use the nano-metre. The main spectral colours occupy approximately the following wavelength bands: violet 450 nm and less, blue 450 to 480 nm, blue-green 480 to 510 nm; green 510 to 550 nm; yellow-green 550 to 570 nm; yellow 570 to 590 nm; orange 590 to 630 nm; red 630 nm and greater. These regions are shown in Fig. 1.1(a). There is a gradual transition from one colour to another throughout the spectrum and it is a matter of opinion as to exactly where one colour ends, and the next begins.

In Fig. 1.1(b) the amount of light reflected at each wavelength by a particular red surface is plotted as a percentage of the amount of light falling on the surface at each wavelength. The curve thus obtained is called the spectral reflectance curve of the sample, and provides a detailed description of the colour properties of the surface. In the case of this red colour it is clear that about 55 per cent of the red light is reflected, 40 per cent of the orange, 20 per cent of the yellow, 15 per cent of the yellow-green, 10 per cent of the green, 10 per cent of the blue-green, 5 per cent of the blue, and 5 per cent of the violet. And these reflectances result in the particular red colour of this surface, actually a red tomato.

Now suppose we take a colour photograph of a scene containing this particular tomato. We shall reproduce it as a patch of colour, either on a transparency or on paper, and it is obvious that if our patch of colour has the same spectral reflectance curve as the original tomato, then it can produce the same effect; for, physically, the two colours will be identical. And since they are

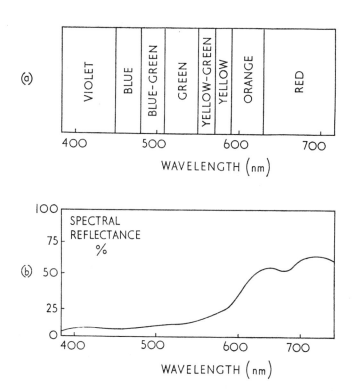

Fig. 1.1. (a) The distribution of colours in the spectrum. (b) The spectral reflectance curve of a red colour.

physically identical they will look alike in all circumstances. Thus if the original and the reproduction are viewed side by side first in sunlight, then in electric filament light, and then in sodium light, they will always look alike, although of course they will both change colour as the illuminant is changed. Moreover, they will look alike in colour to animals and to colour-blind persons.

1.3 The micro-dispersion method of colour photography

Such colour reproduction would indeed be exact but it can only be achieved in practice by methods which are far too inconvenient for general use. There are two methods which have been suggested and they are both photographic: the micro-dispersion method, and the Lippmann method. The former is shown diagrammatically in Fig. 1.2. The camera lens focuses the image on a coarse

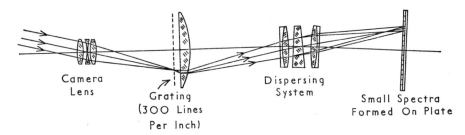

Fig. *1.2*. The micro-dispersion method of colour photography.

grating, consisting of parallel slits, alternatively opaque and transparent, about 1/300th of an inch apart. A large plano-convex field lens then collects the light from all the slits and passes it through a narrow-angle prism. Lenses on both sides of the prism focus images of the slits on a photographic plate, and the image of each slit is drawn out into a small spectrum by the prism. Thus the light from each part of the picture is spread out into a spectrum and hence the spectral reflectance curve of every part of the picture is recorded on the plate. The plate is then developed and fixed in the normal way and a positive print made on another plate (or alternatively the original plate can be reversed), and the positive thus obtained is replaced in the plane of the spectra in exact registration. By passing white light through the system in the reverse direction (from right to left in the diagram), and by using the camera lens as a projection lens, a colour reproduction is obtained in which each part of the picture has the same spectral reflectance curve as that of the original.

However, the difficulties of the method will at once be appreciated. The more important are: the equipment required is bulky and costly, the grating reduces the amount of light, and an extremely fine-grain (and therefore slow) emulsion has to be used in order to record the minute spectra. But the method is of interest in that it provides colour reproduction which is theoretically exact.

1.4 The Lippmann method

The other method of colour photography which is capable of giving exact colour reproduction is one of the most fascinating photographic inventions ever made. In 1891 Professor Gabriel Lippmann of Paris, by special techniques, made a photographic emulsion with grains of almost unbelievable fineness, 0.01 to 0.04μ in diameter. This emulsion he coated on plates, which he exposed in an ordinary camera, except that the emulsion side of the plate was turned away from the lens, and a layer of mercury was poured against it, as shown in Fig. 1.3(a). The emulsion-mercury interface then acted as a mirror, and the reflected and oncoming waves interfered with one another to produce standing waves in the emulsion. This standing wave pattern was duly recorded in the emulsion as latent image, and upon development parallel plates of silver were produced, the distance between successive plates being equal to half the wavelength of the light used in making the exposure. Thus in Fig. 1.3(a), the beam perpendicular to the plate represents green light, and the oblique beam, red light. Since red light is of longer wavelength than green light, the plates of silver are more widely spaced for the oblique beam than for the perpendicular beam.

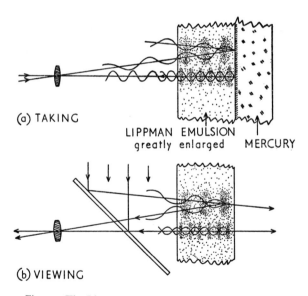

(a) TAKING

LIPPMAN EMULSION
greatly enlarged   MERCURY

(b) VIEWING

Fig. 1.3. The Lippmann method of colour photography.

After processing the plate to a negative, it is viewed by reflected light as shown in Fig. 1.3(b). There is no need to make a positive by reversing the plate, since the developed silver layers of the negative give a positive image when viewed by reflected light. This positive image, moreover, is coloured, for the plates of silver will strongly reflect light of half-wavelength equal to the distance between the plates, and weakly, or not at all, light of other wavelengths. Hence all spectral colours and white are reproduced with exact colour rendering.

Professor Lippmann and other later workers have produced many beautiful colour photographs by this method, and it is probably the most elegant method that will ever be devised. Its disadvantages, however, are of a severe nature. First, the Lippmann emulsions, because of their extremely fine grain, are extremely slow, and exposures of several minutes are necessary to make a Lippmann colour photograph even in bright sunlight. It is impossible to use a fast emulsion because the interference pattern which has to be recorded is smaller than the grain-size of fast emulsions. Secondly, the necessity for viewing the results by reflected light means that it is difficult to project Lippmann colour photographs on to a screen with adequate light; and even when viewed directly by reflected light the angle of viewing is critical.

1.5 Use of identical dyes

In some circumstances it is possible to reproduce the spectral reflectance curves by using the same dyes as were present in the original objects. A textile manufacturer, when trying to reproduce a given colour on an undyed fabric, will achieve exact physical colour reproduction if he uses the same dyes in the same amounts as were used on the pattern. In this book, however, we will generally understand the phrase *colour reproduction* to refer to making pictures of original scenes, and the use of identical dyes is then usually possible only in the special case of copying an existing colour photograph by means of a process which uses the same dyes.

1.6 A simplified approach

In view of the difficulties inherent in the micro-dispersion and Lippmann methods of colour photography, it is not surprising that they have never become popularly used; and, indeed, were it not for the fact that when the human eye views colours it simplifies their complexity somewhat, none of the present-day methods of colour reproduction would work.

The rest of the book, therefore, is devoted to describing the principles and methods of achieving colour reproduction by an approach which is basically much more simple: instead of all the colours of the spectrum being dealt with wavelength by wavelength, their effects are considered in a few groups only, as is the case with the human eye.

Although this approach leads to methods of colour reproduction in photography, television, and printing, which are highly successful in practice, we shall see that a proper understanding of them does sometimes involve some quite complicated considerations. It is therefore suggested that the general reader may prefer to omit Chapters 7, 8, 9, 13, 14, 15, and 19, and possibly also Chapter 6, at the first reading.

REFERENCE

Houston, R. A., *Light and Colour*, p.5, Longmans, Green & Co. (1923).

GENERAL REFERENCES

Evans, R. M., *An Introduction to Colour*, Chapman & Hall (1948).
Friedman, J. S., *History of Colour Photography*, Chapter 3, American Photographic Publishing Co. (1944).
Le Grand, Y., *Light, Colour, and Vision*, Chapman & Hall (1957).
Murray, H. D., *Colour in Theory and Practice*, Chapman & Hall (1952).
Smith, R. C., *Colour Photography*, p. 157 (April, 1962).
Wright, W. D., *The Measurement of Colour*, Hilger and Watts (1964).

CHAPTER 2

Trichromatic Colour Reproduction and the Additive Principle

1. Introduction – *2*. Maxwell's method – *3*. The physiology of human colour vision – *4*. Spectral sensitivity curves of the retina – *5*. Defects of trichromatic colour reproduction

2.1 Introduction

DURING the seventeenth and eighteenth centuries, the idea that there is something of a *triple* nature in colour steadily grew, and by 1722 Jakob Christoffel LeBlon was using a form of three-colour, or *trichromatic*, printing (Weale, 1957; Wall, 1925). By 1807 Thomas Young was instrumental in gaining general acceptance for the view that it is the retina of the human eye which is responsible for this triple feature of colour, and in 1861 James Clerk Maxwell produced the first trichromatic colour *photograph*, not, curiously enough, for its own sake, but as an illustration of the triple nature of colour vision (Maxwell, 1858–1862).

2.2 Maxwell's method

Maxwell's method is fundamental to all modern processes of colour reproduction. He took three photographs—one through a red filter, one through a green filter, and the third through a blue filter, and made three positive lantern slides from the negatives thus obtained. The three slides were placed in three separate projectors, which were arranged to project the three images in register on a white screen, as shown in Fig. 2.1. On placing a red filter in the lantern containing the slide made from the negative taken through the red filter, and green and blue filters respectively in those containing the slides made from the green and blue negatives, a colour reproduction was obtained upon the screen. Physically, all the colours on the screen were mixtures of red, green and blue light only, but, to the eye, white, yellow, orange, mauve, and in fact a whole range of both pale and vivid colours, were seen in addition to red, green and blue.

Today, colour reproduction, whether in photography, television, or printing, may seem to have little to do with Maxwell's method. But the *principle* of his method, reproduction of all colours by mixtures, in varying amount, of beams of red, green and blue light, is retained almost universally; and with modern resources the method itself (triple projection) can produce results of very high quality.

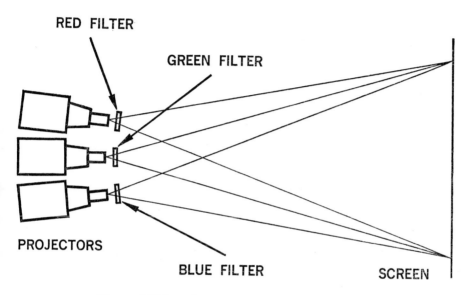

RED FILTER

GREEN FILTER

PROJECTORS

BLUE FILTER   SCREEN

Fig. 2.1. Additive colour reproduction by triple projection.

In Chapter 6 the principles of trichromatic colour reproduction will be derived from the experimental facts of colour matching; this approach, though rigorous, is a little intricate. Therefore in this chapter, as an introduction, we shall adopt a different procedure: we shall take the probable basis of human colour vision as a framework, within which we shall be able to see quite quickly, in general terms, both why trichromatic colour reproduction is successful and what its limitations are. The application of trichromatic principles to colour reproduction does not depend, however, on any particular physiological theory, but rather on the physiological fact that a very wide range of intermediate colours can be produced by mixing beams of red, green, and blue light. This mixing can take place either directly, or by using three dyes or pigments: yellow to absorb blue light, magenta to absorb green light, and blue-green or *cyan* to absorb red light.

2.3 The physiology of human colour vision

The human retina contains two main types of light-sensitive cell, known as rods and cones. By 1900 it was well-established that the colourless vision which occurs at very low levels of illumination, such as weak moonlight or starlight, depends on the bleaching of a photo-sensitive substance called *visual purple*

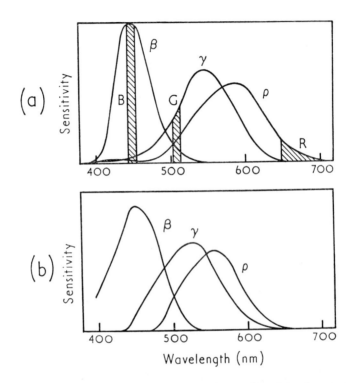

Fig. 2.2. (a) The probable sensitivity curves, β, γ, and ρ of the three types of light receptor believed to be responsible for colour vision as determined by indirect methods, together with the spectral quality of the three best lights, R, G, and B for additive colour reproduction. (b) Spectral sensitivity curves typical of those found from bleaching experiments on pigments in the human retina.

contained in the rods. It was therefore natural to ascribe *colour* vision, with its triple nature, to the bleaching of three different photo-sensitive substances contained in the cones. However, the evidence to support this view decisively has not been easy to come by, partly perhaps because the cones, being less sensitive than the rods, and also being far less numerous, offer much less photo-sensitive material to be found. But in various animals, photo-sensitive pigments have been discovered which absorb in different sections of the visible spectrum, as would be required for a system of colour vision based on such pigments (Dartnall and Lythgoe, 1965; MacNichol, 1964); and measurements have been made showing that, when irradiated with strong light, the colour of the light reflected by the human retina back through the pupil of the eye changes in the way to be expected if three such pigments were being bleached (Rushton, 1957 and 1958; Weale, 1959; Ripps and Weale, 1963; Brown and Wald, 1964), one pigment absorbing mainly red light, another mainly green light, and a third mainly blue light. The probability of this being a correct view of the initial step in human colour vision is greatly enhanced, of course, by the fact that when beams of red, green, and blue light are mixed together as in Maxwell's procedure, a very wide range of intermediate colour sensations, such as white, yellow, purple, pink, brown, etc., can be produced.

It may be said, therefore, that human colour vision probably depends initially on the absorption of light in three photo-sensitive pigments whose main absorptions occur in the red, green, and blue parts of the spectrum. After the light has been absorbed by the pigments, electrical signals are generated in the form of nerve impulses; it is these signals which convey to the brain the colour, and other, information concerning the image of the outside world formed on the retina. The nerve fibres along which these signals travel appear to have many intricate inter-connections with one another, and it seems unlikely that the colour information consists simply of three signals proportional to the absorptions of light by the three pigments. There is evidence that in some animals the signals transmitted are analogous to the luminance and colour-difference signals used in colour television (MacNichol, 1964), and this may also be the case in human colour vision. But once the light has been absorbed in the pigments in the retina, the processing of the subsequent signals will be the same if the absorptions are the same (assuming that the viewing conditions are the same). The key to the success or otherwise of trichromatic colour reproduction must therefore, in the first instance, be sought in the absorptions in the retinal pigments.

2.4 Spectral sensitivity curves of the retina

To understand the retinal absorption stage in any detail, we need to know how the ability of each of the three pigments to absorb light and be bleached (and generate a visual response) varies throughout the spectrum: that is, we need to know the spectral sensitivity curve of each of the three pigment-mechanisms. Indirect methods of measuring them have for many years provided what have been believed to be good approximations to these curves, as shown in Fig. 2.2(a) (Wright, 1946; Thomson and Wright, 1953). Direct measurements, made subsequently, have given similar results, as shown in Fig. 2.2(b) (Rushton, 1957 and 1958; Weale, 1959; Brown and Wald, 1964); these curves have been deduced from measurements of the amount of bleaching caused by different

2A

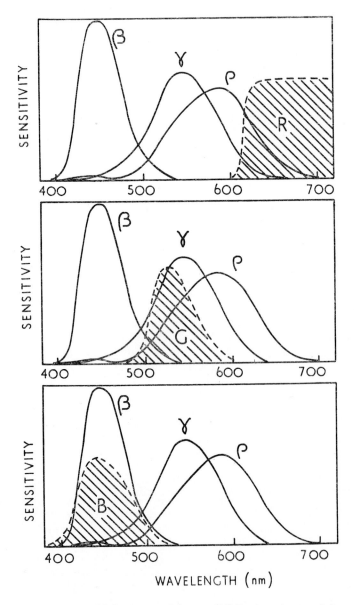

Fig. 2.3. The ρ, γ, β sensitivity curves of the eye (full lines), and transmission curves of red, green, and blue filters typical of those used in additive colour reproduction (broken lines and shaded areas).

wavelengths falling on each retinal pigment as observed from the pupil side of the eye. This type of measurement is greatly complicated in the blue part of the spectrum because some of the products of the bleaching absorb light in variable amounts but do not generate corresponding colour responses; for this reason the results for the blue-absorbing pigment are less certain than those for the red- and green-absorbing pigments, and in some of the investigations results for the blue-absorbing pigment are not given.

It will be seen at once that the sensitivity curves overlap to a considerable extent, one type covering chiefly the red, orange, and yellow parts of the spectrum, another the orange, yellow, green, and blue-green parts, and the third the blue-green, blue and violet parts. We shall regard these three types of sensitivity as belonging to three different types of cone, ρ, γ, and β respectively. (It is possible that some cones, by having more than one pigment present, may have sensitivity curves which are mixtures of those shown, but this does not affect the ensuing arguments (Hunt, 1952 and 1959).)

Considering now Maxwell's method, it is clear that if our reproduction is to be exact, when taking our three separation negatives, our photographic film should analyse the scene in the same way as the eye. The spectral sensitivities, therefore, of the three film-filter combinations should be the same as those of Fig. 2.2. This presents no insuperable difficulties, and can be well enough approximated to, by using panchromatic films and suitable filters. It should be noted that, owing to the broad nature of the ρ and γ curves, the red filter will in fact look orange, and the green filter paler than a spectral green.

How Maxwell was able to operate the process using photographic materials sensitive only in the ultra-violet, blue, and blue-green parts of the spectrum (the only ones available in those days), remained a mystery until Evans showed (Evans, 1961) that Maxwell's red filter also transmitted in the ultra-violet: and red dyes of the type probably used in the tartan bow, which he reproduced, reflect not only in the red but also in the ultra-violet!

With the spectral-sensitivities of our film-filter combinations the same as those of Fig. 2.2, the amounts of photographic image at any point on our negatives will be functions of the responses of the ρ, γ and β cones for the corresponding point at the scene; hence, in our positives the transmission at each point will be proportional to the ρ, γ and β responses (it being assumed that the photographic steps are so arranged that the transmissions of the positives are proportional to the exposures received by the negatives).

If the colour filters used in the three lanterns were of such colours that the red filter stimulated only the ρ-cones, the green, only the γ-cones, and the blue, only the β-cones, exact colour reproduction would result, because each point on the screen would give rise to the same ρ, γ, and β responses in the retina as those to which the corresponding point in the original scene gave rise. But unfortunately, the *if* with which this paragraph began is impossible to achieve.

35

2.5 Defects of trichromatic colour reproduction

From Fig. 2.2(a) it is clear that while a red filter which transmitted only light of wavelength longer than about 650 nm would stimulate only the ρ-cones, and a blue filter which transmitted only light of wavelength about 450 nm would stimulate chiefly the β-cones and hardly at all the γ- and ρ-cones, there is no region of the spectrum to which the γ-cones alone are sensitive, and hence no filter can be found to transmit light which stimulates the γ-cones only. The best that can be done is to choose a filter which transmits a narrow band of light in the green part of the spectrum at a wavelength of about 510 nm as shown at G in Fig. 2.2(a); while the bands of light passed by the red and blue filters are those marked R and and B.

The effect of this deficiency of the green filter is that wherever, on the screen, the green lantern is shining there is an unwanted excess of ρ- and β-response, and this excess will of course be most noticeable when the γ-response is large, as in the case of greens, which will become paler, and least noticeable in the case of reds and blues where the γ-response is small. Whites would have a medium excess of ρ- and β-response which would give them a magenta tinge, but this could be overcome by adjusting the relative intensities of the three lanterns so that whites looked white, and this would also partly correct all pale colours; vivid colours, however, would then be incorrect in hue and relative intensities, but this is usually much more tolerable than a colour tinge in white and greys.

If the filters used in the three lanterns had transmissions as shown at R, G, and B in Fig. 2.2(a) most of the light emitted by the lamps in the lanterns would be wasted by being absorbed by the filters, since each filter only transmits a very narrow band of the spectrum. In order to throw more light on the screen from each lantern, and hence to produce a brighter picture, filters having broader transmission bands (such as those shown in Fig. 2.3) are always used in practice, and this inevitably results in further inaccuracies of colour rendering, since the light from each lantern will give even more of the unwanted cone responses than in the case of the filters of Fig. 2.2(a). When the red, green and blue lights are produced, not by filtering white lights, but by the excitation of phosphors, as is customary in colour television, the situation, as shown in Fig. 2.4, is much the same as in Fig. 2.3.

It is thus clear that the inability of any beams of red, green and blue light to stimulate the retinal cones separately introduces a basic complication into the whole of trichromatic colour reproduction. If the ρ and β curves did not overlap in the blue-green part of the spectrum, then green light could be found which stimulated the γ-cones on their own; but since the ρ and β curves do overlap appreciably the γ-cones cannot be stimulated on their own, and hence simple trichromatic means cannot achieve exact colour reproduction. This is not a difficulty peculiar to any particular method or process, but one that underlies all modern methods of colour reproduction, whether in

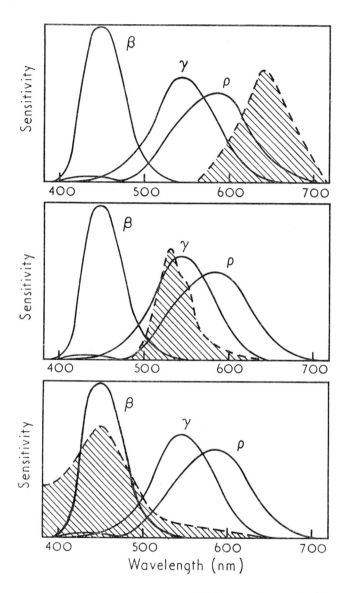

Fig. 2.4. The ρ, γ, β sensitivity curves of the eye (full lines), and spectral emission curves of red, green, and blue phosphors typical of those used in colour television (broken lines and shaded areas).

37

photography, television or printing; it cannot be avoided because it follows from the basic nature of human colour vision.

The position then becomes as shown in Fig. 2.5. If some particular part of the original gives rise to responses ρ_0, γ_0, and β_0, and if the strengths R, G and B of the red, green and blue beams composing this part of the reproduction are proportional to these responses, then the reproduction is spoiled because the red beam gives rise to an unwanted γ-response, γ_R, the green beam gives rise to unwanted ρ- and β-responses, ρ_G and β_G, and the blue beam gives rise to unwanted ρ- and γ-responses, ρ_B and γ_B.

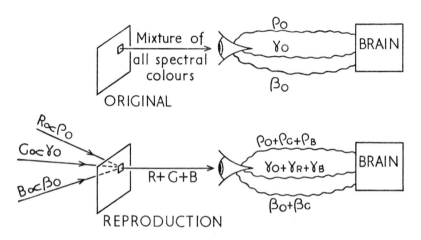

Fig. 2.5. Diagrammatic representation of why a three-colour reproduction of an original scene is inaccurate.

The effect of this may be appreciated in the following way. White and grey sensations may be thought of as corresponding to the values of the responses ρ, γ and β being equal, and the vividness (or *saturation*) of a colour as depending upon the ratio of the largest of the three responses to the other two. Thus for a vivid red colour ρ_0 would be several times as large as γ_0 or β_0, and it follows, of course, that R will be several times as large as G and B. Therefore the unwanted response γ_R will be larger than the unwanted responses ρ_G, β_G, and ρ_B, γ_B. Hence the main effect of the unwanted responses will be to increase γ relative to ρ and β. Thus the ratio of ρ to γ will be reduced and the corresponding colour sensation will become less vividly red. The same effect will operate with, for instance, a vivid green colour. G will be large, and hence ρ_G and β_G will be the main unwanted responses. Hence the ratio of γ to ρ and β will decrease and the colour will become less vividly green. The argument is quite general, and the effect of the defect illustrated in Fig. 2.5 will be to make all colours less vivid (i.e. to *desaturate* them). Thus the overlapping of the ρ and β curves, as shown in Fig. 2.2, resulting as it does in the inability to stimulate the γ-type of cone on its own, means that exact colour reproduction by simple trichromatic means is impossible to achieve. We shall return to the questions of the importance of this defect and the ways in which its effects can be reduced in later chapters, where, incidentally, we shall see that it is not necessarily the best arrangement to have the spectral sensitivity curves of the film-filter combinations the same as those of the ρ, γ and β curves. However, the defects are often unnoticeable in practice, and the pictures which can be obtained by trichromatic reproduction are often extremely pleasing.

REFERENCES

Brown, P. K., and Wald, G., *Science*, **144**, 45 (3rd April, 1964).
Dartnall, H. J. A., and Lythgoe, J. N., *Vision Research*, **5**, 81 (1965).
Evans, R. M., *J. Photogr. Sci.*, **9**, 243 (1961).
Hunt, R. W. G., *J. Opt. Soc. Amer.*, **42**, 198 (1952).
Hunt, R. W. G., *Nature*, **183**, 1601 (1959).
MacNichol, E. F., *Vision Research*, **4**, 119 (1964).
Maxwell, J. C., *Proc. Roy. Inst.*, **3**, 370 (1858–62).
Ripps, H., and Weale, R. A., *Vision Research*, **3**, 531 (1963).
Rushton, W. A. H., *Visual Problems of Colour*, p. 73, N.P.L. Symposium, H.M.S.O., London (1957).
Rushton, W. A. H., *Nature*, **182**, 690 (1958).
Thomson, L. C., and Wright, W. D., *J. Opt. Soc. Amer.*, **43**, 890 (1953).
Wall, E. J., *The History of Three-Colour Photography*, p. 1, American Photographic Publishing Co., Boston (1925).
Weale, R. A., *Nature*, **179**, 648 (1957).
Weale, R. A., *Optica Acta*, **6**, 158 (1959).
Wright, W. D., *Researches on Normal and Defective Colour Vision*, Chapters 21 and 30, Kimpton (1946).

GENERAL REFERENCES

Evans, R. M., Hanson, W. T., and Brewer, W. L., *Principles of Colour Photography*, Chapman & Hall (1953).
Wall, E. J., *The History of Three-Colour Photography*, American Photographic Publishing Co., Boston (1925).

CHAPTER 3

Additive Methods

1. Introduction – *2*. The successive frame method – *3*. The mosaic method – *4*. The lenticular method – *5*. Errors in additive methods

3.1 Introduction

I T will be appreciated that Maxwell's method of colour photography by triple projection offers more hope of practical usefulness than the micro-dispersion and Lippmann methods; and, in fact, triple projection has been used, at least experimentally, both for colour cinematography, and for colour television. But the practical difficulty of getting and retaining exact registration of the three images over the whole of the picture area, and the expense of triplicating the projection apparatus, have militated against Maxwell's original method. The red, green and blue beams of light can be mixed in other ways, however, and leaving aside for the moment the use of dyes, pigments or inks (the so-called subtractive processes), there are three other ways of mixing the red, green and blue beams: the successive frame method, the mosaic method, and the lenticular method. These three methods, together with the triple projection method (and the closely related Ives Chromoscope[1]), are usually called additive methods, since all the colours are produced by adding beams of red, green and blue light to one another in varying proportions.

3.2 The successive frame method

This method, applicable only to cinematography and television, depends for its success on the fact that, if beams of red, green and blue light fall on the retina in quick succession, the individual colours are not seen and the colour sensation is the same as that produced by triple projection. In cinematography,

[1] This is an additive viewer in which virtual images, seen through red, green, and blue filters, are superimposed by means of semi-reflecting mirrors.

Plate 1. Girl on barge. In spite of the basic limitations of trichromatic colour reproduction, very pleasing results can be obtained. *From an Ektachrome transparency by Jack M. Oakley.*

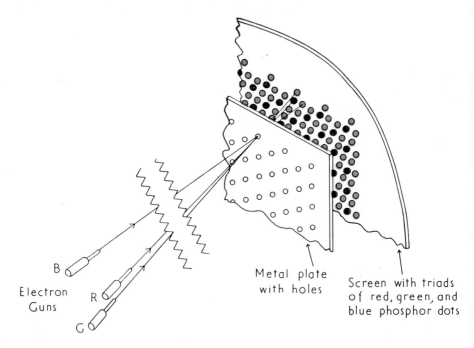

Fig. 3.1. Diagrammatic representation of the shadow-mask type of colour television tube.

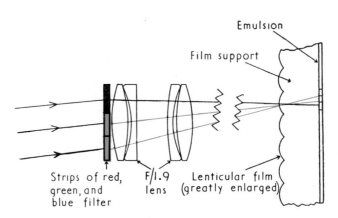

Fig. 3.2. The Lenticular method of additive colour photography (diagrammatic only).

therefore, a filter wheel containing successive segments of red, green and blue filters is rotated in front of the camera lens, in synchronism with the shutter, so that pictures are taken first through one filter, then through another, and then through the third. The film is processed in the usual way to give a black and white positive and this is projected with a similar filter wheel rotating in front of the projection lens and is again in synchronism, this time with the shutter in the projector; thus every time a positive, made from a negative taken through the red filter, is in the gate, a red filter is over the projection lens, and similarly for the green and blue. In a colour television system the same method can be applied with a red, green and blue filter wheel rotating in front of the television camera lens, and a similar wheel rotating in synchronism in front of the television receiver tube.

Unfortunately, in such a system, the blue filter is always much darker than the red and green filters, and the eye can detect the darker filter as a brightness flicker even when the speed of the filter wheel is fast enough to remove all colour flicker. The speed of rotation necessary to lose all sense of flicker depends somewhat on the intensity of the light but for a stationary scene it is usually about 50 rotations per second giving 150 red, green, and blue 'fields' per second. Even at this speed, a moving object can result in objectionable colour fringing (colour 'break-up'), particularly if it is a highly coloured object, so that it is mainly presented in only one of the three colour-pictures. The Columbia system of Colour Television which, in 1950, was standardized by the Federal Communications Commission (F.C.C.) for use in the U.S.A., was a successive frame method of this type working at 144 fields per second. But, owing to defence requirements at that time, the system was never widely used commercially, and this was perhaps as well because the system was not *compatible*, that is, the pictures transmitted in the system could not be received as black-and-white pictures on existing black-and-white television sets; and the rotating disc tends to be too awkward to fit in neatly, and is liable to mechanical failure caused by wear on the bearings. Subsequently the F.C.C. set aside their 1950 decision and standardized a compatible system in 1953 for use in the U.S.A.

In photography, the successive frame method has never achieved commercial success because of the high rates of projection necessary to avoid colour fringing of moving objects.

3.3 The mosaic method

The simplest and most successful additive method has been that used by the mosaic processes. If a very fine mesh of red, green and blue squares is viewed at a distance, the individual colours are not seen; instead, a single uniform colour appears, the nature of which depends upon the relative amounts of light passing through the three types of square. Hence if much more light passes through the red and green, than through the blue squares, the same colour is seen as when red and green are mixed by projection, that is, yellow. It is, therefore, possible

43

to produce a colour photograph like Maxwell's by taking a black-and-white photograph through a mosaic of red, green and blue squares, reversing the negative to a positive or printing a positive from it, and then viewing it through the mosaic in register with the squares on the photograph. Physiologically the success of the method depends upon the fact that the cones of the retina themselves constitute a mosaic, and if the image of the photographic mosaic on the retina is small compared with the retinal mosaic, then the three colours will be as effectively mixed as is the case with triple projection from three lanterns.

In photography, the mosaic processes have had a long and distinguished career. The Autochrome plate, which consisted of a random mosaic of red, green and blue dyed starch grains with the interstices filled with carbon black, came on the market in 1907 and was still a commercial success in the early 1930's. The Agfacolor mosaic process employed a random mosaic of stained resin grains and was rather more transparent. Successful processes employing mosaics of regular lines or squares of red, green and blue were Finlay and Thames (1906, and later revived in England as the Johnson screen plate), and Dufaycolor (1908) in which the mesh eventually (about 1935) reached the astonishing fineness of a million squares to the square-inch and resulted in considerable commercial success. Regular mosaics proved more satisfactory than random mosaics because, in the latter, random clumpings of elements of the same colour gave an increase in apparent mottle.

However, the main interest in mosaic processes is now in connection with colour television, where mosaic dot cathode-ray tubes are very widely used. With a dot tube the arrangement of the camera could, *in theory*, be exactly the same as for the successive frame method. But the receiving tube, instead of being covered with a uniform coating of phosphor, has a regular mosaic of areas of three different phosphors, one of which fluoresces red, another green, and the third blue. Again, *in theory*, it would only be necessary, with such an arrangement, to ensure that the electron beam scans this regular mosaic one line at a time, and the filter wheel in front of the camera rotates at such a speed that whenever the electron beam is exciting a red phosphor dot, the red filter is over the camera lens, and similarly for the green and the blue. A simple calculation, however, shows that this is impracticable. For if we had a television system of 500 lines, with, say 500 dots of each of the three phosphors in each line, the filter wheel would have to rotate 500 x 500 revolutions for each picture, and at 25 pictures per second this requires a rotation of 6,250,000 revolutions per second, which is clearly impossible; amongst other difficulties, no wheel could be made which would not fly apart at such speeds.

To overcome this difficulty it would be necessary in some way to arrange that when, say, the red filter is over the camera lens, the electron beam, as it scans the mosaic of phosphors, only falls on the red phosphor, the green and blue phosphors being missed; but as soon as the green filter comes over the camera, the red and blue phosphors must be missed and only the green phosphor irradiated, and similarly for the blue.

One way of achieving this is shown in Fig. 3.1. The red, green and blue phosphors are deposited on the tube screen, as though they had been fired from three positions R, G and B respectively, through a metal plate containing a large number of small holes situated just behind the tube screen. Each hole is like a pin-hole camera, and for each hole a triad of red, green and blue phosphor dots is situated on the screen. Three electron guns are used in the tube and they fire from the three positions R, G and B. It can then be arranged that whenever the red filter is over the camera lens, only the gun at position R is fired, and hence, since the electron beam travels in a straight line, only the dots of red phosphor are irradiated. As soon as the green filter replaces the red filter over the camera lens the gun at R stops firing and that at G starts, so that only the dots of green phosphor are irradiated; and similarly for the blue. It will be seen that with this arrangement it is possible to have the filter wheel running only at the usual speeds necessary to overcome flicker and colour fringing on moving objects. A variation of this arrangement is to have only one electron gun, and to arrange that the electron beam, after passing through each hole, is steered by electrostatic or electromagnetic focusing on to the appropriate phosphor in synchronism with the camera filter-wheel.

Although the successive frame type of camera can, in this way, be used with mosaic television tubes, in practice, because of compatibility and other considerations, recourse is usually had to a camera similar to the *one-shot* camera used in colour photography: by means of semi-reflecting mirrors three separate but identical images are formed by a single lens, and these pass through red, green, and blue filters on to the light-sensitive surfaces of three television camera tubes; thus the red, green and blue images are available all the time. All three electron guns in the receiver then fire continuously, the broadcast signals controlling their intensities and hence producing the required colours. The methods of transmitting and receiving such *simultaneous* colour pictures together with some further discussion of camera arrangements will be found in Chapters 16 and 17.

It should be noted that in these mosaic colour television tubes it is *not* necessary for the lines of dot-triads to coincide with the picture scanning-lines; it is only required that there be a sufficient number of dots to build up the picture without significant loss of detail. Exact registration of the three guns, the apertures in the metal plate, and the phosphor dots is vital for correct colour; but the exact position of the picture lines on the tube is of no consequence.

Just as the mosaic processes are the most successful in additive colour photography, so it seems that they will be in colour television.

3.4 The lenticular method

An elegant variation of the mosaic method is the lenticular method, which, for a period, had a successful life in commercial colour photography,[1] and which

---

[1] The old *Kodacolor* process 1928–35, not to be confused with the present *Kodacolor* process, which is a subtractive system.

is also feasible for colour television. The principle, when used in photography, is illustrated in Fig. 3.2. A film is used which has minute furrows, or lenticulations, embossed on one side, and a photographic emulsion coated on the other side. The film is used in the camera with the lenticulations towards the camera lens, as shown in the figure, and the radius of curvature of the lenticulations is made so that they focus an image of the camera lens on the emulsion layer. The camera lens itself is covered with red, green and blue filters in strips, parallel to the direction of the lenticulations, so that images of the filters are formed in strips along the entire length of each lenticulation. The result is that the picture is divided up into triads of strips, so that the strips opposite the bottom of each lenticulation are exposed only by light which has passed through the red filter, those opposite the middle of each lenticulation only by green light, and those opposite the top only by blue light. The film is then processed to a positive (or to a negative and then printed in register on to positive lenticular stock) and projected with the same, or a similar array of red, green and blue filter strips over the projection lens. The lenticulations then ensure that the white projection light passing through the bottom strip of each lenticulation emerges only through the red filter strip on the lens, that through the middle strip, only through the green strip on the lens, and that through the top strip only through the blue strip on the lens. Then the projection lens, by focusing the red, green and blue light on to the same point on the screen, additively mixes them, just as effectively as in the case of triple projection. The old Kodacolor process, using 22 lenticulations per millimetre, ran for a number of years with considerable success, and the Eastman Kodak Company in America in 1951 offered an improved version for 35 mm. professional use (*British Journal of Photography*, 1951). Subsequently, lenticular film has been tried as a medium for recording colour television programmes, where the speed and simplicity of the (black-and-white) processing is an important asset (Evans and Smith, 1956; Brown, Combs and Smith, 1956; Crane and Evans, 1958; Duke, 1963). It should be noted that, in lenticular systems, proper colour synthesis only requires that the image be accurately located relative to the lenticulations; location of the entire film relative to the filter strips on the projection lens is not critical.

In colour television, the Lawrence tube or *Chromatron* (Dressler, 1953) employs effectively the same principle, but the 'lenses' are electrostatic fields between wires instead of embossed furrows on film base. One version of the method is shown diagrammatically in Fig. 3.3. The television tube is coated with vertical strips of red, green and blue phosphor, and just behind these strips are a series of vertical wires. Only one electron gun is used, but by varying the electrical potential on the wires the beam can be deflected either left or right or allowed to travel straight on. Thus, when the potential on all the wires is equal, the electron beam is focused on the green phosphor as shown in Fig. 3.3(b). But when potential is applied positively to alternate wires and negatively to intermediate wires the electron beam is focused either on the red phosphor as shown in Fig. 3.3(c), or on the blue phosphor as shown in Fig. 3.3(d),

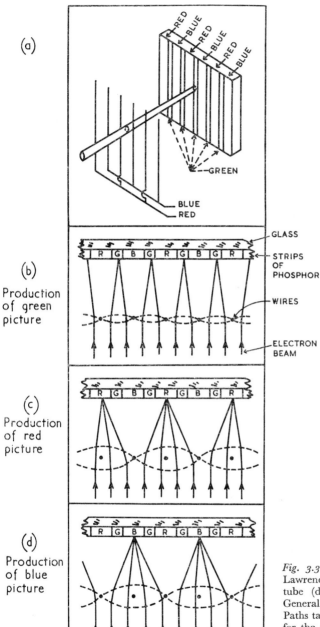

(b)

Production
of green
picture

(c)
Production
of red
picture

(d)
Production
of blue
picture

Fig. 3.3. The arrangement in a
Lawrence type of colour television
tube (diagrammatic only). (a):
General lay-out. (b), (c), and (d):
Paths taken by the electron beam
for the production of green, red,
and blue pictures, respectively.

47

according to which set of alternate wires is chosen. The alterations of the potential can be synchronized with selection from the red, green and blue camera tubes; or the tubes can employ three electron guns, in which case the potential on the wires is kept constant all the time to form electron lenses, which produce images of the guns on the respective phosphor strips; these techniques are described more fully in Chapter 18.

3.5 Errors in additive methods

As far as errors in additive colour reproductions are concerned, the simplest approach is the one adopted in the previous chapter: to regard any deviation of the camera sensitivity curves from the ρ-, γ-, β-curves as leading to error, and to regard the optimum red, green and blue beams as those which most nearly stimulate the ρ-, γ- and β-types of cone separately. In the case of photographic processes in which the same mosaic is used in the camera as is used for viewing the final result, it is clear that to adopt the ρ-, γ- and β-sensitivity curves necessitates red, green and blue beams composed of very broad spectral bands and therefore very far from optimum. For this reason, in such processes, narrower filters (and therefore also sharper sensitivity curves) were used with some overall advantage (Sproson, 1949). The whole subject of errors in additive reproduction will be treated more rigorously in Chapter 6.

REFERENCES

Brown, W. R. J., Combs, C. S., and Smith, R. B., *J. Soc. Mot. Pic. Tel. Eng.*, **65,** 648 (1956).
British Journal of Photography, **98,** 456 (1951).
Crane, E. M., and Evans, C. H., *J. Soc. Mot. Pic. Tel. Eng.*, **65,** 13 (1958).
Dressler, R., *Proc. I.R.E.*, **41,** 851 (1953).
Duke, V. J., *J. Soc. Mot. Pic. Tel. Eng.*, **72,** 711 (1963).
Evans, C. H., and Smith, R. B., *J. Soc. Mot. Pic. Tel. Eng.*, **65,** 365 (1956).
Sproson, W. N., *Phot. J.*, **89B,** 108 (1949).

GENERAL REFERENCES

Cornwell-Clyne, A., *Colour Cinematography*, Chapman & Hall, London (1951).
Koshofer, G., *Brit. J. Photog.*, **113,** 562 and 824 (1966).

CHAPTER 4

The Subtractive Principle

1. Introduction – *2*. The subtractive principle – *3*. Defects of the subtractive principle

4.1 Introduction

IN additive methods of colour reproduction, all the colours are produced by the adding or blending together in different proportions of three primary colours, a red, a green, and a blue. Subtractive colour reproduction, at first sight, seems to be quite different, because all the colours are produced by different proportions of three entirely different colours, a cyan (or blue-green), a magenta, and a yellow. In point of fact, however, the subtractive and the additive methods differ only in manner, and not in principle.

In photography, additive methods suffer from two disadvantages. First, somewhere in the system there must be saturated red, green, and blue filters; these may be in the three lanterns as in the triple-projection method, or in the filter wheel as in the successive frame method, or in the three strips across the projection lens as in the lenticular method, or in the minute patches as in the mosaic methods. But wherever such filters occur there is an inevitable loss of light. Therefore, as compared with black-and-white, an additive colour photograph means either a dimmer picture of the same size, or a smaller picture of the same intensity, or a higher wattage projection lamp and hence a more elaborate cooling system in the projector; all this is unwelcome. And as far as reflection prints are concerned, no additive method has been devised; for only the mosaic processes are possible, and in these the mosaic of red, green, and blue patches, even without any image behind them, will blend to give grey instead of white, and it is, therefore, impossible to reproduce whites at all.

The second disadvantage of the additive methods is that they all require either some special equipment, such as triple projectors, or some sort of mosaic, which results in a loss of definition.

The attraction of the subtractive principle, which was first described by du Hauron in 1862, is that it overcomes all these difficulties; it is therefore widely used not only in photography but also in the printing industry. Projected pictures are as bright as in black-and-white, reflection prints can be made with good whites, and ordinary cameras and projectors can be used. The disadvantages in photography are that subtractive materials are more complicated, with the result that the costs are greater, and the processing often involves the return of the film to the manufacturers or to a laboratory for processing; this involves delay and removes some of the fascination from amateur photography. In colour television the subtractive principle has less advantage because the additive system, using phosphors emitting red, green, and blue light, does not waste light as is the case with the red, green, and blue filters used with beams of white light in additive colour photography.

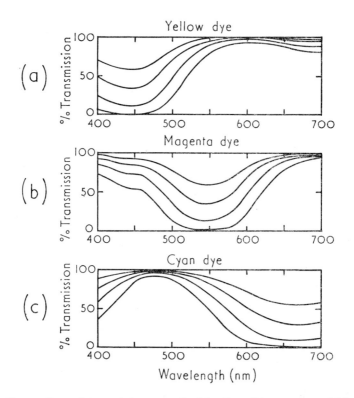

Fig. 4.1. Spectral transmission curves for (a) yellow, (b) magenta, and (c) cyan, dyes at four different concentrations.

4.2 The subtractive principle

White light contains all the colours of the spectrum. But we may regard the spectrum as consisting of three main parts; first, that containing light of wavelengths over about 580 nm, which contains all the reddish part; secondly, that containing light of wavelengths between about 490 and about 580 nm, which contains all the greenish part; and thirdly, that containing light of wavelengths less than about 490 nm which contains all the bluish part. If we looked at the blended light from each of these three parts of the spectrum, we would simply see three colours, red, green, and blue. It therefore follows that when the light from a projector falls on a white screen, or when daylight falls on a piece of white paper, we may regard that light as being an additive mixture of a beam of red light, a beam of green light and a beam of blue light. In order, therefore, to produce a wide range of colours in a beam of white light, all that is required is some means of varying the proportions of the reddish, greenish, and bluish parts, independently.

In Fig. 4.1(a) there is plotted against wavelength the percentage transmission at each wavelength of a yellow dye at four different concentrations. It is seen that for all concentrations the transmission in the reddish part of the spectrum is high, in fact nearly 100 per cent; in the greenish part the variation of transmission with concentration is not large, but in the bluish part of the spectrum the transmission depends very markedly on the concentration of the dye. It is, therefore, clear that if we insert in a projector a slide on which we can vary the concentration of a yellow dye, as this concentration is altered so the amount of bluish light falling on the screen is altered nearly independently of the amount of greenish and reddish light falling on the screen. Similarly, the amount of bluish light reflected from a piece of white paper, viewed in daylight, would be altered by the concentration of a yellow dye on its surface.

In Fig. 4.1(b) similar spectral-transmission curves are shown for a magenta dye at different concentrations. It is clear that the main effect of altering the concentration of the magenta dye is to vary the transmission in the greenish part of the spectrum. It is true that the transmission in the bluish part of the spectrum does alter also, but it does so to a smaller extent. Finally, in Fig. 4.1(c) similar curves are shown for a cyan dye at different concentrations, and the main effect of varying the concentration is to alter the transmission in the reddish part of the spectrum, and to a less extent the transmission in the greenish and bluish parts of the spectrum.

If, therefore, we now have a slide in a projector, or a surface layer on a piece of white paper, on which we can vary at will the concentrations of a cyan, a magenta, and a yellow dye, we have the means of varying the relative and absolute intensities of the reddish, greenish, and bluish parts of the white light, and, therefore, we can produce a very wide range of colours at different intensities. This is the subtractive principle, and it is clear that, although the colours of the dyes used are cyan, magenta, and yellow, this is merely incidental to the fact that it is dyes of these colours which correspond respectively to a red-absorbing, a green-absorbing, and a blue-absorbing substance. In the printing trade the colours of the inks are often referred to as 'blue', 'red' and 'yellow', but their functions are still to act as absorbers of red, green, and blue light respectively.

All that is necessary to produce a subtractive colour reproduction is to be able to control the concentrations of the three dyes independently at each point on the transparency or piece of paper. Assuming that this can be done, the successive stages of subtractive colour photography are as follows:

(1) Black-and-white records of the original scene are made by means of red, green, and blue light (as in the additive system).

(2) Dye-image positives are made from the negatives, the red negative giving a cyan image, the green negative a magenta image, and the blue negative a yellow image.

(3) When superimposed in register, the three dye images are viewed in white light.

The third step is illustrated in Plate 9 (page 250), although in this case, as is general in printing, a fourth image has also been printed in a black ink. This is because it is difficult to attain good blacks with the type of cyan, magenta and yellow inks that have to be used in practice.

4.3 Defects of the subtractive principle

On many occasions, subtractive colour photographs produced by some of the modern commercial processes are so pleasing to the eye that the impression is made that almost perfect colour rendering has been achieved. In point of fact, however, as far as colour rendering is concerned, all subtractive processes suffer not only from the defects inherent in the additive method (which were described in Chapter 2), but also from some further defects of their own.

In Fig. 4.2 are shown again the probable sensitivity curves of the three types of light-sensitive cell, or cone, ρ, γ and β, operating in the human retina. As with the additive process, in order to obtain exact colour reproduction, we may regard it, for the moment, as necessary that the effective sensitivities of the three photographic emulsions used to record the three negatives should be the same as the three curves of Fig. 4.2. This can be done, but it is further required that the cyan dye controls a band of wavelengths to which only the ρ-cones respond, the magenta dye a band to which only the γ-cones respond, and the yellow dye a band to which only the β-cones respond. In Fig. 4.2 the approximate bands of wavelength controlled by the cyan, magenta, and yellow dyes of Fig. 4.1 are shown, and it is clear that, as with the additive process, the ρ-, γ- and β-responses are not independently controlled by the three dyes, and exact colour reproduction is, therefore, impossible. With the additive system, the red, green, and blue lights need not consist of such broad bands of wavelengths as those controlled by the subtractive dyes, and, because of this, additive systems are theoretically superior in this respect.

A further disadvantage of the subtractive system, as can be seen from Fig. 4.1, is that the best available cyan and magenta dyes have appreciable absorptions in parts of the spectrum where they should have 100 per cent transmission. This often results in blue and green colours being reproduced considerably darker than in the original scene.

Various measures can be adopted in an endeavour to minimize the fundamental shortcomings of subtractive colour processes, and these are often quite effective. In the first place, the processes can be operated so that the reproduction is more contrasty than the original. This results in a general improvement in the vividness of all colours, but at the expense of tone reproduc-

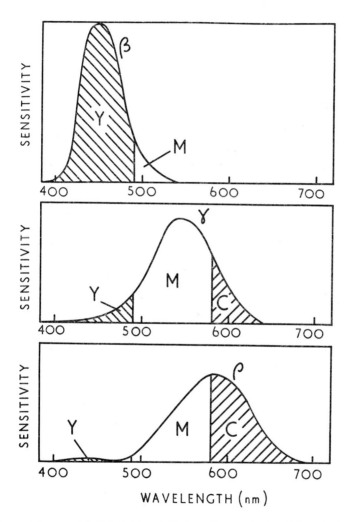

Fig. 4.2. The areas labelled C, M, and Y, show the magnitudes of the retinal responses controlled by the absorptions of the cyan, magenta, and yellow dyes respectively. In an ideal system the absorption of each dye would control one retinal response only.

53

tion. Correct tone reproduction, however, is not always essential for a pleasing reproduction, and indeed in many cases an increase of contrast improves the tone rendering. This is particularly true of scenes for which the lighting is rather flat, and with many modern subtractive processes a combination of flat lighting and a high-contrast process yields very pleasing results.

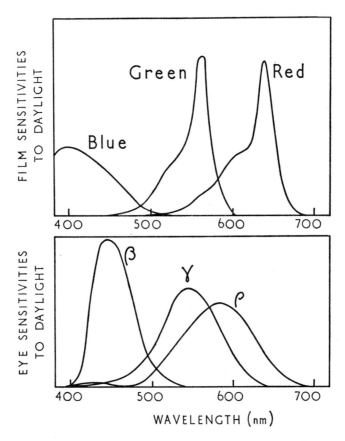

Fig. 4.3. Spectral sensitivities typical of those used in trichromatic colour photography, compared with the probable sensitivities of the three colour mechanisms of the eye.

Another beneficial measure is to use sensitivity curves for the three images which are more widely separated than those of Fig. 4.2 and a typical set of such curves is shown in Fig. 4.3. This again improves the vividness of most colours, but sometimes introduces errors in hue and lightness. For instance, the sensitivity of photographic materials to ultra-violet light results in blue skies being reproduced very much more saturated than would be the case if the sensitivity curves matched those of the eye. But by the same token distant grassland is often reproduced too light and bluish rather than green.

Another measure is to make each dye-image dependent on more than one of the three exposures in such a way as to increase colour saturation: this can be done by means of *inter-image effects* or *masking* (to be described in Chapter 13).

It will be realized that these three expedients cannot correct for the fundamental limitations of the process, which spring from the nature of the colour mechanism of the eye and the shape of the spectral absorption curves of the best available cyan, magenta, and yellow dyes. What is claimed for modern subtractive processes is that they produce pleasing colour pictures, and that the inevitable inaccuracies are balanced in such a way as to be least noticeable.

REFERENCE
Du Hauron, L. Ducos, *The Photographic News*, **13**, 319 (1869).

GENERAL REFERENCE
Evans, R. M., *Eye, Film, and Camera in Colour Photography*, Wiley, New York (1959).

CHAPTER 5

Visual Appreciation

1. Introduction – *2.* The basis of judgement – *3.* Variations in hue – *4.* Variations in lightness – *5.* Variations in saturation – *6.* Priorities – *7.* Factors affecting apparent colour balance – *8.* Integrating to grey

5.1 Introduction

THE trichromatic theory of colour vision has been the subject of attacks from many quarters during its long history, but the fact that colour matching is manifestly a phenomenon of three variables means that there is really no escape from it in some form. That vision, and especially colour vision, is essentially a highly complex process is undeniable; but the evidence continues to accumulate that, whatever complications may befall the retinal signals on their way to the brain, the initial step is the absorption of light in the retina by three photosensitive substances having different spectral absorptions. Thomas Young therefore did a great service to the subject by the emphasis he laid on the retina as the true source of trichromacy. Maxwell fully grasped the significance of this, and indeed, as we have seen, used his famous demonstration at the Royal Institution in 1861, not primarily to demonstrate to the world for the first time that colour photography was possible, but as an illustration of the truth of the trichromatic theory.

The beginnings of colour photography are thus to be found in the works of a physiologist and a physicist. But the honours for the remarkable commercial success of the modern colour photographic process are undoubtedly due neither to physiologists nor to physicists, but to chemists. It is they who have produced the photographic emulsions with the required sensitivities in the different parts of the spectrum; it is they who have developed the techniques of colour development that play so vital a part in the modern process.

When it comes to the question of assessing how successful the chemists have been, however, the physicist once more plays his part. Most of our detailed knowledge of the nature of the colour mechanism of the human eye has so far come as a result of the work of physicists. They can, therefore, tell us what particular concentrations of dyes, or intensities of lights, are required to reproduce any particular colour as in the original. They are also able to explain, as will be

56

shown in Chapter 6, why this exact colour reproduction is impossible to achieve by simple means. The physicist can indeed prove his assertions, in a very striking way, by making critical comparisons between the colours of objects and the colours of their reproductions in colour photographs or on colour television tubes: the differences are both real and considerable.

Sometimes the imperfections inherent in trichromatic colour photography and television are apparent to the user; some particular colour may appear obviously incorrect in the reproduction. One example of this is the tendency of very pale colours to lose their colour altogether and appear white or grey. Another, in colour photography, is the tendency for certain flowers to be reproduced pink instead of blue although every other colour in the picture appears satisfactory. The reason for this last defect is that certain blue flowers, in addition to reflecting strongly in the blue part of the spectrum and thus appearing blue to the eye, also strongly reflect light in the extreme red end of the spectrum; light of this latter wavelength scarcely affects the eye because the sensitivity of the human retina in this part of the spectrum is very low, but the colour film usually has a high sensitivity in the extreme red, as shown in Fig. 4.3, with the result that the film records the redness of the flower to the exclusion of its blueness. If the sensitivity of the colour film were curtailed in this part of the spectrum, so that it was more nearly like that of the eye, these particular colours would be reproduced more satisfactorily. But such an arrangement would reduce the saturation or vividness of most red colours.

In spite of the inability of simple trichromatic methods to reproduce colours correctly, in some conditions it is the exception, rather than the rule, for the result to *look* incorrect. Moreover, the physicist tells us that the main defect is that colours are reproduced insufficiently vivid (because of the unwanted eye-responses, see Fig. 2.3) and, in the case of subtractive reproductions, too dark (because of the unwanted dye absorptions, see Fig. 4.1); and yet the user often feels that, far from the colours being too pale and too dark, there is rather a tendency for them to appear, if anything, too vivid and too bright, and the process is accused of exaggerating the colours. In short, the physicist defines the shortcomings of the process, and can indeed demonstrate them and measure them, but when the photographer takes a colour film or the viewer looks at his colour tube, the defects often seem to have disappeared.

To explain this apparent anomaly it has to be remembered that although colours may be conveniently defined in terms of physical quantities such as spectral transmission and reflection curves, they are perceived as sensations in the mind. We must therefore consider the psychological as well as the physical side of the story.

5.2 The basis of judgement

Let us examine the basis on which colours are criticized in a reproduction. It is only on rather special occasions that the reproduction and the original are seen side by side; more usually the reproduction is seen at a different place or time, and the time interval may vary from a few hours to several weeks or even months or years. The human memory therefore plays an important part. It might be thought, then, that the process involved in appraising colours in a reproduction consists of making mental comparisons between the sensation produced in the mind by the reproduction, and a recollection from the memory of the colour sensation produced by the original object at the time when the picture was taken. It is, however, a fact that the average person generally feels competent to appraise the colours in pictures taken by people other than himself, of objects which he has never seen, at times when he was not present. This implies that colours in a reproduction are not generally appraised by comparing them either with the original object, nor even with some mental recollection thereof. By what means are they then judged?

There seems no alternative to the idea that the basis of judgement is usually a comparison between the colour sensations aroused by the reproduction, and a mental recollection of the colour sensations previously experienced when looking at objects similar to the one being appraised.

Let us take an example. Green grass is a fairly common component in colour pictures; when trying to assess whether it is correctly reproduced or not, we make a mental comparison between the colour sensation we experience when looking at the reproduction, and our impression of what green grass usually looks like. The physicist will tell us that trichromatic colour processes are particularly bad at reproducing green colours, and that the result will tend to be both darker and less vivid than it should be. Why is it then, that the green colour we see in the picture for green grass seems perfectly satisfactory? The answer is that green grass in original scenes can be any of a very wide range of colours. The apparent colour varies with the type of grass, the dampness of the soil, the direction, colour, and intensity of the lighting, the clarity of the atmosphere, the time of year, and even with the colour and size of the objects surrounding the grass. In short, our standard of comparison, a recollection of the usual colour of green grass, is an extremely vague one, and, consequently, provided that the reproduction of the green grass is included somewhere in the range of colour sensations produced by actual samples of green grass, we are satisfied. These variations in the colours of natural objects are thus of considerable importance. But they are not the only factors which result in a wide range of colour sensations being associated with a given type of object.

Looking at colours is one of a large number of complex activities for which we use our bodies, with scarcely a thought for the processes involved. At first

---

Plate 2. Pincer's Fish. By avoiding the directional reflections on the glass wall of the tank, the colours are seen without the interference of any diffuse white light reflected from their surfaces: hence very vivid colours can be seen. *From a Kodachrome transparency by Kroehnert.*

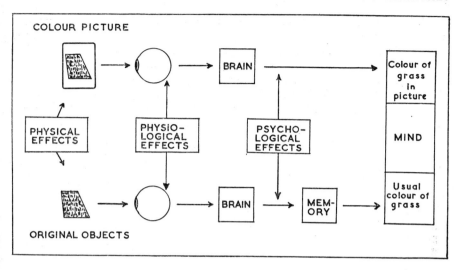

Fig. 5.1. Diagrammatic representation of the processes involved in viewing a colour reproduction of grass (upper line), and (lower line) in viewing original grass. The physical, physiological, and psychological effects differ in the two cases, and also from one original area of grass to another. The standard conception in the memory, therefore, of the usual colour of grass is so vague that the desaturation of grass green inherent in colour reproductions often passes unnoticed, and this applies to many other colours also.

sight it might be thought that our memories could easily supply us with a fairly definite *average* 'green grass' sensation, so that our judgement of the colour reproduction would be clear and fairly exact. But such is far from being the case.

In Fig. 5.1 an attempt has been made to indicate diagrammatically the factors which complicate the issues. The upper line represents the processes involved in viewing a colour picture of the grass. The light from the reproduction enters the observer's eye, resulting in messages being sent to the brain, and these messages are interpreted by the mind as the colour sensations corresponding to the colour of the grass in the picture. The lower line shows a similar sequence for original grass, the colour sensations of which have been stored in the memory.

Plate 3. Girl with harps. Red, orange, yellow, and brown colours generally reproduce well for two reasons. First, the gamut of colours which can be reproduced is usually least deficient in the yellow and orange parts of the spectrum; secondly, yellow dyes and inks usually transmit very well in the yellow, orange, and red parts of the spectrum (and magentas in the red part of the spectrum). *From an Ektachrome transparency by Jack M. Oakley.*

The colour sensation produced by the reproduction of the grass will depend upon the physical composition of the light by which it is illuminated, upon the physiological state of adaptation of the eye when viewing it, and upon any psychological effects that the picture as a whole or in part may have on the observer. Similarly, the colour sensation corresponding to any original grass will be affected by the physical, physiological, and psychological conditions under which it is seen, which will not only differ from those obtaining when the reproduction is viewed, but will also vary from day to day for any one area of grass and from one area of grass to another.

It will be clear from the above that the final comparison, shown diagrammatically on the extreme right of Fig. 5.1, between the colour of the grass in the picture and our impression of the usual colour of grass, is complicated at every step by extraneous effects, which not only result in the impressions we have of the usual colours of objects being extremely vague but also prevent the comparison itself being made with any precision. We shall now discuss some of these effects in more detail.

5.3 Variations in hue

To take the case of green grass again, the hue will depend to a considerable extent on the type of grass, some grasses being a yellowish-green, and others almost a bluish-green; new spring grass is usually rather yellower than older grass. This applies also to foliage, and here the range of hues is even greater; bright yellow-green in spring, green in summer, yellow in early autumn and red or brown in late autumn. Fruits vary tremendously in hue as they ripen, the unripe fruit generally being green, the hue gradually changing to yellow, orange, or red, as the fruit reaches maturity. Flesh-colour, even of so-called 'white' races, varies from light pink or almost white to various shades of tan and brown according to the type of skin and the amount of sun-burn.

The apparent hue of any object is likely to vary, moreover, with the colour of the background against which it is seen. Even the green of a tree, for instance, will apparently change in hue if seen first against a blue sky and then against brown earth.

The colour of the light illuminating a scene will also result in variations in hue. If the sun is low in the sky, for instance, the light will be yellowish, and, although the eye compensates for this physiologically, such compensation is only partial, and objects look yellowish when illuminated by low-altitude sunlight. Furthermore, it is well known that some colours change quite markedly in appearance when taken from daylight into artificial light. This is particularly noticeable with certain mauve colours which tend to look much redder in tungsten-filament lighting.

5.4 Variations in lightness

The apparent lightness of surface colours is affected by a wide variety of factors. Any fabric or cloth tends to hang in folds, and the troughs of the folds look darker than the crests. Leaves, blades of grass, petals of flowers, and other similar objects, tend to cast shadows on one another, again with the result that the amount of light reflected varies very greatly from point to point. Of course the magnitude of this variation is a function, not only of the configuration of the objects, but also of the type of lighting. Strongly directional lighting, such as clear sunlight, casts very deep shadows, whereas diffuse lighting results in softer shadows. Haze in the atmosphere can lighten dark objects and darken light objects if they are relatively distant, and dust on surfaces can act in the same way.

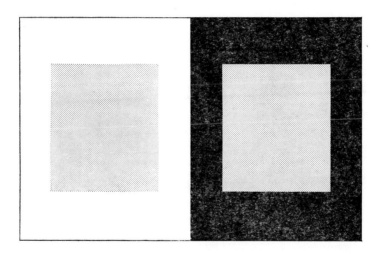

Fig. 5.2. The two grey squares reflect exactly the same amount of light, but the black surrounding the one makes it look lighter than the other which is surrounded by white.

As with hue, so also with lightness, the background can play an important part; a dark background makes colours appear lighter and a light background makes them appear darker. This effect is illustrated in Fig. 5.2, where the two grey patches reflect exactly the same amount of light, but the right patch appears lighter than the left one, because the former has a black surround and the latter a white surround. This difference has an important practical consequence when prints on paper are made from colour transparencies. The latter are seen by projection in a dark room and therefore have a dark surround, while the former usually have white borders. It is clear from Fig. 5.2 that the effect of the black border is to 'subtract grey' from the picture areas, and this gives projected transparencies an inherent advantage over reflection prints.

5.5 Variations in saturation

The saturation, or vividness, of colours as seen by the eye is subject to even more variation than hue or lightness.

It is common experience that a scene which looks a little dull and drab when viewed under an overcast sky, becomes apparently much more vivid and colourful when the sun comes out. The colours all seem to become more saturated. This is principally due to two factors. First, the general level of lighting intensity is raised, and secondly the lighting becomes directional instead of diffuse.

To the camera, however, a variation in the intensity of the light makes no difference to the result, provided that it is adequately compensated by altering the iris diaphragm or the exposure time or both. But the eye, of course, cannot adjust its exposure time, and the control on the iris of the eye is limited to a range of about 8:1 in intensity, so that a major portion of the adjustment in the eye is effected by changes in the actual sensitivities of the different mechanisms of the retina. We are all familiar with the difficulty of seeing our way about in a dimly lit room if we have just been in brilliant sunlight. After some minutes, however, the sensitivity of the retina has risen sufficiently for us to see quite well. In the eye, these changes in sensitivity, known as *adaptation*, are accompanied by quite marked changes in colour vision, which result in colours appearing pale when the intensity is low, and vivid when the intensity is high. An extreme example of this is the appearance of colours by moonlight, when they are desaturated almost to the extent of being indistinguishable from greys. Even at dusk colours are very drab, and the effect is by no means absent at higher intensities. For this reason colour reproductions usually look better the more intensely they are illuminated (Bartleson, 1965).

The second effect arises from the fact that all surfaces, whether coloured or not, reflect from their topmost layer a certain proportion of the incident light which is added to that reflected from the body of the surface. This light reflected from the topmost layer is the same colour as the illuminant, and therefore when a coloured surface is viewed in white light, some of the white light is added to the coloured light reflected from the body of the surface and the colour is therefore desaturated. Most surfaces exhibit some degree of gloss, and this means that, if the lighting is directional, the white light reflected from the topmost layer of the surface will be confined chiefly to a single direction, and will only rarely enter the eye, so that the coloured light, which is reflected diffusely from the body of the surface, usually enters the eye alone, and no desaturation takes place. If, on the other hand, the lighting is diffuse, no matter what the direction of viewing, the coloured light diffusely reflected by the body of the surface will always be mixed with some white light specularly reflected from the topmost layer. This is explained diagrammatically in Fig. 5.3, and practical examples are shown in Plates 2 (page 59) and 8 (page 249).

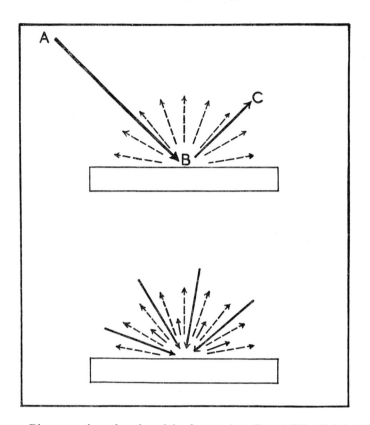

Fig. 5.3. Diagrammatic explanation of the desaturating effect of diffuse lighting. Full lines indicate white light, dotted lines indicate coloured light. In the upper diagram the surface receives strongly directional lighting AB, and, when viewed in any direction other than CB, the coloured light diffusely reflected by the surface is seen alone. In the lower diagram the surface is diffusely illuminated, and, no matter what the direction of viewing, the coloured light diffusely reflected by the surface is always mixed with some white light specularly reflected from the top-most layer of the surface.

As far as adaptation is concerned the variation of saturation with light and dark adaptation is an unalterable fact which usually acts adversely, since many colour pictures depict brightly-lit outdoor scenes and are viewed at lower levels of illumination. Occasionally, however, the effect operates to the advantage of the picture. For instance, a colour photograph may have been taken on a very dull day using an exposure sufficiently prolonged to give a correctly exposed result. It may then be viewed by brighter light and a gain in saturation obtained. To take an extreme case, a colour photograph may be taken by moonlight. The eye at this low illumination can only just perceive colours and they appear very desaturated indeed. But by giving the colour photograph a sufficiently long exposure (about 1,000,000 times that given in sunlight) all the colours are reproduced with exactly the same brilliance as if the colour photograph had been taken in sunlight. Hence, on viewing the photograph with a bright light, the sensations caused by the photograph are very much more saturated than those evoked by the original.

Atmospheric haze will desaturate the colours of distant objects in that it absorbs part of the coloured light coming from the objects and superimposes white light instead. The clarity of the atmosphere can make a tremendous difference to the apparent saturation of distant objects.

Just as dust affects the lightness of surface colours, so also it affects their apparent saturation. Again it absorbs some of the coloured light and superimposes white light so that it always results in a loss of saturation. Dust, of course, soon collects on out-door objects in a hot dry spell of weather, but is quickly removed by a shower of rain. Some coloured surfaces show very remarkable increases in saturation when they are wetted, even in the absence of dust.

The colour of the lighting can also have an effect on saturation in spite of the considerable physiological compensation which the eye makes for differences in illuminant colour. Tungsten-filament lighting and daylight differ considerably in blue content, and this affects the apparent saturations of blue and yellow colours.

The colours of blue skies vary considerably in saturation according to the state of the atmosphere and the position of the sun, the range extending from white near the sun, especially in the presence of haze, to deep blue opposite to the sun, especially in very clear weather. This variation also makes the blueness of areas of water, such as rivers, seas and lakes, very variable in saturation.

5.6 Priorities

Since most of the effects described above, such as those due to atmospheric haze, variation in illumination from directional to diffuse, presence of dust or water on surfaces, adaptation, etc., produce changes in the *saturations* of colours, while only a few effects produce changes in hue, we would expect our mental standards of hue to be more precise than those of saturation. Thus a pale red tomato, for example, is more acceptable in a reproduction than an orange or a magenta one. Correctness of hue would, therefore, seem to be more important than correctness of saturation. Moreover, the variations in saturation which occur in natural colours are generally similar to those produced by adding white light uniformly over the whole field of view. Hence if, in a reproduction, all colours are desaturated by about the same amount, one would expect the result to look more natural than if colours of different hues and saturations were desaturated to different extents, so that some colours shone out like signal lights, while others were grossly desaturated.

The above considerations would seem to suggest that, as far as colour is concerned, the requirements for a successful colour reproduction are, in order of importance:

(1) Correctness of hue,

(2) Approximately equal desaturation of colours of all hues,

(3) Approximately proportional desaturation of colours of all saturations.

The importance of the first requirement is illustrated by the prime importance of overall colour *balance* in colour reproduction. When a picture becomes unacceptable because of a general excess of magenta, for instance, it is the violent change of hue undergone by pale colours which is the most objectionable feature.

The second requirement is sometimes violated by blue skies in colour photographs: the ultra-violet sensitivity of most photographic materials frequently renders them more saturated than other colours. An example of this is apparent to some observers in Plate 5 (page 190).

The third requirement is often difficult to achieve with very pale colours, or with very strongly lit colours in colour photographs; their high luminance puts them on the low contrast toe of photographic materials, and they are often so desaturated as to be indistinguishable from white.

We can now summarize the situation. For fundamental and unavoidable reasons, simple trichromatic methods of colour reproduction cannot result in exact colour rendering, and the errors inherent in most systems are considerable when measured physically. But when the colour of an object in a colour picture is appraised by an observer, it will generally look acceptable, provided it falls somewhere within the range of colours which that object customarily exhibits in everyday life. Practically all colours met with in everyday experience are subject to wide variations in hue, lightness and saturation, and this means that no precise colour standards of familiar objects can possibly be carried in the memory. In particular, the variations in saturation are very great and this obscures the unavoidable tendency of all processes to produce losses in saturation. Furthermore, physiological and psychological effects make it extremely difficult to compare sensations produced by original and reproduction colours with any precision.

There are, however, some objects whose colours are particularly critical. Thus the reproduction tolerances for human flesh, and for most foodstuffs, are smaller than average; and in advertising work manufacturers are often very concerned that their products and packages be depicted with little or no apparent errors of colour reproduction.

67

5.7 Factors affecting apparent colour balance

It is clear from the above discussion that exact colorimetric fidelity is not necessary for a colour reproduction to be acceptable. In fact, some workers have reported that optimum reproduction of some well-known colours, such as flesh, is achieved when a definite difference exists between the original and reproduction colours (MacAdam, 1951; Bartleson and Bray, 1962).

There is one property of the appearance of original scenes, however, which remains remarkably constant, and that is the colour of greys. A grey scale, seen in a very wide range of conditions, continues to look approximately grey (Evans, 1943). This is partly because of the physiological adaptations of the eye to the prevailing illuminant; but, as has already been mentioned, this effect is only partial, and the consistency of the appearance of greys is also partly caused by the ability of observers subconsciously to discount the colour of an illuminant when looking at objects in its light: this psychological effect takes place more or less instantaneously, whereas the physiological adaptation may take several minutes to complete.

It might, therefore, be thought that consistency of perceived greys would also extend to their reproductions: unfortunately this is not so. One reason for this is that colour reproductions do not generally fill more than a small part of an observer's field of view, and this reduces both the physiological and the psychological adjustments which take place. Secondly, both these adjustments affect all areas and all densities of a scene approximately equally, but reproductions may have greys with deviations which vary according to their geometrical or tonal position in the picture. The avoidance of local areas of colour balance different from that of the whole picture is therefore essential for proper reproduction of greys in pictures: this means that colour photographic materials must be coated and processed very uniformly; colour television cameras and receivers must be free of local variations in sensitivity; and half-tone reproductions must be printed uniformly all over. Consistency of colour balance at all tone levels from white to black is equally important, and this requires close control of the relative response characteristics of the red, green, and blue 'channels' of the reproduction system.

Assuming that consistency of the reproduction of greys has been achieved with both area and tone-level, their correct reproduction is possible but not automatic: it is also necessary that the greys be of the correct colour, and this is not necessarily the same as the illuminant colour. Let us consider, by way of example, the case when transparencies are being projected by tungsten light in a darkened room.

The situation is summarized in Fig. 5.4. In the upper left-hand part of the diagram a neutral grey scale is illuminated with tungsten light, which being yellowish, results in yellowish stimuli reaching the eye. But the prevailing illuminant being yellowish, the sensitivity of the eye to yellow light is relatively decreased and this compensates for the yellowness of the stimuli entering the eye, thus giving rise to a neutral grey impression in the mind. The reproduction is therefore also required to give a neutral grey impression to the mind, and the eye, seeing a screen lit by tungsten light in a darkened room will be partially, but not quite wholly, adapted to tungsten light. It is therefore necessary that the neutral grey scale be reproduced on the transparency as slightly blue in order to overcome the slightly yellowish appearance of the tungsten light on the screen.

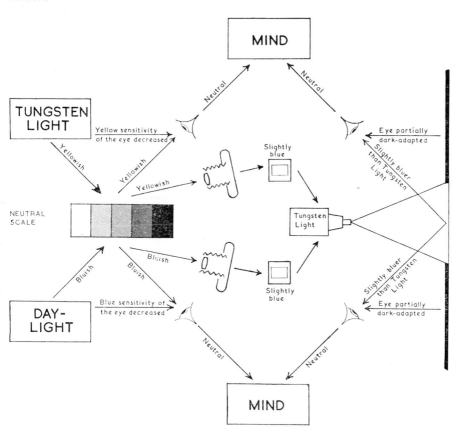

Fig. 5.4. The effects of colour adaptation on colour reproduction.

Considering now the bottom half of the figure, when the neutral grey scale is illuminated by daylight, which is bluish, the eye will receive bluish stimuli, but will have decreased sensitivity to blue so that a neutral grey impression will still be produced in the mind. But the projection conditions have not changed, so that the neutral scale must again be reproduced on the transparency as slightly blue. It is therefore clear that when the photograph is taken in tungsten light, *yellowish* light must produce a slightly blue result, whereas when it is taken in daylight, *bluish* light must produce the same slightly blue result. It is therefore clear that different films must be used for the two situations, a film with a faster blue layer for tungsten light, and a film with a slower blue layer for daylight, or, alternatively, appropriate filters must be used over the camera lens. Kodak materials balanced for daylight use are known as *Daylight type*, those balanced for tungsten light of colour temperature[1] 3400 to 3500°K as *Type A*, and for tungsten light of colour temperature 3100 to 3200°K as *Type B*, and those balanced for clear flash lamps as *Type F*. In negative-positive colour photographic systems considerable compensation for illuminant colour can be made at the printing stage.

In colour television similar compensation for the colour of the light illuminating the scene must also be made, and this can be done by altering the relative amplifications of the signals from the red, green, and blue images in the television camera, so that they are always equal to one another for white (and grey) objects in the scene.

If two illuminants of markedly differing colour, such as daylight and tungsten light, are mixed in the same scene, the result in the colour reproduction is usually very unpleasant, and mixed lighting must, therefore, usually be avoided. The appearance of the original scene is often quite tolerable and this seems to be because the light sources are usually visible and subconscious allowance is made for their colour effects, whereas in the colour picture the sources are nearly always excluded; also many colour reproduction systems operate at high contrasts and with ultra-violet and infra-red sensitivities greater than those of the eye: hence the difference in colour between the two sources may be increased in the reproduction.

5.8 Integrating to grey

Correct colour balance is particularly necessary in the case of reflection colour prints, because their surroundings provide a reference balance against which they can easily be compared. Hence special techniques are usually needed when making reflection prints and one of the most successful, known as 'integrating to grey', was first suggested by Evans (Evans, 1951). Evans argued that because any colour reproduction will tend to adapt the eye towards its average colour balance, it would be an advantage if the light from the print, when integrated, appeared grey in colour, because then the eye would be adapted to it immediately. Accordingly, in printing colour negatives, it is often arranged that the cyan, magenta, and yellow layers of the print material receive exposures inversely proportional to the red, green and blue transmissions of the negative, respectively. In this way, prints which approximately 'integrate to grey' can be

[1] Colour temperature is defined in Section 8.2.

made rapidly by semi-automatic methods to a consistently high standard of acceptance, the proportion requiring special treatment because of unusual subject
matter being surprisingly small. This method of printing has been applied in
various ways. (Bartleson and Huboi, 1956; Hunt, 1960). This subject is dealt
with more fully in Chapter 14.

REFERENCES

Bartleson, C. J., *Phot. Sci. and Eng.*, **3**, 114 (1959).
Bartleson, C. J., *J. Opt. Soc. Amer.*, **50**, 73 (1960).
Bartleson, C. J., *Phot. Sci. Eng.*, **9**, 174 and 179 (1965).
Bartleson, C. J., and Bray, C. P., *Phot. Sci. Eng.*, **6**, 19 (1962).
Bartleson, C. J., and Huboi, R. W., *J. Soc. Mot. Pic. Tel. Eng.*, **65**, 205 (1956).
Evans, R. M., *J. Opt. Soc. Amer.*, **33**, 579 (1943).
Evans, R. M., *U.S. Patent 2,571,697. British Patent 660,099* (1951).
Hunt, R. W. G., *J. Photogr., Sci.* **8**, 186 and 212 (1960).
MacAdam, D. L., *J. Soc. Mot. Pic. Tel. Eng.*, **56**, 502 (1951).

GENERAL REFERENCES

Evans, R. M., *Eye, Film, and Camera in Colour Photography*, Wiley, New York (1959).

CHAPTER 6

The Colour Triangle

6.1 Introduction

IN Chapters 2 and 4 the errors of trichromatic colour reproduction by both the additive and the subtractive principles were considered in terms of the assumed sensitivity curves of the three types, ρ, γ, and β, of retinal cone. This approach to the subject has the advantage of being direct and simple, but it requires some assumptions concerning the eye, and is of a qualitative, rather than a quantitative nature. For a quantitative approach it is necessary first to consider in some detail the phenomenon of trichromatic colour matching. Before we do this, however, a brief consideration of some aspects of colour terminology is advisable (British Standard 1611:1953; C.I.E. International Lighting Vocabulary, 1967).

6.2 Colour terminology

It is generally agreed that colours have three main attributes: *hue*, which denotes whether the colour appears red, orange, or blue etc.; *saturation*, which denotes the extent to which the colour appears to be admixed with white, grey or black (high saturation denoting the appearance of little admixture, low saturation denoting the appearance of much admixture); and *luminosity* or *lightness*, which denote the extent to which colours appear to emit more or less light, the former term being used for light sources, and the latter for surface colours. The appearance of any given colour, however, can change with the viewing conditions; thus a surface which by daylight appears a light saturated red, for instance, becomes a dark desaturated red at twilight and practically grey by moonlight. For this reason it has been found helpful to divide colour terms into *subjective* and *objective* terms.

Subjective terms denote the appearance of the colour to an observer; thus hue, saturation, luminosity, and lightness, as defined above, are all subjective terms. Objective terms relate to quantities obtained with measuring instruments, and (unlike subjective terms) are unaffected by changes in the adaptation of the observer. It is convenient to measure quantities which are correlated with the subjective terms defined above and the objective terms involved are as follows:

Subjective Term:	Hue	*Objective Term:*	Dominant Wavelength
	Saturation		Purity
	Luminosity		Luminance
	Lightness		Luminance Factor
	Hue and Saturation		Chromaticity

The term *luminance* has been adopted internationally to denote what previously was called *photometric brightness*, or just *brightness*. The change was made because, to many people, the brightness of a colour denotes its colourfulness rather than its luminous intensity per unit projected area, which is now therefore called *luminance*. Thus if the intensity of illumination on a surface is doubled, the luminance of that surface is doubled, but the brightness of the colour (in the sense of its colourfulness) might remain unchanged. In America, *brightness* is often used in the sense of *luminosity*.

The term *luminance factor* is a measure of the extent to which an object reflects or transmits more or less light; the more specific term *reflection factor* or *reflectance* is often used for surface colours; for transmitting colours, such as filters, *transmission factor* or *transmittance* is often used.

There are occasions when it is extremely important to distinguish between the objective and subjective attributes of colours; but in many contexts only general attributes are in view and strict observance of the above terminology would be pedantic. In these cases the subjective terms are used in this book, since they are more widely understood. In America the Munsell system of colour specification is widely used, and in this system *Hue* is used in the objective sense, *Value* is used instead of Luminance Factor, and *Chroma* instead of Purity. The Munsell system has the special feature that, though an *objective* system, it is scaled *subjectively*: that is, equal steps of Munsell Hue, Chroma and Value have been chosen to represent as far as possible equal differences in Hue, Saturation and Lightness respectively. A consequence of this is that in a shadow series, having constant hue and saturation, chroma decreases with decreasing lightness, because at low lightnesses it is more difficult to see colour differences than at high lightnesses. Thus, on a page of Munsell samples of constant hue, if (as they should) the columns of chips represent constant chroma, the colour saturation tends to increase with decreasing lightness.

6.3 Trichromatic matching

If, as in Fig. 6.1 arrangements are made whereby colours can be compared in appearance with an additive mixture of red, green, and blue light, it is found

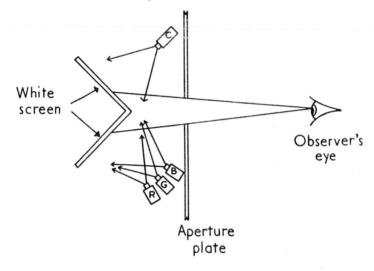

Fig. 6.1. The principle of trichromatic matching. The upper white screen is illuminated only by light of the test colour C. The lower white screen is illuminated only by a mixture of red, green, and blue light from the three lanterns R, G, and B. By adjusting the amounts of red, green, and blue light in the mixture, it can be made identical in appearance to the colour C.

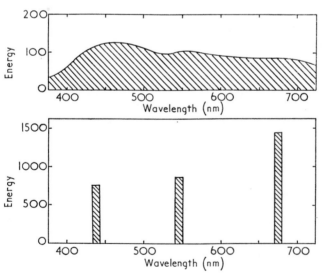

Fig. 6.2. The upper curve shows the spectral energy distribution of a white light; the energy distribution shown in the lower diagram refers to a light which, to the eye, appears exactly the same colour. (Note the different energy scales used.)

that by varying the relative and absolute amounts of the red, green and blue lights it is always possible to make the appearance of the mixture identical with that of any chosen colour. (A few colours of very high purity appear to be exceptions to this rule, but, as we shall shortly see, they can also be matched by using a special technique.)

This phenomenon of trichromatic matching is easily explained in terms of a trichromatic theory of colour vision. For if all colours are analysed by the retina into only three different types of response, ρ, γ, and β (proportional, for instance, to absorptions in three different photo-sensitive pigments), the eye will be able to detect no difference between two stimuli which give rise to the same ρ-, the same γ- and the same β-signal, no matter how different the two stimuli may be in spectral composition. In fact the spectral difference between two matching stimuli can be quite startling as shown in Fig. 6.2, where a stimulus consisting of energy throughout the whole of the spectrum is matched by light from three narrow bands of the spectrum only. But both these energy distributions give rise to identical ρ-, γ-, and β-responses, so that the two stimuli are indistinguishable to the eye. (Such stimuli, which are spectrally different but visually identical, are known as *metameric pairs*, or *metamers*.)

With some colours of very high purity, and most colours of the spectrum, it is found that although the red, green, and blue mixture can reproduce the same hue and luminosity, the saturation of the mixture is never quite sufficient to match these colours. The case is particularly marked for the blue-green colours of the spectrum. A mixture consisting of blue and green only can be made to reproduce the correct hue and luminosity, but the mixture is always paler than the test colour.

At first sight, it might be thought that this fact invalidates trichromatic theories of colour vision, but it is in fact predicted by them. In Fig. 6.3 the

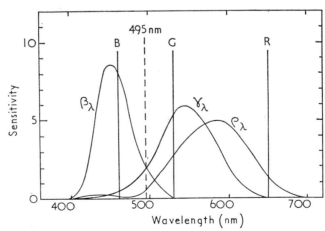

Fig. 6.3. A typical set of sensitivity curves, $\rho\lambda$, $\gamma\lambda$, and $\beta\lambda$, representing the probable sensitivity curves of the three types of light receptor believed to be operating in the eye. (Reproduced from Fig. 2.2(a).)

75

assumed sensitivity curves of the three retinal receptors ρ, γ and β, are reproduced from Fig. 2.2(a). Let us consider the case where our red, green, and blue beams of light R, G, and B are the most saturated available, that is monochromatic light of wavelengths 650 nm for the red, R, 530 nm for the green, G, and 460 nm for the blue, B, and suppose that we are trying to match monochromatic light of wavelength 495 nm (a blue-green). It is clear that the red stimulus will give only a ρ-response, and no γ- or β-response. The green stimulus will give chiefly a γ-response, but also a considerable ρ-response, but very little β-response. The blue stimulus will give mainly a β-response, together with a small γ-response, but very little ρ-response. An arbitrary scale has been included in Fig. 6.3 so that the responses given by unit energy of each of the three stimuli R, G, and B, can be tabulated from Fig. 6.3 thus:

For unit energy of R $\qquad \rho=1.26 \quad \gamma=0 \quad \beta=0$

,, ,, ,, ,, G $\qquad \rho=2.7 \quad \gamma=5.7 \quad \beta=0$

,, ,, ,, ,, B $\qquad \rho=0.08 \quad \gamma=0.4 \quad \beta=8.0$

Now for unit energy of light of wavelength 495 nm, from Fig. 6.3:

$$\rho=0.5 \qquad \gamma=2.0 \qquad \beta=2.0$$

and therefore in order to match it with a mixture of R, G and B it is necessary to choose amounts of them which give rise to the same response magnitudes.

Since only the B stimulus produces any β-response it is clear that we must have a quarter of a unit of B in order to produce the required 2.0 β-response. Thus we have:

For $\frac{1}{4}$ unit of B $\qquad \rho=0.02 \quad \gamma=0.1 \quad \beta=2.0$

We now need more γ-response, and since R produces none, we must produce it by means of G. We therefore need a γ-response of 1.9 units which will be given by $\frac{1}{3}$ of a unit of G. Thus we have:

For $\frac{1}{3}$ unit of G $\qquad \rho=0.9 \quad \gamma=1.9 \quad \beta=0$

Hence for $\frac{1}{4}$ unit of B together with $\frac{1}{3}$ unit of G:

$$\rho=0.92 \quad \gamma=2.0 \quad \beta=2.0$$

It is thus clear that already we have almost twice as much ρ-response as we should have and we have not yet added any R. To do so would merely increase the ρ-response still further, without altering the γ- and β-responses, thus making the mixture even less like the test colour of wavelength 495 nm. It is therefore clear that no mixture of lights of wavelengths 650, 530, and 460 nm can ever be made to match light of wavelength 495 nm, and this is borne out by experiment. The fact, however, is predicted by the curves of Fig. 6.3, which are the quantitative expressions of trichromatic theories of colour vision, and the theories are in no way invalidated. It is because the ρ- and β-curves of Fig. 6.3 overlap, thus making it impossible to stimulate the γ-cones on their own, that saturated blue-green colours cannot be matched by additive mixtures of red, green, and blue light.

If monochromatic lights of different wavelengths are chosen for the three matching stimuli, or if matching stimuli each comprised of broad spectral bands of light are used, there will always be some saturated colours which cannot be matched; occasionally light of wavelength 495 nm may be matched, as when for instance one of the three matching stimuli consists of light of this wavelength; but in this case there will be other spectral colours which cannot be matched.

To revert, however, to our stimuli R, G, and B of wavelengths 650, 530, and 460 nm, it is clear that if, instead of adding some of the stimulus R to the mixture of $\frac{1}{4}$ unit of B and $\frac{1}{3}$ unit of G, we add it in the right amount to the test colour of wavelength 495 nm, we can obtain a colour match once more. Thus we already have 0.92 ρ-response in the mixture, but only 0.5 ρ-response in the test colour. So the addition of 0.42 ρ-response to the test colour will make it match the mixture of G and B. This amount of ρ-response is given by $\frac{1}{3}$ unit of R thus:

For $\frac{1}{3}$ unit of R $\qquad \rho = 0.42 \quad \gamma = 0 \quad \beta = 0$

We, therefore, now have the situation that:

Unit energy of 495 nm $+ \frac{1}{3}$ unit of R is matched by $\frac{1}{3}$ unit of G $+ \frac{1}{4}$ unit of B

It is customary to regard this addition of one of the three matching stimuli to the test colour instead of to the mixture as a negative quantity of R and we therefore write:

Unit energy of 495 nm is matched by $\frac{1}{3}$ unit of G $+ \frac{1}{4}$ unit of B $- \frac{1}{3}$ unit of R

Using this conception of negative amounts, it is possible to match *all* colours by choosing suitable proportions of three matching stimuli which are additively mixed.

6.4 Colour-matching functions

Since, as we have just seen, it is possible to match all colours by means of additive mixtures of three matching stimuli, it is possible to match all the colours of the spectrum. When this has been done the results are often presented as three curves, as shown in Fig. 6.4, in which the amount of R, the amount of G, and the amount of B needed to match unit energy of each wavelength of the spectrum, are plotted against wavelength. As would be expected, the maximum of each curve is in a region of the spectrum where the colour is similar to the matching stimulus in question, and it will also be noted that all three curves have negative portions, the largest being that of the R stimulus in the blue-green parts of the spectrum. The units used for the amounts of R, G and B are not always energy units, since it is generally more convenient to use arbitrary units such that some specified white stimulus is matched by equal amounts of the three matching stimuli. In Fig. 6.4 the white stimulus used for defining the units is one in which the amount of energy per unit wavelength is constant throughout the spectrum; this hypothetical white source is of some importance in colorimetry and is known as the *equal-energy source*, with the abbreviation S_E. If a different white had been used for defining the units, or if the units had been defined photometrically (as, for instance, candelas/square foot or lumens/square foot) or if units of energy had been used, the curves would not have differed in shape but only in height, all the ordinates of any one curve being multiplied by the same factor, but the three factors being different for the three curves.

The ordinates of these *colour-mixture curves* or *colour-matching functions*, are generally denoted by the symbols $\bar{r}_\lambda$, $\bar{g}_\lambda$, $\bar{b}_\lambda$ or $\bar{r}(\lambda)$, $\bar{g}(\lambda)$, $\bar{b}(\lambda)$, so that the interpretation of the curves may be written thus:

Unit energy of light of wavelength λ is matched by
$\bar{r}_\lambda$ units of R $+\bar{g}_\lambda$ units of G $+\bar{b}_\lambda$ units of B.

It is convenient to abbreviate this to:

$$1.0(\lambda) \equiv \bar{r}_\lambda(R) + \bar{g}_\lambda(G) + \bar{b}_\lambda(B)$$

where the equivalent sign ($\equiv$) is used to mean that the equation represents an equivalence of colours to the eye, and the symbols in brackets do not represent *quantities*, but merely indicate to which stimuli the coefficients (1.0, $\bar{r}_\lambda$ etc.) refer.

Experiment shows that these equations usually obey the ordinary rules of algebra so that, for instance:

$$k(\lambda) \equiv k\bar{r}_\lambda(R) + k\bar{g}_\lambda(G) + k\bar{b}_\lambda(B)$$

Moreover if we have k_1 energy units of wavelength λ_1 and k_2 energy units of wavelength λ_2, represented by the equations

$$k_1(\lambda_1) \equiv k_1\bar{r}_1(R) + k_1\bar{g}_1(G) + k_1\bar{b}_1(B)$$
$$k_2(\lambda_2) \equiv k_2\bar{r}_2(R) + k_2\bar{g}_2(G) + k_2\bar{b}_2(B)$$

then experiment shows that:

$$k_1(\lambda_1) + k_2(\lambda_2) \equiv (k_1\bar{r}_1 + k_2\bar{r}_2)(R) + (k_1\bar{g}_1 + k_2\bar{g}_2)(G) + (k_1\bar{b}_1 + k_2\bar{b}_2)(B)$$

This additive property of equations can be extended to any number of wavelengths so that generally we can write:

$$k_1(\lambda_1) + k_2(\lambda_2) + \ldots \equiv (k_1\bar{r}_1 + k_2\bar{r}_2 + \ldots)(R) + (k_1\bar{g}_1 + k_2\bar{g}_2 + \ldots)(G)$$
$$+ (k_1\bar{b}_1 + k_2\bar{b}_2 + \ldots)(B)$$

But all colours, whether saturated or pale, light or dark, and of whatever hue, consist of mixtures of spectral colours in varying amounts. Therefore, if we know the spectral energy distribution of any stimulus, with the aid of the curves of Fig. 6.4 (or tabulated values of $\bar{r}_\lambda$, $\bar{g}_\lambda$ and $\bar{b}_\lambda$) it is possible to calculate the amounts of R, G and B necessary to match it, and the results of such calculations agree with the values obtained when the stimulus is matched experimentally.

Suppose then that we have some stimulus, C, represented by some spectral energy distribution curve E_λ. By means of the curves of Fig. 6.4 we can calculate the amounts of R, G and B needed to match it, and obtain the equation:

$$(C) \equiv R_c(R) + G_c(G) + B_c(B)$$

where

$$R_c = E_1\bar{r}_1 + E_2\bar{r}_2 + \ldots \quad \ldots + E_n\bar{r}_n$$

there being similar expressions for G_c and B_c, and the numerals 1 to n indicating a series of wavelengths equally spaced at a convenient interval throughout the entire visible spectrum. These amounts R_c, G_c and B_c are known as *tristimulus values*.

Suppose now that in an additive colour photographic system the colours of the red, green and blue lights forming the final picture are the same R, G and B as we have been considering, namely monochromatic lights of wavelength 650, 530 and 460 nm respectively. And suppose that the three filter-emulsion combinations on which the image of the original scene is focused, have spectral sensitivity curves exactly the same as those of Fig. 6.4 (we shall consider the

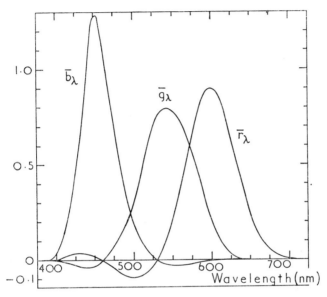

Fig. 6.4. Colour-matching functions showing the amounts, $\bar{r}_\lambda$, $\bar{g}_\lambda$, and $\bar{b}_\lambda$ of red, green, and blue light required to match unit energy of each wavelength of the spectrum, using matching stimuli of wavelengths 650, 530, and 460 nm respectively. The amounts of the stimuli are measured in arbitrary units chosen so that equal amounts of the three stimuli are needed to match the 'equal energy' white source, S_E.

practical realization of the negative parts of these curves presently). Considering the red negative only, the exposure N_R will be proportional to

$$E_1\bar{r}_1 + E_2\bar{r}_2 + E_3\bar{r}_3 + \ldots \quad \ldots + E_n\bar{r}_n$$

Assuming that the photographic system is linear, the amount of latent image, I_R, formed in the negative, will be proportional to N_R, and the transmission T_R on the positive will be proportional to I_R and therefore also to N_R. But the expression for N_R is exactly the same as that for R_C, the amount of the stimulus R needed to match the colour C. Therefore the projection of the positive with transmission T_R will automatically result in kR_C of stimulus R being projected on the screen, and k will be constant over the picture area, so that over the entire picture area the amount of R will be proportional to the amount needed

79

to match the colours of the original scene. Similarly the transmission of the green positive T_G will be proportional to G_c, the amount of stimulus G needed to match the colours of the original, and the transmission of the blue positive T_B will be proportional to B_c, the amount of stimulus B needed to match the colours of the original. Hence any colour in the original is represented by:

$$(C) \equiv R_c(R) + G_c(G) + B_c(B)$$

and in the reproduction by:

$$(C') \equiv kR_c(R) + kG_c(G) + kB_c(B)$$

It is thus only necessary to make $k=1$, that is, to adjust the overall intensity of the picture so that the luminance of the reproduction is the same as that of the original, to obtain exact[1] colour reproduction of all the colours in the original scene (Hardy and Wurzburg, 1937, Harrison and Horner, 1937).

The conditions which must be satisfied in order to obtain this result are:

(1) The spectral sensitivity curves of the filter-emulsion combinations, used to record the three negatives, must be identical with the colour-matching functions of the three stimuli used to form the final picture;

(2) The transmission at any point on the positives must be proportional to the exposures at the corresponding point on the negatives;

(3) The overall luminance must be adjusted so that the picture has the same luminance as the original.

Conditions 2 and 3 may not be too difficult to realize, but the negative portions of the colour-matching functions make condition 1 almost impossible to achieve in a photographic system. What is required is a filter-emulsion combination wherein exposure by light in some parts of the spectrum bleaches the latent image formed by light in other parts of the spectrum. Thus in the case of the 'red' negative, for instance, exposure to light from the blue-green part of the spectrum (wavelengths 460 to 530 nm) must *reduce* the amount of latent image formed by light in the red (and blue) parts of the spectrum. By using two *toe-recording* photographic negatives, one for the positive parts of the curve, and the other for the negative part, and binding up a photographic positive made from the latter in exact registration with the former, the result can, at least in theory, be achieved (See MacAdam 1938, page 405). In practice, however, the method is cumbersome and only approximate, and, as far as photography is concerned, no convenient method of introducing the negative parts of the sensitivity curves has yet been found. In colour television, however, the problem is a good deal simpler, at least, in principle. Thus if one television pick-up tube had a spectral sensitivity identical to the positive parts of the red colour-matching functions, and another tube a spectral sensitivity corresponding to its negative parts, as shown in Fig. 6.5, then by subtracting the second from the first a red signal would be derived based on a composite spectral sensitivity

---

[1] By *exact* it is simply meant here that the reproduction colours all have the same tristimulus values as the original colours. For a discussion as to whether this is the most *desirable* state of affairs reference should be made to Chapter 9.

curve equivalent to the complete matching function. Similar arrangements could be made for the green and blue signals, using a total of six different tubes in all. This arrangement is very cumbersome, however, and it is more convenient in practice to use only three, all-positive, curves and to obtain the correct signals by means of a technique known as *matrixing*. If to the red matching function a

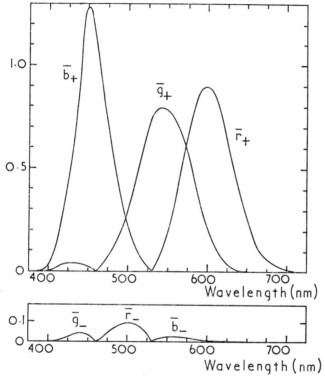

Fig. 6.5. The positive portions (above), and the negative portions (below), of the colour-matching functions of Fig. 6.4.

small fraction of the green matching function is added, a composite all-positive curve can be obtained. If the signal obtained from a tube having such a sensitivity, then has subtracted from it the same small fraction of the green signal, the final signal will be based on the true red matching function. When this technique is applied to obtain signals based on all three colour-matching functions, the correct fractions to be subtracted involve three simultaneous equations, and it is these equations which matrixing is usually intended to imitate. The result can be a television system having exactly the required sensitivity curves of Fig. 6.4. (This is discussed more fully in Section 16.13.)

If then, we have such a colour television system, employing these sensitivity curves, and red, green and blue lights on the viewing tube which are identical with R, G and B (that is monochromatic lights of wavelengths 650, 530, and 460 nm respectively), we have clearly fulfilled condition 1. Assuming that conditions 2 and 3 are also fulfilled, we should then have exact colour reproduction. But let us consider the case of a blue-green light, of wavelength 495 nm, for example, in the original scene. Fig. 6.4 tells us that it will require a negative amount of red in its match so that we can write:

$$k(\lambda_{\text{BG}}) \equiv -R_{\text{BG}}(\text{R}) + G_{\text{BG}}(\text{G}) + B_{\text{BG}}(\text{B})$$

Now, all the colours on our television tube are formed by mixtures of the stimuli R, G, and B, but these mixtures can now only be all positive mixtures. For the meaning to be attached to the symbol $-R_{\text{BG}}$ is that this amount of stimulus R must be added to the blue-green light; but of course the blue-green light is part of the original scene and, even if we could add red light to it, once it had been added, we would no longer have the same colour. It is clear, therefore, that although the algebra tells us that we have exact colour reproduction, in fact whenever the electronic signals call for one or more of the three stimuli R, G or B to be present in a negative amount, the television tube is unable to oblige. This defect only occurs when the final signals called for are negative. A colour in the original scene can contain light from the blue-green part of the spectrum, for instance, and still be reproduced exactly provided that it also contains light from some other part of the spectrum which makes the resultant quantity of R either zero or positive. Thus a colour consisting of a mixture of light from the blue-green and yellow-green parts of the spectrum would give rise to the following situation:

$$k_1(\lambda_{\text{BG}}) \equiv -R_{\text{BG}}(\text{R}) + G_{\text{BG}}(\text{G}) + B_{\text{BG}}(\text{B})$$
$$k_2(\lambda_{\text{YG}}) \equiv R_{\text{YG}}(\text{R}) + G_{\text{YG}}(\text{G}) - B_{\text{YG}}(\text{B})$$
$$k_1(\lambda_{\text{BG}}) + k_2(\lambda_{\text{YG}}) \equiv (R_{\text{YG}} - R_{\text{BG}})(\text{R}) + (G_{\text{BG}} + G_{\text{YG}})(\text{G}) + (B_{\text{BG}} - B_{\text{YG}})(\text{B})$$

Then provided that $R_{\text{YG}} - R_{\text{BG}}$ and $B_{\text{BG}} - B_{\text{YG}}$ are both positive, this mixture will be reproduced perfectly correctly on our television screen, despite the fact that neither part of the mixture can be reproduced correctly on its own.

Hence, we can say that, with this television system, all colours will be reproduced perfectly correctly, except for those very saturated colours which cannot be matched by an all-positive mixture of the red, green, and blue lights used in the television tube. In point of fact, these unmatchable colours are only rarely encountered in nature, so that the limitation is of little practical consequence.

6.5 The colour triangle

The consideration of many of these questions is greatly facilitated by the use of the *colour triangle*, which may be thought of as a kind of colour map, in which all colours are represented in a systematic way by points in a triangle.

Given three defined matching stimuli R, G and B, which could, for instance, be our three monochromatic lights of wavelengths 650, 530, and 460 nm, the amounts of these three stimuli needed to match any colour enable it to be related systematically to all other colours. Thus the equation:

$$k(C) \equiv R_c(R) + G_c(G) + B_c(B)$$

represents k *units* of the colour C. Now the *amount*, k, of the colour C can be regarded as a physical or photometric quantity, measured, for instance, in ergs per square centimetre per second, if energy units are used, or in candelas or lumens per square foot (or as a percentage of the incident light) if light units are used. The *colour*, red or yellow, vivid or pale etc., is governed largely by the ratio of the three quantities R_c, G_c and B_c to one another. It is therefore customary to divide the equation by the sum of the three quantities to give:

$$\frac{k}{R_c + G_c + B_c}(C) \equiv r(R) + g(G) + b(B)$$

where

$$r = R_c/(R_c + G_c + B_c)$$
$$g = G_c/(R_c + G_c + B_c)$$
$$b = B_c/(R_c + G_c + B_c)$$

Since the *amount* of C is now of secondary importance, we may write the equation without specifying it, using the proportional sign thus:

$$(C) \propto r(R) + g(G) + b(B).$$

r, g, and b are known as *chromaticity co-ordinates*. It is clear that the sum $r+g+b$ is always equal to unity, so that if r and g are known, b can always be deduced from:

$$b = 1 - r - g$$

We can therefore plot r and g and obtain a diagram on which all colours are represented. In Fig. 6.6. this has been done with g as ordinate and r as abscissa, the curved line representing the locus of the spectral colours, and the point W, the particular white which was used to define the units of the three stimuli. The matching stimuli themselves and the white, W, have the following values of r and g:

(R)	$r=1$	$g=0$
(G)	$r=0$	$g=1$
(B)	$r=0$	$g=0$
(W)	$r=0.333$	$g=0.333$

and hence occupy the corners and the centre of the triangle as shown.

Since r, g and b will always have the same signs as R_c, G_c and B_c, it is inevitable that the value of r is negative in the blue-green part of the spectrum, as shown in the figure.

6.6 The centre of gravity law

Suppose we have two colours, C_1 and C_2, whose positions on the colour triangle are known. It is important to know where the point C_3, representing a mixture of given quantities of C_1 and C_2, will be situated. If C_1 and C_2 are represented by:

$$(C_1) \propto r_1(R) + g_1(G) + b_1(B) \quad \text{where } r_1 + g_1 + b_1 = 1$$
$$(C_2) \propto r_2(R) + g_2(G) + b_2(B) \quad \text{where } r_2 + g_2 + b_2 = 1$$

and the quantities in the mixture are m_1 units of C_1 and m_2 units of C_2, we have to proceed as follows: m_1 and m_2 are usually given in photometric units[1] (usually units of luminance), so that we have to know the photometric values (for example in candelas per square foot) of the units in which the amounts of R, G and B are being measured. These values will not necessarily be the same for the three stimuli; they will generally be different, for instance, when the units are defined by stipulating that equal amounts of R, G and B match a particular white. Let the three photometric values or luminances be denoted by L_R, L_G, and L_B. Then with the amount of C_1 measured in photometric or luminance units, we may write:

$$L_1(C_1) \equiv r_1(R) + g_1(G) + b_1(B)$$

where $L_1 = L_R r_1 + L_G g_1 + L_B b_1$. Hence 1 photometric unit of C_1 is represented by the equation:

$$1.0(C_1) \equiv \frac{r_1}{L_1}(R) + \frac{g_1}{L_1}(G) + \frac{b_1}{L_1}(B)$$

and therefore m_1 photometric units by:

$$m_1(C_1) \equiv \frac{m_1}{L_1}r_1(R) + \frac{m_1}{L_1}g_1(G) + \frac{m_1}{L_1}b_1(B)$$

Similarly m_2 photometric units of C_2 are represented by:

$$m_2(C_2) \equiv \frac{m_2}{L_2}r_2(R) + \frac{m_2}{L_2}g_2(G) + \frac{m_2}{L_2}b_2(B)$$

where $L_2 = L_R r_2 + L_G g_2 + L_B b_2$. Therefore the mixture is represented by:

$$m_1(C_1) + m_2(C_2) \equiv \left(\frac{m_1}{L_1}r_1 + \frac{m_2}{L_2}r_2\right)(R) + \left(\frac{m_1}{L_1}g_1 + \frac{m_2}{L_2}g_2\right)(G) + \left(\frac{m_1}{L_1}b_1 + \frac{m_2}{L_2}b_2\right)(B)$$

The new values of r and g are obtained by dividing this equation by the sum of the coefficients of (R), (G) and (B), and this sum reduces to $m_1/L_1 + m_2/L_2$. We therefore obtain:

$$(C_3) \propto r_3(R) + g_3(G) + b_3(B)$$

where

$$r_3 = \left(\frac{m_1}{L_1}r_1 + \frac{m_2}{L_2}r_2\right) \bigg/ \left(\frac{m_1}{L_1} + \frac{m_2}{L_2}\right)$$

and similar expressions for g_3 and b_3. The geometrical interpretation of this formula is very simple indeed: C_3 always lies on the line joining C_1 and C_2 and divides it in the inverse ratio:

$$\frac{m_2}{L_2} \bigg/ \frac{m_1}{L_1}$$

[1] For a list of photometric units and their meanings, see Appendix 2.

as shown in Fig. 6.6. C_3 is in fact at the centre of gravity of weights m_1/L_1 placed at C_1 and m_2/L_2 placed at C_2, hence this rule of colour mixture is often referred to as the Centre of Gravity Law.

It has a number of important consequences in the colour triangle. First, since the spectral locus maintains a convex curvature throughout, all mixtures of spectral colours, and therefore *all* colours, must lie either within or upon the spectral locus, but never outside it; thus, by joining the two ends of the spectral locus with a straight line, the area containing *all* colours is enclosed. Points lying outside this area have one of their three values more negative than is ever required in colour matching.

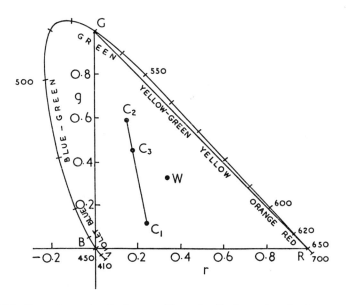

Fig. 6.6. The colour triangle for matching stimuli of wavelengths 650, 530, and 460 nm, showing the locus of spectral colours and the white point W. The units are such that equal quantities of the three stimuli are needed to match the equal energy white.

Secondly, when white light is added in gradually increasing amounts to any colour of the spectrum the position of the point representing the resultant mixture gradually moves in from the spectral locus, along a straight line, towards the white point. Thus, on the colour triangle, the straight line joining the white point to any spectral colour represents colours of constant dominant wavelength[1] but of varying purity, the purest colours lying near or upon the

---

[1] MacAdam (1950, 1951) and others have shown that these lines represent colours which are only approximately constant in *hue*.

spectral locus, and the least pure colours lying near the white point, with intermediate colours in between. The hues are distributed around the spectral locus in accordance with Fig. 1.1, and have been marked in Fig. 6.6. The purest magentas and purples lie along the line joining the ends of the spectral locus.

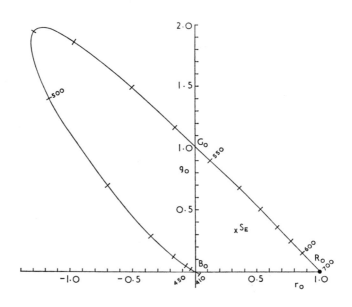

Fig. 6.7. The colour triangle for matching stimuli of wavelengths 700, 546.1, and 435.8 nm, the units being such that equal quantities of the three stimuli are needed to match the equal energy white, S_E.

The colour triangle now makes clear the limitations of our colour television system. All colours represented by points lying within the triangle R, G, B will be reproduced correctly. But points lying outside, requiring, as they do, one of the amounts to be negative, cannot be correctly reproduced; the reproduction colour will move in to the edge of the triangle. The most severe limitation is in the case of blue-green colours of high purity.

6.7 Other colour triangles

If, instead of using matching stimuli of wavelengths 650, 530 and 460 nm, we had used three other lights, R_o, G_o, and B_o say, we would have obtained a colour triangle similar to that of Fig. 6.6, but with R_o, G_o and B_o at the corners of the triangle and the other colours somewhat shifted in position. Thus, Fig. 6.7 shows the triangle for matching stimuli R_o, G_o and B_o of wavelengths 700, 546.1 and 435.8 nm, and Fig. 6.8 that for matching stimuli R_s, G_s and B_s consisting of bands of wavelengths from 700 to 580 nm, from 580 to 490 nm, and from 490 to 400 nm isolated from a tungsten filament lamp operating at a colour temperature (this term is defined in Section 8.2) of 2854°K.

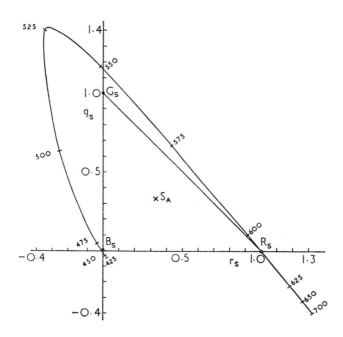

Fig. 6.8. The colour triangle for matching stimuli obtained by isolating three spectral bands from a tungsten filament lamp at a colour temperature of 2854°K (S_A). The spectral bands were: 700 to 580 nm (R_s), 580 to 490 nm (G_s), and 490 to 400 nm (B_s). The units are such that equal quantities of the matching stimuli are needed to match the colour of the light from the lamp (S_A).

It is obviously desirable that a triangle should be chosen for which, if possible, equal distances in any part of the triangle represent equal colour differences. Actually no triangle can be found which is perfect in this respect, but that shown in Fig. 6.9 is at least approximately uniform in colour differences. It will be seen to be different from those of Figs. 6.6, 6.7 and 6.8 in that the apices

U, V and W lie outside the spectral locus. A full description and explanation of this triangle will be deferred to the next chapter; for the moment it is sufficient

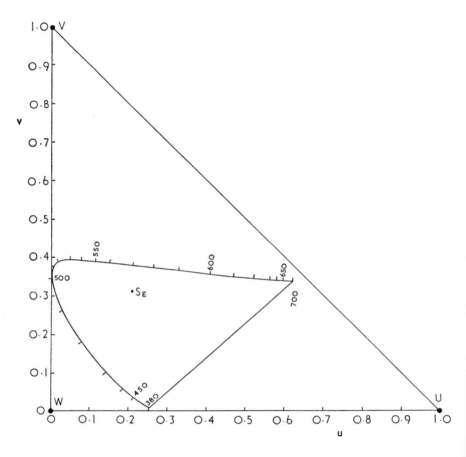

Fig. 6.9. UVW colour triangle, in which the colours are approximately uniformly distributed in the region enclosed by the spectral locus (which includes all colours).

to remark that it has the same properties as the other triangles: the point representing the mixture of any two colours lies on the line joining the points representing the constituent parts of the mixture, and divides that line in the inverse ratio $(m_2/L_2)/(m_1/L_1)$ as before.

6.8 Additive colour reproduction

With the aid of the colour triangle the limitations of additive colour reproduction can now be seen more rigorously. We have already seen that, in a system in which the sensitivity curves have the required negative parts, the only limitation is that colours lying outside the triangle formed by the reproduction stimuli will move to the edge of this triangle. It is therefore obviously desirable that this triangle should cover as much as possible of the domain of all colours.

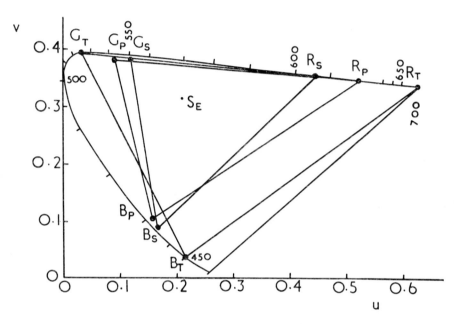

Fig. 6.10. Triangles showing the gamut of colours which can be matched when different matching stimuli are used. $R_TG_TB_T$: theoretical additive stimuli, monochromatic wavelengths 700, 525, and 450 nm. $R_PG_PB_P$: practicable additive stimuli, filters of Fig. 6.11(a) illuminated by light of Fig. 6.11(b). $R_SG_SB_S$: the stimuli of Fig. 6.8, being 'theoretical subtractive' stimuli.

In Fig. 6.10 the triangle R_T, G_T, B_T shows about the best that can be done. If G_T were moved to slightly shorter wavelengths the saturated blue-greens would improve at the expense of the saturated yellows, but the latter are far more numerous in nature than the former, so that the position of G_T is probably near the optimum. These stimuli, being on the spectral locus, consist of monochromatic lights, and their wavelengths are approximately 700, 525, and 450 nm.

It is always difficult to obtain very bright beams of purely monochromatic light, and therefore most additive colour photographic systems use reproduction stimuli consisting of red, green, and blue filters, made of glass or dyed gelatin, with transmission curves similar to those shown in Fig. 6.11(a), illuminated by a tungsten light source having an energy distribution curve similar to that shown in Fig. 6.11(b). The positions of such stimuli on the triangle are shown

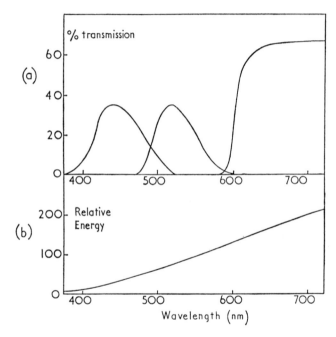

Fig. 6.11. (a) Transmission curves of filters typical of those used as the reproduction stimuli in additive colour photography. (b) Spectral energy distribution curve of a tungsten filament lamp of colour temperature 2854°K, often used to illuminate these filters.

by the points R_P, G_P and B_P, and it is seen that the limitation in the blue-green, green, and magenta directions is now much more marked. In television systems the red is generally worse than R_P, the green similar to G_P, and the blue similar to B_P (see Fig. 18.12).

As has already been mentioned, in colour photography the negative parts of the sensitivity curves are very difficult to realize, so that in practice they have to be ignored. Now, each set of reproduction stimuli will have slightly different colour-matching functions; and it is clear that the further the spectral locus lies outside the reproduction triangle, the greater will be the negative portions of these functions, and thus also in the case of the sensitivity curves (which must be identical to them), and hence the greater the errors introduced in ignoring them. Thus in colour photography the choice of reproduction stimuli is doubly important. Not only does a small reproduction triangle limit the gamut of reproducible colours, but it also magnifies the consequences of ignoring the negative parts of the corresponding colour-matching functions. And the absence of the negative sensitivities in colour photography could result in practically all colours being incorrectly reproduced, since one of the three matching stimuli is negative for almost every wavelength of the spectrum. The only exception is in the red, orange, and yellow parts of the spectrum, and these are often the colours reproduced best. See Plate 3 (page 60).

The importance of different types of departure of the sensitivity curves from the theoretical colour-matching functions has been the subject of several studies (Evans, Hanson, and Brewer, 1953, chapter 13; MacAdam, 1953; Neugebauer, 1956; Gosling and Yule, 1960).

6.9 The Ives-Abney-Yule compromise

We have seen in Chapter 5 that a common way in which colours vary in real life is by a uniform addition of white to all colours, such as occurs in a hazy atmosphere. For this reason, errors in colour reproduction which are equivalent to the addition of a little white to all colours, are not very noticeable. In Fig. 6.12, three points P_1, P_2 and P_3 are shown, at the apices of a triangle which just includes the domain of all real colours. If stimuli plotting in such positions were available (which, of course, they are not) all colours would be matched by all positive mixtures of them, and there would be no negative portions to the colour-matching functions. It is in fact quite easy to calculate what the colour-matching functions would be, and, being all positive, the spectral sensitivity curves of our reproduction system could be quite easily matched to them. If then for our reproduction stimuli, we chose three colours Q_1, Q_2 and Q_3 lying on lines joining P_1, P_2 and P_3 to the point W representing a white stimulus, then Q_1, Q_2 and Q_3 could be considered as being mixtures of P_1, P_2 and P_3 with the white light W. The use of them, therefore, as reproduction stimuli instead of P_1, P_2 and P_3 would merely add white light to the scene, and hence not produce errors of a very noticeable character. The hues would all be correct, and the desaturation would be quite uniform for all colours. This approach is known as the Ives, Abney, and Yule compromise (see MacAdam, 1938, page 415). The colour-matching functions which would correspond to the 'stimuli' P_1, P_2 and P_3 are shown in Fig. 6.13, and a colour reproduction system in which these curves were used for the camera sensitivities, and the stimuli Q_1, Q_2 and Q_3 were used as reproduction stimuli, should produce errors which are entirely confined to the addition of some white to all colours (although black would still be obtainable, of course, by having zero amounts of Q_1, Q_2 and Q_3). This

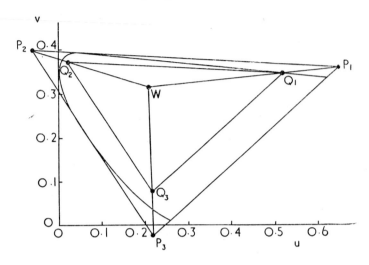

Fig. 6.12. The Ives-Abney-Yule compromise. By using spectral sensitivity curves corresponding to the 'super-saturated' stimuli P_1, P_2, P_3 and real reproduction stimuli Q_1, Q_2, Q_3, the reproduction errors for all colours will be confined to a slight admixture of white.

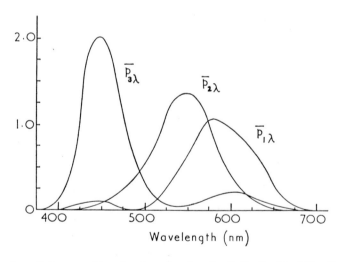

Fig. 6.13. Colour-matching functions for the stimuli P_1, P_2, P_3 of Fig. 6.12. Since the spectral locus lies entirely within the triangle P_1, P_2, P_3, these curves have no negative portions.

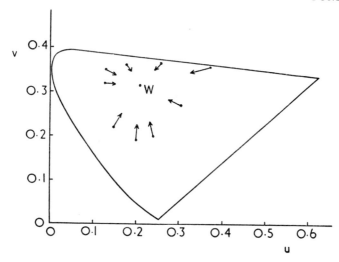

Fig. *6.14.* Errors typical of those resulting from the use of the Ives-Abney-Yule compromise shown in Fig. 6.12.

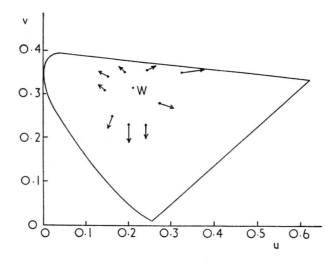

Fig. *6.15.* Increases in colour saturation typical of those which can be obtained by increasing tone contrast from 1.0 to 1.5.

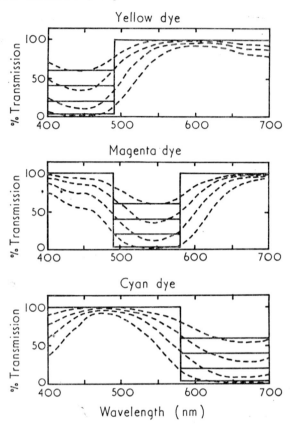

Fig. 6.16. Full lines: spectral transmission curves of 'ideal' subtractive dyes at four different concentrations. Broken lines: spectral transmission curves of dyes typical of those used in practice (reproduced from Fig. 4.1) at four concentrations.

type of error is represented in the colour triangle by the shifting of points inwards towards the white point as shown in Fig. 6.14. Now, one of the favourite ways of seeking to compensate for losses in saturation in colour reproduction is to raise the contrast uniformly of all three images. The effect of this is to increase the ratio of the largest to the smallest of the three amounts Q_1, Q_2 and Q_3 of the stimuli (Q_1), (Q_2) and (Q_3), and this in turn will result in an increase in colour saturation, since whites and greys correspond to the values of Q_1, Q_2 and Q_3 being equal. Fig. 6.15 shows typical results obtained at a contrast of 1.5, and it is seen that, by operating the Ives, Abney and Yule compromise at this contrast level, it is possible to counteract the errors of Fig. 6.14 almost exactly, and thus restrict the errors of the system almost exclusively to a distortion of contrast, which may not be very noticeable if the system is normally used with fairly flat lighting. It is still impossible to reproduce colours lying outside the triangle Q_1, Q_2, Q_3 but these rarely occur in nature.

The Ives, Abney and Yule compromise, either with or without increased contrast, is equally applicable to additive colour photographic systems and to colour television systems. For the former it is useful because of the inability to incorporate the negative parts of colour-matching functions; with the latter, because it avoids analysis of the picture through further filters or providing matrixing circuits in order to simulate their effects.

6.10 Subtractive colour reproduction

In subtractive systems, the function of the cyan dye is to absorb red light, that of the magenta dye to absorb green light, and that of the yellow dye to absorb blue light, so that, ideally, the three dyes should have spectral transmission curves as shown by the full lines in Fig. 6.16. These curves are such that at every wavelength two of the dyes have 100 per cent transmission, while only the third dye absorbs. If the absorption bands were narrower than those shown, so that at some wavelengths no light was absorbed, then, no matter how concentrated the deposits of the three dyes, it would not be possible to form black. If, on the other hand, the absorption bands were wider than those shown, the colours would be darker than they need be. The two wavelength values at which the absorption bands change must be at about 500 and 600 nm in order that the colours controlled by the dyes are in fact red, green, and blue and not, for instance, orange, cyan and violet which would limit unnecessarily the range of colours that could be formed. The exact optimum position of these two wavelength values is somewhat indeterminate, but most estimates (see for example Clarkson and Vickerstaff, 1948) give values around 490 and 580 nm and these have been used in Fig. 6.16.

The reproduction stimuli corresponding to these dyes will be the three blocks of wavelengths 580 to 700 nm, 490 to 580 nm, and 400 to 490 nm, suitably weighted according to the spectral energy distribution of the light source used. For a tungsten filament light source operating at a colour temperature of 2854°K the reproduction primaries are at R_s, G_s and B_s in Fig. 6.10. These points are the centres of gravity of the appropriate blocks of wavelengths after weighting for the light source and the colour-matching functions of the UVW triangle.

The gamut of colours that can be matched with mixtures of the three dyes of Fig. 6.16 is then the triangle R_s, G_s, B_s in Fig. 6.10. It is seen that there are large regions of colours which cannot be matched with these dyes, most notably in the green and magenta parts of the diagram, and it is clear that processes of colour photography which use dyes for forming their colours, that is, subtractive processes, will be unable to match many colours of high saturation. It is important, however, to remember that additive processes are theoretically restricted to a triangle such as R_T, G_T, B_T, and in practice are restricted to one, such as R_P, G_P, B_P, that is not usually very much larger than R_s, G_s, B_s; moreover, as we shall see, the dyes which have to be used in practice enable some colours outside the R_s, G_s, B_s triangle to be reproduced.

Assuming that we are using the 'ideal' dyes described in Fig. 6.16, what must be the spectral sensitivities of the three layers or parts of our process in order that colours be reproduced accurately? Once again they are, of course, colour-matching functions, in this case those corresponding to the stimuli R_s, G_s and B_s. They are shown in Fig. 6.17. It is seen that the curves show large negative portions, and this is a direct consequence of the fact that the spectral locus in Fig. 6.8 lies so far outside the triangle R_s, G_s, B_s.

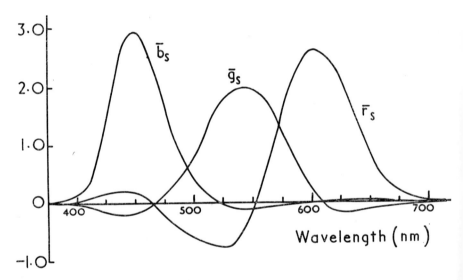

Fig. 6.17. Colour-matching functions for the 'theoretical subtractive' stimuli R_s, G_s, B_s of Figs. 6.8 and 6.10.

We have already seen that in photographic processes, unless cumbersome and complicated procedures are used, it is impossible for the emulsions to have any negative sensitivities at all. This means that, not only will colours which plotted outside the triangle R_s, G_s, B_s be desaturated, but also all colours which plotted inside that triangle will be reproduced incorrectly, and, although the most usual fault will be desaturation, errors in hue may also occur, unless, for instance, the Ives, Abney and Yule compromise is used.

If it were possible in a photographic system to use emulsions having negative as well as positive portions to their sensitivity curves, correct reproduction of all colours within the triangle R_s, G_s, B_s might still not occur. It would be further necessary that the tone reproduction of each emulsion be correct, and in practice all photographic systems distort the rendering of tones to some extent.

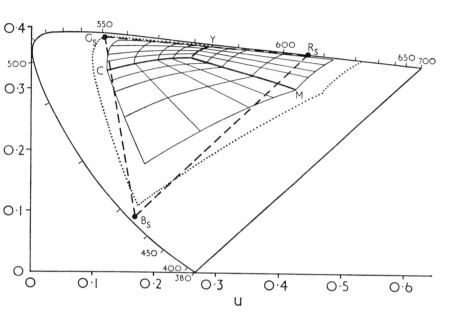

Fig. 6.18. Gamuts of chromaticities that can be reproduced with the dyes of Fig. 6.16 when illuminated by a tungsten filament lamp at a colour temperature of 2854°K. Broken line: gamut produced by the 'ideal' dyes (which produce the stimuli R_s, G_s, B_s). Full lines: gamuts produced by various combinations of the four different concentrations of the three typical practical dyes shown in Fig. 6.16. The dotted lines show how the gamut is extended by using, in addition, a fifth concentration, equivalent in the case of each dye to the two highest concentrations combined together; such high concentrations are seldom present in pictures but the chromaticities they produce indicate approximately the limits of a typical modern subtractive film. The five concentrations represent minimum transmissions in the main absorption bands of approximately 56 per cent, 31 per cent, 10 per cent, 1 per cent, and 0·1 per cent. which is equivalent to densities of approximately 0·25, 0·5, 1·0, 2·0, and 3·0.

In colour photography this is sometimes an advantage. As we have seen, an equal increase in the contrast of all three layers results in increased saturation; and many processes of colour photography have, with advantage (Horner, 1951), a gradually increasing contrast from highlight to shadow.

97

So far, we have been thinking entirely in terms of dyes having transmission curves as shown by the full lines of Fig. 6.16. In practice no such dyes exist, and instead use has to be made of dyes having transmission curves of the type shown in Fig. 4.1 (shown dotted in Fig. 6.16). They differ in several respects from the 'ideal' curves of Fig. 6.16, but photographically their greatest defect is that they do not transmit 100 per cent of the light in the regions where they are supposed to. These unwanted absorptions result in many colours, particularly blues and greens, being reproduced too dark, but the sloping sides of the absorption bands enable a few colours outside the triangle R_s, G_s, B_s to be matched. The reason for this can be seen from Fig. 6.16. As the concentration of the dyes increases the sloping sides of the absorption bands effectively narrow the red, green and blue blocks of wavelengths so that the reproduction stimuli become slightly more like monochromatic stimuli and hence more saturated. (For a method of analyzing the effect of this on colour reproduction, see MacAdam, 1938, page 466.) The gamut of colours obtainable with dyes similar to those of Fig. 4.1 is shown in Fig. 6.18, and is seen to lie partially outside the triangle R_s, G_s, B_s, and particularly so in the cyan and magenta directions where the triangle R_s, G_s, B_s, is most restricted.

6.11 Umberger's theory of subtractive dye systems

The interpretation of problems in subtractive colour reproduction would be greatly facilitated if it were possible to describe additive stimuli which, for real dyes as well as for the 'ideal' or block dyes, represented the colour of the light controlled by each dye. Various attempts have been made to do this and one of the most interesting has been described by Umberger (Umberger, 1963).

It is convenient to consider the spectral absorption properties of the dyes in terms of their variation of density (rather than transmission) with wavelength; a set of three such spectral density curves is shown in Fig. 6.19. In transparency materials, the density,* D_λ, of a dye at any wavelength is usually quite accurately proportional to its concentration, c_1, (this is not so for reflection prints because of the effects of inter-reflections in the dye-layer). For transparencies we may therefore write:

$$D_\lambda = a_{1\lambda} . c_1,$$

where $a_{1\lambda}$ represents the spectral density function of the dye at unit concentration. The spectral transmission, T_λ, is therefore given by·

$$\log T_\lambda = -D_\lambda = -a_{1\lambda} c_1$$

If now, two further dyes having spectral density functions $a_{2\lambda}$ and $a_{3\lambda}$ are added at concentrations c_2 and c_3 respectively, then the spectral transmission, T_λ, is given by

$$\log T_\lambda = a_{1\lambda} c_1 - a_{2\lambda} c_2 - a_{3\lambda} c_3$$

* Optical density is equal to $\log_{10} \dfrac{100}{T}$, where T is the percentage transmittance or reflectance.

If now a change from c_1 to c_1' is made in the concentration of one of the dyes, the transmission, T_λ', is given by

$$\log T_\lambda' = -a_{1\lambda}c_1' - a_{2\lambda}c_2 - a_{3\lambda}c_3$$

These two transmission curves, together with the spectral energy distribution curve, E_λ, of whatever light source is used to illuminate the transparency, will constitute two colours $E_\lambda T_\lambda$ and $E_\lambda T_\lambda'$; and the difference between these two expressions,

$$E_\lambda T_\lambda - E_\lambda T_\lambda',$$

represents the energy distribution of a colour, P_1, which when added to $E_\lambda T_\lambda'$ produces $E_\lambda T_\lambda$. In other words this colour, P_1, is acting as the additive stimulus corresponding to the dye whose concentration was altered from c_1 to c_1'.

The problem is to evaluate the expression, $E_\lambda T_\lambda - E_\lambda T_\lambda'$, in a useful manner. To do this, we consider the effect of very small changes in c_1; differentiating the expression for $\log T_\lambda$ with respect to c_1, we obtain:

$$\frac{\mathrm{d}T_\lambda}{T_\lambda \mathrm{d}c_1} = -2.3 a_{1\lambda}$$

where $2.3 = \log_e 10$ approximately.

But for very small changes in c_1, $\mathrm{d}T_\lambda = T_\lambda' - T_\lambda$. Therefore,

$$E_\lambda T_\lambda - E_\lambda T_\lambda' = -E_\lambda \mathrm{d}T_\lambda = 2.3\, T_\lambda E_\lambda a_{1\lambda} \mathrm{d}c_1.$$

This shows that the stimulus P_1 depends on the transmission curve T_λ of the area of film under consideration; and hence P_1 will be dependent on the colour being considered. Subtractive dyes therefore have corresponding stimuli which are *unstable* (we have already noted that they tend to become more saturated at high concentrations).

If we consider, for a moment, grey colours, then T_λ will be approximately constant throughout the spectrum, and to a first approximation can be replaced by a constant T_n. Then:

$$E_\lambda T_\lambda - E_\lambda T_\lambda' = 2.3\, T_n\, E_\lambda a_{1\lambda} \mathrm{d}c_1 = k E_\lambda a_{1\lambda} \mathrm{d}c_1$$

where k is a constant. The nature of P_1 then becomes very simple: its spectral energy distribution is obtained by taking the spectral *density* curve $a_{1\lambda}$ and regarding it as the *transmission* curve of an additive filter; the spectral energy distribution thus obtained, $E_\lambda a_{1\lambda}$, is then proportional to the spectral energy distribution, $E_\lambda T_\lambda - E_\lambda T_\lambda'$, of P_1. (Higher accuracy can be obtained by evaluating $T_\lambda E_\lambda a_{1\lambda}$, if it is desired to avoid the approximation involved in regarding the neutral as non-selective.)

This definition of P_1, though simple, may seem to be of limited application because it applies only to neutral colours and to very small changes in dye concentrations. If, however, T_λ is regarded now, not as the spectral transmission of a patch of uniform colour, but as the integrated transmission of the light from the whole picture area of the transparency, the arguments above remain true, but become more general. For while few patches of uniform colour in a transparency will be neutral, the integrated light from the whole of the transparency will very often be approximately neutral. The energy distribution, $E_\lambda a_{1\lambda}$, can then be regarded as the stimulus corresponding to the dye for the whole picture. As far as the restriction to very small changes in dye concentration is concerned, the results will provide useful approximations to larger changes, but the instability of the stimuli precludes the possibility of finding a stimulus representative of large changes in dye concentration.

Energy distributions, $E_\lambda a_{2\lambda}$ and $E_\lambda a_{3\lambda}$, can of course be determined to represent stimuli P_2 and P_3 representing the dyes having spectral density curves $a_{2\lambda}$ and $a_{3\lambda}$ respectively. The three stimuli, P_1, P_2, and P_3, can then be used for various purposes, such as the determination of theoretical sensitivity curves for the set of dyes being used, and the movements of colours on the colour triangle as the concentrations of the dyes are varied from neutral. Other sets of stimuli can be worked out for non-neutral colours if required, using the formulae: $T_\lambda E_\lambda a_{1\lambda}$, $T_\lambda E_\lambda a_{2\lambda}$, $T_\lambda E_\lambda a_{3\lambda}$.

For a more detailed analysis of the subtractive system, including the effects of changes in spectral sensitivity, contrast, and dye characteristics on the accuracy of colour reproduction, reference should be made to Chapters 13 and 14 of Evans, Hanson, and Brewer, 1953.

6.12 Subtractive quality

Enough, however, has been said to show that there are fundamental limitations to the fidelity of colour reproduction by subtractive photographic means. Some colours are too saturated to be matched by the dyes available; all colours, whether matchable or not, may be reproduced to some extent erroneously, because of the impossibility of incorporating negative sensitivities in the three emulsions; the tone reproductions of the three emulsions are not usually exactly linear and therefore may introduce errors; and the dyes available absorb in parts of the spectrum where they should have 100 per cent transmission. On the other hand, increased contrast can help to combat losses in saturation, and the dyes that we have to use can match a few more colours than can the theoretical dyes. The net result, however, is that the basic process of subtractive colour photography can involve considerable distortion. But modern processes use various devices to improve quality, and, as we have seen in Chapter 5, the visual tolerances can be fairly large. In consequence, the practical results can be extremely pleasing.

6.13 Two-colour reproductions

If all the colours in a scene were such that the points representing them in the colour triangle lay on a straight line, then it would be possible to obtain an exact colour reproduction by means of a two-colour additive system. Similarly, if all the colours of a scene could be matched by a mixture of only two dyes, exact two-colour subtractive reproductions could be obtained. The colours in most scenes, however, are not confined even approximately to the above type of restrictions, but two-colour (usually cyan and orange) reproductions can sometimes be surprisingly realistic, and in cinematography have been used commercially (Cornwell-Clyne, 1951, p. 343).

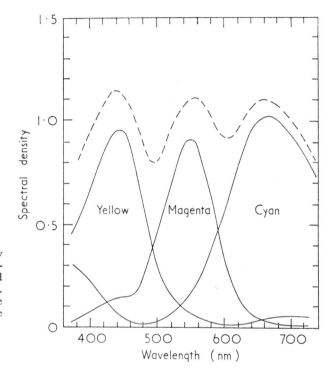

Fig. 6.19. Spectral density curves of the typical practical cyan, magenta, and yellow dyes of Fig. 6.16. The broken line shows the total density of all three dyes.

Some interesting effects are obtained in two-colour additive systems if red and white are used as the mixture colours (Cornwell-Clyne, 1951, p. 261; Land, 1959). Because the eye has a strong tendency to discount the overall pinkish colour balance, the white light appears cyan and the reproduction exhibits a wide range of mixture colours. Judd and others have shown that a number of other effects occur and give rise to quite a wide range of hues being perceived (Belsey, 1964; Judd, 1960; Rushton, 1961) but Wilson has shown that, contrary to some claims, these reproductions are not independent of the contrasts of the two images (Wilson and Brocklebank, 1960 and 1961).

A remarkable property of these projections is that if the two images are in good registration quite acceptable colour reproduction can be obtained for some subject matter; if the registration is slightly out, the appearance is slightly impaired; but if the registration is grossly out, the observer sees only reds, pinks and whites. It is clear from these registration effects that more is involved than a general adaptation to the pink colour of the light, for this would be largely independent of registration; what apparently happens is that if the registration is good enough for the two images to give the appearance of a single meaningful scene, then the visual mechanism instantaneously largely discounts the average pink colour, and discerns the objects in the scene as though they were illuminated with a whitish light.

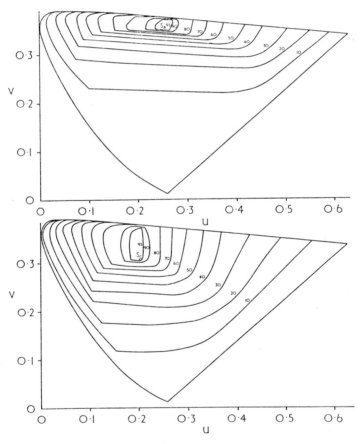

Fig. 6.20. Theoretical chromaticity limits for non-fluorescent colours at the percentage reflectances (or transmittances) shown, for tungsten light (above) and daylight (below).

The acceptability of two-colour reproductions, whether of the red-plus-white type, or of the more usual type in which blue-green and orange dyes are used, is markedly dependent on the subject matter. Indoor scenes are often very realistic, probably because light sources very deficient in blue content, such as candles and yellowish tungsten lamps, are commonly experienced, and the low level of the blue signal tends to reduce vision to nearly two variables. Outdoor scenes, on the other hand, are generally less acceptable, and the inability to render the hue difference between blue sky and green foliage is a serious drawback.

6.14 Colour gamuts of reflecting and transmitting colours

When considering the gamut of colours which a system can reproduce, it is useful to bear in mind that there are theoretical limits to the chromaticities which (non-fluorescing) coloured surfaces or filters can attain for any given total reflectance or transmittance. These limits have been worked out by MacAdam (MacAdam, 1935) and are shown in Fig. 6.20. They relate to colorants having spectral absorption bands with vertical sides like those of Fig. 6.16, full lines; real colours have sloping sides to their spectral absorption bands and are hence even more restricted in chromaticity than indicated by Fig. 6.20. Surface colours are even further restricted because of light reflected from their top-most surfaces (see Figs. 5.3 and 11.4), the desaturating effect of which can be very great for dark colours.

REFERENCES

Belsey, R., *J. Opt. Soc. Amer.*, **54**, 529 (1964).
British Standard 1611 (1953). *Glossary of Colour Terms used in Science and Industry.*
C.I.E. *International Lighting Vocabulary*, 3rd Edition, C.I.E. Paris (1967).
Clarkson, M. E., and Vickerstaff, T., *Phot. J.*, **88B**, 26 (1948).
Cornwell-Clyne, A., *Colour Cinematography*, Chapman & Hall, London (1951).
Evans, R. M., Hanson, W. T., and Brewer, W. L., *Principles of Colour Photography*, Wiley, New York (1953).
Gosling, J. W., and Yule, J. A. C., *Proc. Tech. Assoc. Graphic Arts*, **12**, 157 (1960).
Hardy, A. C., and Wurzburg, F. L., *J. Opt. Soc. Amer.*, **27**, 227 (1937).
Harrison, G. B., and Horner, R. G., *Phot. J.*, **77**, 706 (1937).
Horner, R. G., *Phot. J.*, **91B**, 44 (1951).
Judd, D. B., *J. Opt. Soc. Amer.*, **50**, 254 (1960).
Land, E. H., *Proc. Nat. Acad. Sci.*, **45**, 115 and 636 (1959).
MacAdam, D. L., *J. Opt. Soc. Amer.*, **25**, 361 (1935).
MacAdam, D. L., *J. Opt. Soc. Amer.*, **28**, 399 (1938).
MacAdam, D. L., *J. Opt. Soc. Amer.*, **40**, 589 (1950).
MacAdam, D. L., *J. Opt. Soc. Amer.*, **41**, 615 (1951).
MacAdam, D. L., *J. Opt. Soc. Amer.*, **43**, 533 (1953).
Neugebauer, H. E. J., *J. Opt. Soc. Amer.*, **46**, 821 (1956).
Rushton, W. A. H., *Nature*, **189**, 440 (1961).
Umberger, J. Q., *Phot. Sci. Eng.*, **7**, 34 (1963).
Wilson, M. H., and Brocklebank, R. W., *J. Phot. Sci.*, **8**, 141 (1960).
Wilson, M. H., and Brocklebank, R. W., *Contemporary Physics*, **3**, 19 (1961).

CHAPTER 7

Colour Standards and Calculations

1. Introduction – *2.* Standard illuminants – *3.* The standard observers –
4. Colour Transformations – *5.* Properties of the XYZ system – *6.* Uniform
colour space – *7.* Nomograms – *8.* Subjective effects – *9.* Estimation of
sensation magnitudes – *10.* Physical colour standards

7.1 Introduction

IN the previous chapter, various aspects of colour reproduction were considered in a quantitative way with the aid of the colour triangle. We saw, however, that there was no one unique triangle, but several different triangles which could be used. Certain standards have been set up internationally in order to simplify the intercomparison of colour data, and in this chapter we shall briefly review these standards, and describe methods for calculating data from them.

7.2 Standard illuminants

We have already mentioned in Section 5.3 the well-known fact that certain colours exhibit marked changes in appearances as they are viewed in illuminants of different colour. It is therefore clear that an essential step in specifying colour is accurate definition of the illuminants involved. In 1931, in order to simplify the problem, the C.I.E. (Commission Internationale de l'Eclairage) recommended the use of three standard illuminants, A, B, and C, whose spectral energy distribution curves are as shown in Fig. 7.1. Standard Illuminant A (S_A) consists of a tungsten filament lamp operating at a colour temperature of $2854°K$[1], while standard illuminants B and C (S_B and S_C) consist of S_A together with certain liquid filters, as shown in Table 7.1. S_A is intended to be representative of tungsten filament lighting, S_B representative of sunlight, and S_C representative of light from an overcast sky.

[1] Equivalent to 2581 degrees Centigrade or Celsius (°C). This colour temperature is usually achieved at a filament temperature of about 2530°C. See Section 8.2.

But, although S_B and S_C represent the spectral energy distribution of day-light fairly well over most of the spectrum, they are seriously deficient at wavelengths below 400 nm; this makes them unsuitable for use with samples which absorb energy of these wavelengths and then re-emit it by fluorescence at longer wavelengths. The increasingly widespread use of dyes and pigments which fluoresce (as a means of producing brilliant whites for instance), has led to the standardization by the C.I.E. of a series of energy distributions representing daylight at all wavelengths between 300 and 830 nm. One of these distributions is shown in Fig. 7.1. In Fig. 7.2 this distribution is shown again together with

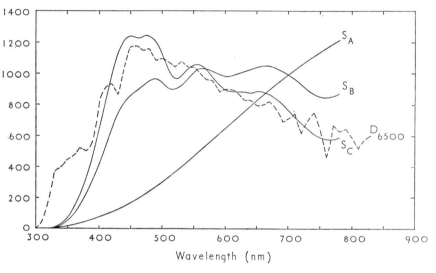

Fig. 7.1. Relative spectral energies of C.I.E. standard sources A, B, and C. S_A is representative of tungsten filament lamps. Within the range of wavelengths from 400 to 700 nm S_B approximates sunlight, and S_C approximates light from an overcast sky. The relative energies of C.I.E. standard illuminant D_{6500} (representing typical average daylight) are shown by the broken line, and it is seen that S_C is seriously deficient in energy at wavelengths below 400 nm.

two others: that labelled 6500 represents a standard daylight for general use; that labelled 5500 represents a yellower daylight such as may be provided by sun-light with sky-light; and that labelled 7500 represents a bluer daylight such as may be provided by a north sky. It should be noted that these standard daylights are defined as spectral energy distributions, whereas S_A, S_B, and S_C are defined as actual physical sources: the former are more useful for calculations, the latter for viewing. However, tables of the spectral energy distributions of S_A, S_B, and S_C are also available, and the distributions of Fig.

7.2 can be provided approximately by actual sources. In addition to these sources the hypothetical illuminant E (S_E), consisting of equal energy per unit wavelength throughout the visible spectrum, is often referred to in colorimetry. The spectral energy distributions shown in Fig. 7.2 were founded on measurements made in several different locations in the world (Judd, MacAdam and Wyszecki, 1964).

There are, as yet, no standard illuminants representative of the different types of fluorescent lamp but such standards may eventually be set up.

These standard illuminants are only intended to be representative of ranges of illuminants, so that any actual sample of sunlight, for instance, might well be redder or bluer than D_{5500}, according to the solar altitude, weather conditions, and so on.

In Appendix 3 the spectral energy distributions are given for standard illuminants A, B, C, D_{5500}, and D_{6500}.

TABLE 7.1

FILTERS FOR USE WITH STANDARD ILLUMINANT A, IN ORDER TO CONVERT IT TO STANDARD ILLUMINANTS B AND C

Each filter consists of two solutions, each one centimetre in thickness and contained in a double cell made of colourless optical glass.

Chemical	Quantities	
	For S_B	For S_C
Copper Sulphate ($CuSO_4.5H_2O$)	2.452 gm.	3.412 gm.
Mannite ($C_6H_8(OH)_6$)	2.452 gm.	3.412 gm.
Pyridine (C_5H_5N)	30.0 c.c.	30.0 c.c.
Water (distilled) to make	1000 c.c.	1000 c.c.
Cobalt Ammonium Sulphate ($CoSO_4.(NH_4)_2SO_4.6H_2O$)	21.710 gm.	30.580 gm.
Copper Sulphate ($CuSO_4.5H_2O$)	16.110 gm.	22.520 gm.
Sulphuric Acid (Sp.Gr. 1.835)	10.0 c.c.	10.0 c.c.
Water (distilled) to make	1000 c.c.	1000 c.c.

These illuminants are expressed in the C.I.E. System as follows:

$$(S_A) \propto 0.44757(X) + 0.40745(Y) + 0.14498(Z)$$
$$(S_B) \propto 0.34842(X) + 0.35161(Y) + 0.29997(Z)$$
$$(S_C) \propto 0.31006(X) + 0.31616(Y) + 0.37378(Z)$$

7.3 The standard observers

We have seen in previous chapters that a given colour C can be matched by an additive mixture of suitable proportions R_c, G_c and B_c of three matching stimuli R, G and B. When different observers match the same colour, using the same matching stimuli, however, it is found that there are slight differences in the amounts which they require to effect a match. Some of these differences are random, and disappear if the results of several matches by each observer are averaged. But there remain real differences which must be attributed to differences in the colour vision of the individual observers. Some observers are very different from the average and these are classed as colour defective (or 'colour blind'), but the results of most observers are scattered over only a limited range. In 1931 the C.I.E. defined a *Standard Observer* by averaging the results from investigations by W. D. Wright and J. Guild on the colour matching in a 2° field of 17 non-colour-defective observers, and by K. S. Gibson and E. P. T. Tyndall on the relative luminances of the colours of the spectrum, averaged for a large number of observers. These standard-observer data consist of colour-matching functions for stimuli of wavelengths 700 (R_o), 546.1 (G_o) and 435.8 nm (B_o), with units such that equal amounts of the three stimuli are required to match light from the equal energy illuminant S_E (Fig. 7.3).

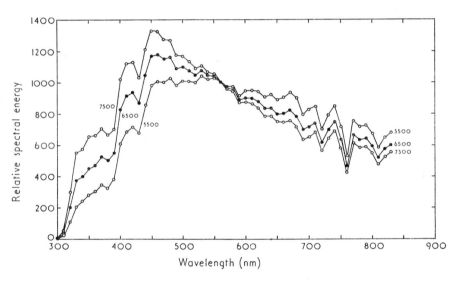

Fig. 7.2. Relative spectral energies of C.I.E. standard distributions D_{5500}, representing typical sun-light with sky-light; D_{6500} representing typical average day-light; and D_{7500} representing typical 'north-sky' light.

With the aid of these curves, given the spectral energy distribution curve of any colour, it is possible to calculate (by the method described in Section 6.4) the amounts of the three stimuli required by the standard observer to match that colour in a 2° field; and this constitutes an exact specification of the colour, which has international significance. Moreover, a calculated specification of this type is derived from purely physical data (the spectral energy distribution curve of the colour) without any further colour matching being necessary.

The colour triangle corresponding to these stimuli and units is that shown in Fig. 6.7, and the position of any colour in that triangle is calculable from the amounts R, G, and B of the three stimuli by the usual formulae:

$$r = R/(R+G+B)$$
$$g = G/(R+G+B)$$

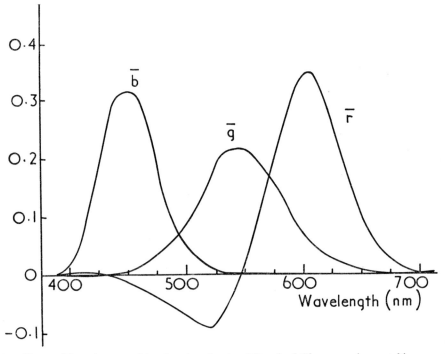

Fig. 7.3. The colour-matching functions for the 2° Standard Observer, using matching stimuli of wavelengths 700, 546.1, and 435.8 nm, with units such that equal quantities of the three matching stimuli are needed to match the equal energy white, S_E.

The standard observer data adopted in 1931 by the C.I.E. has stood the test of time remarkably well, and has provided a system of colour specification which has been widely and successfully used. But slight errors have occasionally seemed detectable in two respects: the values adopted for the relative luminances of spectral colours; and the effect of the angular size of the field of view. A very thorough re-determination of colour matching data was therefore carried out at the National Physical Laboratory at Teddington (Stiles and Burch, 1958; Stiles, 1955) using both a 2° matching field (the same as that used in establishing the 1931 data) and also a 10° matching field. The results with the

2° field were in close agreement with the 1931 C.I.E. data except that they confirmed earlier suspicions that at the extreme violet end of the spectrum this data ascribed too little luminance to the spectral colours. Although these discrepancies are quite large, in that at some wavelengths the correct values are several times larger than the standardized values, colour specifications are not improved appreciably in practice by revising the data to correct these faults. The reason for this is that at the wavelengths concerned the luminance is so low that the contribution of either the incorrect or the correct values is very small for the vast majority of colours.

Comparison of the results for the 2° and 10° field size measurements showed that significant differences did occur between them, and 10° Standard Observer data has been adopted for use when large field sizes are involved (C.I.E., 1960 and 1964). However, in colour reproductions, the interest generally lies much more in patches of colour of about 2° angular size than 10°, and the 1931 C.I.E. data may therefore be used with a fair degree of confidence.

7.4 Colour transformations

If Fig. 6.7 is compared with the colour triangles shown in some of the other figures of the previous chapter it will be seen that the spectral locus has an unusually large bulge into the negative r region. This is because the wavelength 546.1 is rather a yellow green. For this and other reasons, the C.I.E. defined three new stimuli X, Y and Z in terms of which standard-observer results could be expressed. It is possible to calculate the amounts of X, Y and Z needed to match any colour from the amounts of R, G and B needed to match it, provided that *transformation equations* relating the two systems are known. Thus if we have:

$$c(C) \equiv R(R) + G(G) + B(B)$$

and we know that:

$$1.0(R) \equiv A_1(X) + A_2(Y) + A_3(Z)$$
$$1.0(G) \equiv A_4(X) + A_5(Y) + A_6(Z)$$
$$1.0(B) \equiv A_7(X) + A_8(Y) + A_9(Z)$$

we can substitute for (R), (G) and (B) and obtain:

$$c(C) \equiv X(X) + Y(Y) + Z(Z)$$

where

$$X = A_1 R + A_4 G + A_7 B$$
$$Y = A_2 R + A_5 G + A_8 B$$
$$Z = A_3 R + A_6 G + A_9 B$$

The position of C in the XYZ triangle can then be calculated by obtaining:

$$x = X/(X+Y+Z) \qquad y = Y/(X+Y+Z)$$

The transformation equations relating the two systems thus contain the coefficients A_1 to A_9, but, as can be seen above, they can be contained either in three equations representing colour matches (as for 1.0 (R), 1.0 (G), and

109

1.0 (B)) or in three ordinary algebraic equations (as for X, Y, and Z). In Great Britain the former method has sometimes been adopted, but without the use of a distinguishing notation for equations representing colour matches. In America the latter method has generally been used. Unfortunately, the meaning of a given set of equations is quite different according to which method is being used, so that great care has to be taken in interpreting such equations in the literature. However, if one set of equations is known, they can be written in the other form by inspection using the above example as a guide.

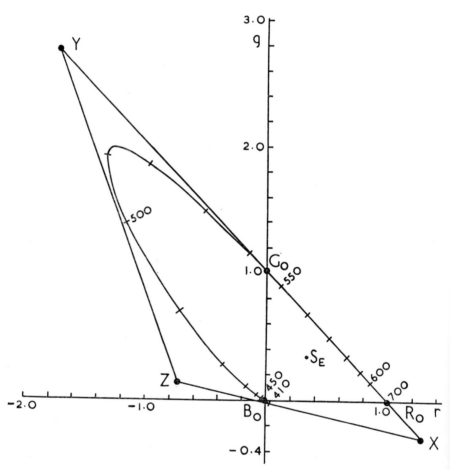

Fig. 7.4. The positions of the matching stimuli X, Y, and Z in the Standard Observer colour triangle R_0 G_0 B_0 reproduced from Fig. 6.7.

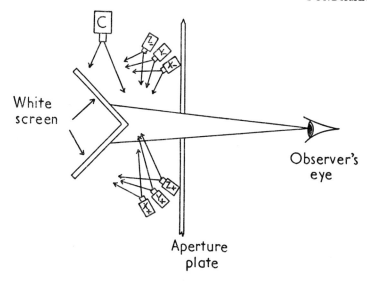

White
screen

Observer's
eye

Aperture
plate

Fig. 7.5. Showing diagrammatically how matching stimuli having negative coefficients greater than those of pure spectral colours can be used. Light from the X_- lantern is of a different colour from that of the X_+ lantern, but the amounts of light from these two lanterns always vary in the same proportion; and similarly for the other two pairs of lanterns.

Sets of equations of both types can be solved as three simultaneous equations to obtain the reverse transformation equations:

$$1.0\ (X) \equiv B_1(R) + B_2(G) + B_3(B)$$
$$1.0\ (Y) \equiv B_4(R) + B_5(G) + B_6(B)$$
$$1.0\ (Z) \equiv B_7(R) + B_8(G) + B_9(B)$$

$$R = B_1 X + B_4 Y + B_7 Z$$
$$G = B_2 X + B_5 Y + B_8 Z$$
$$B = B_3 X + B_6 Y + B_9 Z$$

These considerations apply not only to the relationship between the stimuli R, G, B and X, Y, Z, but equally to the relationship between any two sets of colour-matching stimuli, the values of the coefficients A_1 to A_9 and B_1 to B_9 depending on the particular stimuli involved and the units adopted for them.

The actual definition of X, Y and Z in terms of R_0, G_0 and B_0 for the 2° standard observer data is as follows:

$$1.0(X) \equiv 2.3646(R_0) - 0.5151(G_0) + 0.0052(B_0)$$
$$1.0(Y) \equiv -0.8965(R_0) + 1.4264(G_0) - 0.0144(B_0)$$
$$1.0(Z) \equiv -0.4681(R_0) + 0.0887(G_0) + 1.0092(B_0)$$

The stimuli X_{10}, Y_{10}, Z_{10} used for the $10°$ standard observer are slightly different, and are related to R_0, G_0, B_0 by a similar set of equations having slightly different values.

The positions of X, Y and Z in the $R_0G_0B_0$ colour triangle are derived from these equations by dividing each by the sum of the coefficients and are as shown in Fig. 7.4. It is seen that they lie outside the spectral locus, and that therefore the negative amounts in their specifications are greater than those required in matching even spectral colours. This means that a colorimeter employing these matching stimuli X, Y and Z, must be arranged so that increasing the amount of X, for example, not only adds some colour (X_+) to the mixture but also adds a proportional amount of another colour (X_-) to the test colour, and similarly for Y and Z, as shown diagrammatically in Fig. 7.5. Only in this way can negative amounts greater than those required by spectral colours be realized. Such a colorimeter can be made quite simply, however, but in point of fact the more conventional type (as shown in Fig. 6.1) is generally used, and the results then transformed into the XYZ system algebraically. It is frequently desirable to transform not the actual values R, G and B to X, Y and Z, but only the proportional values r, g, and b, to x, y and z, where $r+g+b=1$ and $x+y+z=1$. When this is required it is convenient to have the transformation equations in the form:

$$x=\frac{a_1r+a_2g+a_3}{a_7r+a_8g+a_9}$$

$$y=\frac{a_4r+a_5g+a_6}{a_7r+a_8g+a_9}$$

$$z=1-x-y$$

The values of the coefficients in these equations are related to those of the equations given above as follows:

$$a_1=A_1-A_7 \qquad\qquad a_4=A_2-A_8$$
$$a_2=A_4-A_7 \qquad\qquad a_5=A_5-A_8$$
$$a_3=A_7 \qquad\qquad\qquad a_6=A_8$$
$$a_7=A_1+A_2+A_3-A_7-A_8-A_9$$
$$a_8=A_4+A_5+A_6-A_7-A_8-A_9$$
$$a_9=A_7+A_8+A_9$$

And similar expressions in terms of B_1 to B_9 give the coefficients of the reverse equations

$$r=\frac{b_1x+b_2y+b_3}{b_7x+b_8y+b_9}$$

$$g=\frac{b_4x+b_5y+b_6}{b_7x+b_8y+b_9}$$

$$b=1-r-g$$

The following relationships are also useful:

$$A_1 = a_1 + a_3 \qquad A_2 = a_4 + a_6 \qquad A_3 = a_7 + a_9 - a_1 - a_3 - a_4 - a_6$$
$$A_4 = a_2 + a_3 \qquad A_5 = a_5 + a_6 \qquad A_6 = a_8 + a_9 - a_2 - a_3 - a_5 - a_6$$
$$A_7 = a_3 \qquad\quad A_8 = a_6 \qquad\quad A_9 = a_9 - a_3 - a_6$$

Similar expressions relate B_1 to B_9 with b_1 to b_9.

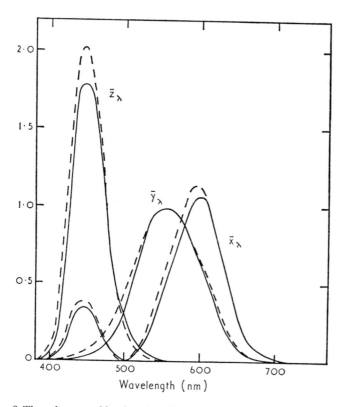

Fig. 7.6. The colour-matching functions for the C.I.E. matching stimuli X, Y, and Z. Full lines: for the 2° Standard Observer, using X, Y, Z; broken lines: for the 10° Standard Observer, using X_{10}, Y_{10}, Z_{10}.

The way in which the positions of the points in the colour triangle are altered by transformations from one set of matching stimuli to another can be expressed very simply. All colour triangles based on the 2° standard observer data of Fig. 7.3 are *projective transformations* of the triangle of Fig. 6.7 (and Fig. 7.4); similarly all colour triangles based on the 10° standard observer data are projective transformations of one another.

A projective transformation of a triangle is such that it could be obtained by taking a plane and a point, P, suitably situated in space relative to the triangle, and transferring each point of the triangle by means of straight lines drawn through the point, P, until they meet the plane. This is shown in Fig. 7.7. The point M is situated in the RGB triangle. The point P and the plane containing the XYZ triangle have been suitably placed in space. The position of the colour which plots at M in the RGB triangle is then given by N in the XYZ triangle where N is the point of intersection of the line MP with the plane of the XYZ triangle.

That this is indeed the geometrical interpretation of the transformation equations is easily proved as follows.

In Fig. 7.7 let R'O'X' be the line of intersection of the RGB and XYZ planes, and let O' be such that PO' is at right angles to R'X'. Let O'G' and O'Y' also be at right angles to R'X' and in the RGB and XYZ planes respectively. Draw MM' at right angles to O'G', and NN' at right angles to O'Y'. Draw PQ parallel to O'Y' and PS parallel to O'G'. Using the small letters on the figure to represent the distances adjacent to them, from similar triangles we have:

$$\frac{x'}{r'}=\frac{PN'}{PM'}=\frac{k}{g'-k} \quad \therefore \quad x'=\frac{kr'}{g'-k}$$

$$\frac{y'}{g'}=\frac{O'N'}{O'M'}=\frac{h}{g'-k} \quad \therefore \quad y'=\frac{hg'}{g'-k}$$

But r' and g' are co-ordinates of M using axes O'R' and O'G', and x' and y' are co-ordinates of N using axes O'X' and O'Y'. They will therefore be related to r and g, and x and y by equations of the type:

$$r'=c_1 r-c_2 g+c_3$$
$$g'=c_2 r+c_1 g+c_4$$
$$x'=c_5 x-c_6 y+c_7$$
$$y'=c_6 x+c_5 y+c_8$$

On substituting in the equations for x' and y' (above), equations of the form:

$$x=\frac{a_1 r+a_2 g+a_3}{a_7 r+a_8 g+a_9}$$

$$y=\frac{a_4 r+a_5 g+a_6}{a_7 r+a_8 g+a_9}$$

are obtained. Hence the projective transformation is the geometrical equivalent of the colorimetric transformation equations.

7.5 Properties of the XYZ system

It will be recalled that since the stimuli X, Y and Z lie outside the spectral locus they consist of light added, not only to the comparison mixture, but also to the test colour C (Fig. 7.5). In the XYZ system it has been arranged that although the *colour* of the light added by the X stimulus to the test colour (X_) is different from that added to the comparison beam (X_+), the *luminance* is the same.

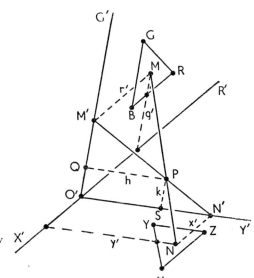

Fig. 7.7. Diagram showing the geometry of projective transformations.

Similarly, in the case of the Z stimulus, the luminances of the two parts of the stimulus are the same. It therefore follows that all the luminance of the test colour has to be balanced by the Y stimulus. Thus, variation of the amounts of X and Z affect the *colour* of the match, but leave any difference in luminance unchanged. This is an advantage. For supposing that we had two colours C_1 and C_2, whose colour-matching data were known. In the RGB system we have:

$$k_1(C_1) \equiv R_1(R) + G_1(G) + B_1(B)$$
$$k_2(C_2) \equiv R_2(R) + G_2(G) + B_2(B)$$

Now if we want to compare the luminances of these two colours it is necessary to convert the units used for R, G and B into luminance units. Suppose that the factors for doing this are L_R, L_G and L_B. Then the luminances are:

$$L_1 = L_R R_1 + L_G G_1 + L_B B_1$$
$$L_2 = L_R R_2 + L_G G_2 + L_B B_2$$

115

But in the XYZ system if:

$$k_1(C_1) \equiv X_1(X) + Y_1(Y) + Z_1(Z)$$
$$k_2(C_2) \equiv X_2(X) + Y_2(Y) + Z_2(Z)$$

then the luminances are:

$$L_1 = L_X X_1 + L_Y Y_1 + L_Z Z_1$$
$$L_2 = L_X X_2 + L_Y Y_2 + L_Z Z_2$$

But L_X and L_Z are zero, and hence these expressions reduce to:

$$L_1 = L_Y Y_1$$
$$L_2 = L_Y Y_2$$

which are much simpler expressions. Moreover, when it is only required to compare the luminance of one colour with that of another we have:

$$L_1/L_2 = Y_1/Y_2$$

which is an extremely simple relationship.

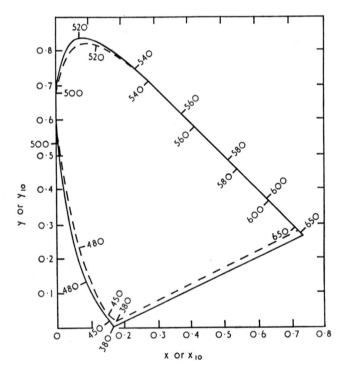

Fig. 7.8. The x, y triangle for the $2°$ Standard Observer (full line) and for the $10°$ Standard Observer (broken line) using x_{10}, y_{10}.

The XYZ system is used very widely for colorimetric specifications. The colour-matching functions $\bar{x}_\lambda$, $\bar{y}_\lambda$, and $\bar{z}_\lambda$ for the system are shown in Fig. 7.6 for both the 2° and the 10° standard observers. It will be noted that there are no negative portions to the curves, because, as can be seen from Fig. 7.4, no part of the spectral locus lies outside the triangle XYZ and therefore every colour of the spectrum can be matched by an all positive mixture of X, Y and Z. In Fig. 7.8 the XYZ colour triangles based on the 2° and 10° standard observers are shown, y being plotted against x, where:

$$y = Y/(X+Y+Z)$$
$$x = X/(X+Y+Z)$$

(For the 10° standard observer, the stimuli X_{10}, Y_{10}, Z_{10} are used throughout.)

In order to obtain the XYZ specification of a colour it can either be matched on a colorimeter as in Fig. 7.5, which gives the direct answer (Hunt, 1954); or, which is more usual, it can be matched on a conventional red, green and blue colorimeter and the results transformed by means of transformation equations; or, which is more usual still, its XYZ specifications can be calculated from its spectral energy curve. To this end, values $\bar{x}_\lambda$, $\bar{y}_\lambda$ and $\bar{z}_\lambda$ are available in standard works on colorimetry and the calculation proceeds as follows.

Suppose we have a transparency or surface whose transmission or reflection factor at, say, 400 nm, is t_1, illuminated by a source whose energy at that wavelength is E_1. Then the values of X, Y and Z for that wavelength are given by:

$$X_1 = t_1 E_1 \bar{x}_1$$
$$Y_1 = t_1 E_1 \bar{y}_1$$
$$Z_1 = t_1 E_1 \bar{z}_1$$

where $\bar{x}_1$, $\bar{y}_1$, $\bar{z}_1$, are the values of $\bar{x}$, $\bar{y}$, $\bar{z}$, respectively, at 400 nm. At another wavelength, say 410 nm, we would have:

$$X_2 = t_2 E_2 \bar{x}_2$$
$$Y_2 = t_2 E_2 \bar{y}_2$$
$$Z_2 = t_2 E_2 \bar{z}_2$$

These products must in fact be worked out at regular wavelength intervals (generally every 5 or 10 nm) throughout the entire visible spectrum and then summated thus:

$$X = t_1 E_1 \bar{x}_1 + t_2 E_2 \bar{x}_2 + t_3 E_3 \bar{x}_3 + \ldots \ldots = \Sigma t E \bar{x}$$
$$Y = t_1 E_1 \bar{y}_1 + t_2 E_2 \bar{y}_2 + t_3 E_3 \bar{y}_3 + \ldots \ldots = \Sigma t E \bar{y}$$
$$Z = t_1 E_1 \bar{z}_1 + t_2 E_2 \bar{z}_2 + t_3 E_3 \bar{z}_3 + \ldots \ldots = \Sigma t E \bar{z}$$

In order to reduce the amount of work, tables for $E\bar{x}$, $E\bar{y}$ and $E\bar{z}$ are available for a number of different sources. These tables are sometimes multiplied by a factor which results in $\Sigma E\bar{y}$ being equal to 100. This means that a perfectly reflecting or transmitting colour ($t=1$ at all wavelengths) has a value of $Y=100$. For any other colour the value of Y then gives the *percentage* reflection or transmission directly, since the Y values of any two colours are proportional to their luminances.

The dependence of luminance entirely on the Y stimulus in the XYZ system, means that the $\bar{y}_\lambda$ colour-matching function represents the relative

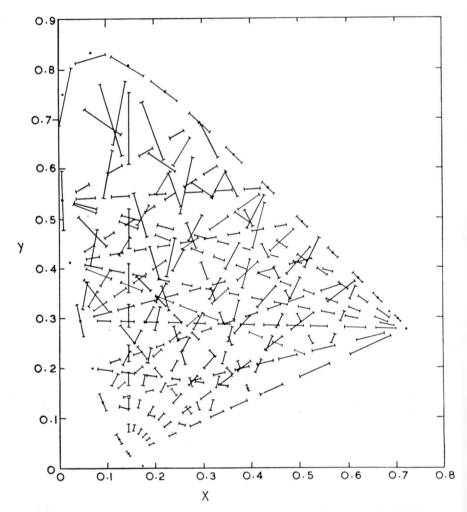

Fig. 7.9. Visually equal chromaticity steps at constant luminance on the C.I.E. x, y triangle (after W. D. Wright).

luminances of the colours of the spectrum; this is an important function in photometry, where it is known as the *spectral luminous efficiency* function, V_λ.

The use of the Centre of Gravity Law in the XYZ system is also simplified by the dependence of the luminance on the Y stimulus only. Suppose we wish to determine the chromaticity of a mixture of m_1 photometric units of a colour C_1 and m_2 photometric units of a colour C_2 where the chromaticity co-ordinates of C_1 and C_2 are x_1, y_1, z_1 and x_2, y_2, z_2, respectively. Then from Section 6.6 the mixture is at the position of the centre of gravity of weights:

$$m_1/(L_x x_1 + L_y y_1 + L_z z_1)$$
$$m_2/(L_x x_2 + L_y y_2 + L_z z_2)$$

But these reduce to $m_1/L_y y_1$ and $m_2/L_y y_2$, because L_x and L_z are both zero. But the same result is given by weights m_1/y_1 and m_2/y_2, so that these simple expressions can be used.

7.6 Uniform colour space

Unfortunately, although the XYZ system has a number of advantages, it has one serious disadvantage. In the XYZ triangle colours are by no means uniformly distributed. This is demonstrated in Fig. 7.9 where the short lines in the

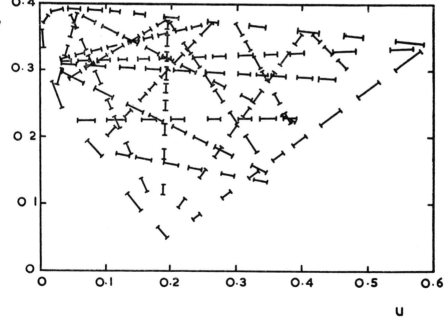

Fig. 7.10. Some of the steps of Fig. 7.9 replotted in the *u, v* triangle.

triangle all represent colour differences which appear of equal magnitude to the eye in a 2° field. It is seen that towards the top of the triangle, where green colours are situated, the lines are much longer than towards the bottom left of the triangle, where blue colours are distributed; the maximum difference is in fact as great as twenty times. Incidentally the distances shown by these lines correspond to three times a just noticeable difference in colour in a patch which subtends an angle of 2° at the observer's eye (Wright, 1941).

Although no linear projection of the triangle can eliminate the differences in the lengths of these lines completely, by choosing a different triangle, they can be very considerably reduced. Fig. 7.10 shows a selection of the lines shown in Fig. 7.9, but on the UVW triangle which was extensively used in the previous chapter. It is seen that the lines are now much more nearly uniform in length, and in fact the maximum difference is now only about four to one, and over much of the triangle is not greater than two to one.

This particular 'uniform chromaticity' triangle is one that was proposed by D. L. MacAdam (1937) and has the advantage that, like the XYZ system, two of the stimuli, U and W, affect only the *colour* of a match, the luminance being affected only by the stimulus V. Its relation to the XYZ system is given by the conveniently simple equations:

$$u=2x/(6y-x+1.5) \qquad x=1.5u/(u-4v+2)$$
$$v=3y/(6y-x+1.5) \qquad y=v/(u-4v+2)$$

Its use as an approximately uniform chromaticity triangle was approved provisionally by the C.I.E. at its 1959 meeting at Brussels; the colour-matching functions, $\bar{u}_\lambda$, $\bar{v}_\lambda$, $\bar{w}_\lambda$ corresponding to the UVW stimuli, and other data, have been published by Nimeroff (Nimeroff, 1964). The $\bar{v}_\lambda$ curve is the same as the $\bar{y}_\lambda$ curve of the XYZ system. By analogy with the previous section the Centre of Gravity Law is operated using weights m_1/v_1 and m_2/v_2, where v_1 and v_2 are the v-co-ordinates of the two colours C_1 and C_2 being mixed in the proportions m_1 and m_2 photometric units, respectively. Values of $\bar{u}_\lambda$, $\bar{v}_\lambda$, $\bar{w}_\lambda$ and u_λ, v_λ, w_λ are given in Appendix 3.

At its 1963 meeting in Vienna the C.I.E. used this triangle as the basis for a uniform colour solid, in which lightness as well as chromaticity is accommodated. Three quantities U^*, V^*, W^* are derived as follows:

$$U^*=13W^*\ (u-u_0)$$
$$V^*=13W^*\ (v-v_0)$$
$$W^*=25Y^{\frac{1}{3}}-17$$

where u, v are as given above; u_0, v_0 are the values of u, v for the chromaticity corresponding to the achromatic or grey axis in the solid; and Y is the tristimulus value based on the $\bar{y}_\lambda$ curve (or on the $\bar{v}_\lambda$ curve) and expressed as a percentage. For reflection samples u_0, v_0 are usually taken as equal to the values of u, v for the illuminant being used. If two colours have values U_1^*, V_1^* W_1^* and U_2^* V_2^*, W_2^*, then the magnitude of the visual difference, D, between them is given by:

$$D^2=(U_1^*-U_2^*)^2+(V_1^*-V_2^*)^2+k(W_1^*-W_2^*)^2$$

The U^*, V^*, W^* colour solid approximates to that of the Munsell system and this is why U^* and V^* are made to increase as W^* increases: chromaticity differences being more noticeable at high than at low lightnesses (Wyszecki, 1963; Wyszecki and Wright, 1965). When $k = 1$, the formula, like the Munsell system, is appropriate for colour differences occurring across a narrow dividing

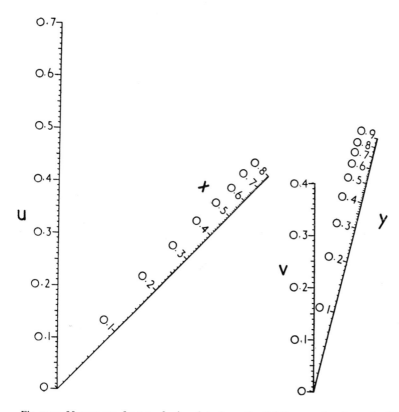

Fig. 7.11. Nomogram for transferring data from the C.I.E. x, y triangle to the C.I.E. u, v triangle and vice-versa. A straight-edge placed across the four scales gives the values of u and v corresponding to those of x and y and vice-versa.

line; if the colours are more widely separated, it may be desirable to reduce the value of k to about $\frac{1}{4}$, because differences in lightness are then less noticeable (Judd and Wyszecki, 1963). A table of values of Y and W^*, together with other data and a worked example, are given in Appendix 3, which the reader may find it convenient to refer to at this point.

7.7 Nomograms

A useful device for transferring data from one colour triangle to another is a nomogram. In Fig. 7.11 a nomogram is shown for obtaining the values of u and v directly from x and y, or vice versa. It is only necessary to place a straight edge across the nomogram so that it cuts the x and y scales at the values of the point concerned: the corresponding values of u and v are then given by the intersection of the straight edge with the u and v scales. To obtain the values of x and y corresponding to known values of u and v the straight edge is aligned with the values of u and v and the values of x and y are then read off directly.

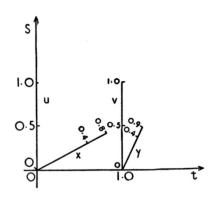

Fig. 7.12. Showing the co-ordinates s and t used in working out nomograms for colorimetric transformations. The nomogram of Fig. 7.11 was worked out in these co-ordinates and then plotted with the s-scale doubled in length in order to give more convenient scales.

Since a nomogram of this type is so useful, and appears to be little known, it is of interest to record briefly here how it can be derived. In Fig. 7.12 two variables s and t are plotted along two axes at right angles. The scale of u, which is uniform, runs along the s axis, and the scale of v, which is also uniform, runs parallel to it, at a distance of 1 unit from it along the t axis. If the equation for x is:

$$x = \frac{a_1 u + a_2 v + a_3}{a_7 u + a_8 v + a_9}$$

then the x-scale in the nomogram is given by:

$$s = \frac{a_3 - a_9 x}{(a_7 + a_8)x - (a_1 + a_2)}$$

$$t = \frac{a_8 x - a_2}{(a_7 + a_8)x - (a_1 + a_2)}$$

And if the equation for y is:

$$y = \frac{a_4 u + a_5 v + a_6}{a_7 u + a_8 v + a_9}$$

then the y-scale in the nomogram is given by:

$$s = \frac{a_6 - a_9 y}{(a_7 + a_8)y - (a_4 + a_5)}$$

$$t = \frac{a_8 y - a_5}{(a_7 + a_8)y - (a_4 + a_5)}$$

It sometimes happens, in calculating nomograms, that a scale passes through the infinity point and the useful values of the scale are very awkwardly placed. In these cases it is sometimes profitable to calculate the nomogram for different pairs of variables, such as y, z and v, w. Alternatively one of the scales can be reversed in direction, for instance by writing $v' = -v$ and working out the nomogram for v', and then using the negative part of the v' scale as a positive scale for v. Also it is useful to remember that since, in projective transformations, all straight lines remain straight lines, any projective transformation of the nomogram is permissible, and sometimes a more convenient shape can be arrived at. We have made use of this in Fig. 7.11, in which the nomogram of Fig. 7.12 has been stretched in the vertical direction by a factor of 2 to give more convenient scales.

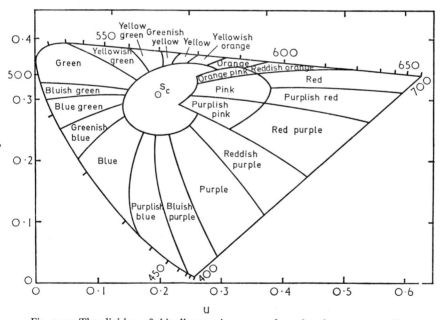

Fig. 7.13. The division of this diagram into a number of regions corresponding to various hues surrounding a central region to which no hue name is given is from Kelly's work (Kelly, 1943) on colour designations for lights. It refers to observation of self-luminous areas against a dark background.

In Appendix 1 the way in which Matrix Algebra can be used in colorimetric calculations is described.

7.8 Subjective effects

It is important to recognize the limitations of colour triangles and colour solids as a means of describing the appearance of colours.

In Fig. 7.13 the UVW triangle is shown divided into areas to which various colour names have been ascribed. This is obviously a useful means of interpreting the meaning of the position of any colour in the triangle, but unfortunately it is subject to some severe limitations. In the first place different observers will tend to use different names to describe the same colours; but, worse still, the same observer will use different names to describe the same colour when seen

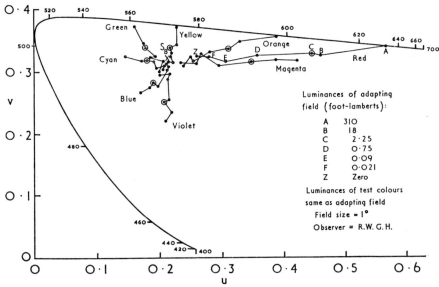

Fig. 7.14. Variation in the appearance of eight different test colours as the adapting luminance is varied from 310 foot-lamberts (outer points, A) to zero (inner points, Z). Intermediate levels (in foot-lamberts) 18, 2.25, 0.75, 0.09, and 0.021 (Hunt, 1952 and 1953). If the average reflectance of a typical scene is taken as 25 per cent, these luminance levels are approximately equivalent to the following levels of illumination in foot-candles (ft.-c.):

 A. 1200 ft.-c.: cloudy daylight or operating theatre.
 B. 70 ft.-c.: dull daylight or drawing office.
 C. 10 ft.-c.: twilight or corridors.
 D. 3.0 ft.-c.: twilight or good street lighting.
 E. 0.4 ft.-c.: poor street-lighting.
 F. 0.1 ft.-c.: ten-times full moonlight.

under different conditions. The conditions for which the names of Fig. 7.13 were worked out were for coloured lights (as opposed to surfaces, for instance) seen against dark backgrounds. If the viewing conditions are changed, however, to surface colours seen against a light background, for instance, the colour sensations will also change and these colour names may no longer be useful.

The extent of some of the changes brought about by changing the viewing conditions is indicated by the results shown in Fig. 7.14. These results were obtained using the experimental arrangement shown diagrammatically in Fig. 7.15. Provision was made for the right eye to see a patch of colour composed of a red, green and blue mixture, the amounts of which the observer could

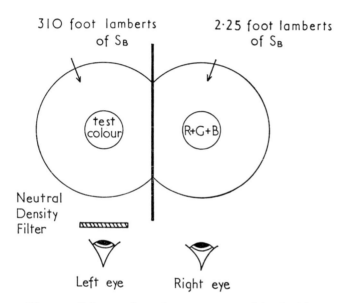

Fig. 7.15. Diagram of the experimental arrangement used in obtaining the results of Fig. 7.14. The right eye always saw the red, green, and blue mixture under the same conditions of adaptation. Changes in appearance of test colours occasioned by changes in the left eye adaptation were measured by matching them with the red, green, and blue mixture seen by the right eye.

vary at will. Surrounding this patch, and controlling the state of adaptation of the eye, was a surround field of standard illuminant B, which was kept at constant luminance of 2.25 foot-lamberts (for a list of photometric units and their meanings see Appendix 2). The left eye viewed a test colour in a central patch, with a surround field of standard illuminant B at various levels, which controlled the adaptation of the left eye. Since the adaptation of the two eyes proceeds largely independently[1] it is possible to measure the changes in colour appearance produced by changing the adaptation in one eye, by recording the different stimuli needed to produce the same changes in the other eye in which the adaptation is held constant.

This binocular matching method was first extensively used by Wright (1934 and 1946), and has since been used by a number of workers including Burnham, Evans and Newhall (1952), Winch and Young (1951), MacAdam (1956), and Hunt (1950, 1952, 1953, and 1965).

The outermost points in Fig. 7.14 show the stimuli necessary to produce in the right eye sensations which matched those produced in the left eye by the eight different test colours used when surrounded by 310 foot-lamberts of standard illuminant B. By putting neutral filters over the left eye, the luminance of the left-eye surround field was reduced from 310 to 18, 2.25, 0.75, 0.09, 0.021 and zero foot-lamberts. The stimuli needed by the right eye to match the eight test colours when the left eye was adapted to these different luminance levels, are also shown in Fig. 7.14, and the results for the seven levels for each test colour are connected by straight lines. The lines thus provide a description of the way in which colours appear to become less saturated or vivid as the general illumination level falls. It is seen that the changes in the saturations of the colours with changes of adaptation are very considerable, and involve changes in the names indicated for the stimuli by Fig. 7.13. The general conclusion is that colour triangles or solids show relationships between *stimuli*, but that the corresponding colour *sensations* vary with the conditions of viewing. Thus Fig. 7.14, although used to describe the effects of altering the viewing conditions, is none the less, like all colour triangles, still merely a diagram for plotting *stimuli* (in this case those needed by the right eye in order to match some stimuli in the left eye) and not a diagram relating *sensation* magnitudes.

In Fig. 7.16 some results are shown for another set of measurements (Hunt, 1965) made in a manner similar to that shown in Fig. 7.15, but in this case the right eye was adapted to a luminance of 1050 foot-lamberts (at a colour temperature of 4000°K) and the left eye was allowed an unimpeded view of the outside world. The right-eye adapting luminance was equivalent to a scene of average reflectance (say about 25 per cent) illuminated by sun-light (about 4000 foot-candles) and this made it possible to match colours seen by the left eye in bright sun-light. Fig. 7.16 shows the combined effect of changing both the colour and the intensity of the adapting light in the left eye: the arrows depict the way in which the appearances of various colours change as the left-eye adaptation is changed from bright sun-light at 4000 foot-candles to tungsten light at 2.2 foot-candles, and it is clear that the colours become generally yellower and less saturated. Calculation of values analogous to W^*, as shown in the caption to Fig. 7.16, also show a marked drop in luminosity when the colours are viewed

---

[1] The pupil diameters always alter together and they both have the diameter characteristic mainly of the illumination falling on whichever eye happens to be more brightly illuminated; but pupil diameter contributes only a small factor in adaptation phenomena.

in the tungsten-light condition. It is thus clear that adaptation in this case has corrected only partially for the yellower and dimmer nature of the tungsten-

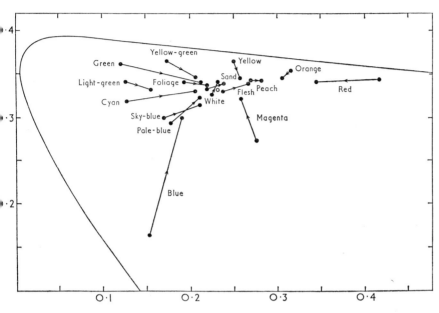

Fig. 7.16. Variation in the appearance of sixteen different test colours as the adapting conditions were changed from bright sun-light at an illumination level of 4,000 foot-candles to tungsten room-light at 2.2 foot-candles; the conditions of reference were 1050 foot-lamberts at 4000°K.

The following changes in apparent lightness (evaluated as $25 Y^{\frac{1}{3}} - 17$) also occurred:

| | Apparent lightness | |
Colour	Bright sun	Tungsten room
White	86	53
Yellow	78	44
Flesh	71	39
Sand	67	35
Orange	60	31
Light-green	60	23
Yellow-green	62	31
Peach	55	34
Sky-blue	55	18
Pale-blue	57	29
Foliage	52	18
Red	43	20
Magenta	39	19
Green	40	16
Cyan	29	10
Blue	27	11

light condition, and in addition a desaturating effect of the type shown in Fig. 7.14 has taken place.

Judd has proposed empirical formulae for calculating the subjective appearance of colours in terms of an eight-point scale for hue, and eleven-point scales for saturation and lightness. In order to make the calculations it is necessary to have the C.I.E. specifications not only for the sample colour but also for the illuminant and for the background, and to know whether the colour will be seen as a reflection surface or as a source of light (Judd, 1940). His formulae were in fairly good agreement with a number of experimental tests and have also been used to predict the colours seen in two-colour projections (Judd, 1960). Evans has investigated the conditions required for the sensation of fluorescence to be experienced (Evans, 1959), Crawford the conditions for illuminants to provide 'natural' appearance of coloured objects (Crawford, 1959), and Burnham the effects of a straight-forward shift in colour of adapting light (Burnham, 1959).

7.9 Estimation of Sensation Magnitudes

Sensations, by their very nature, can only be measured, if at all, by introspection; and, because of the inherent difficulties of this approach, colorimetry has rightly been based entirely on relationships between stimuli, sensations only being classed as equal, or equally different, in some or all respects. Stevens, however, has persevered with the method of asking observers to estimate the magnitudes of sensations of luminosity and lightness and has found that a power-law relationship exists between the luminance of a stimulus and the corresponding estimated subjective magnitude (Stevens and Stevens, 1963). He has found, moreover, that a power-law exists in a number of other stimulus-sensation relationships such as loudness, electric-shock, weight-lifting, heat, and cold. In the case of luminance the exact relationship found was that sensation magnitude is proportional to the cube root of the luminance in the absence of contrast effects; but in their presence it changes more rapidly with luminance, the exact value depending on the conditions, but not normally exceeding the cube of the luminance. Others have found similar relationships (Hopkinson, 1956; Padgham and Saunders, 1966) while the writer has derived similar relationships between the physiological response and luminance (Hunt, 1953).

7.10 Physical colour standards

As was mentioned in section 6.2, the Munsell Colour System, although objective in nature in that it consists of samples of painted cards, is scaled subjectively in that equal steps on its scales represent as nearly as possible equal subjective colour differences. It is no doubt partly for this reason that it has gained wide recognition as a very useful method of colour specification. One disadvantage to be reckoned with surface colour standards, however, is the difficulty of preventing them from deteriorating with use; this is avoided if transparent glass samples are used, although at the expense of some inconvenience when surface colours are being compared. The Tintometer system uses cyan, magenta, and yellow glasses, which are calibrated on scales of approximately equal visual increments for each colour and are of excellent permanence. Both the Munsell and the Tintometer systems have found wide application, and their usefulness as portable physical sub-standards of colour has been greatly enhanced by the publication of C.I.E. specifications for their samples (Kelly, Gibson, and Nickerson, 1943; Schofield, 1939), thus making it possible to transfer results from either system to the C.I.E. system or vice-versa. In the case of the Munsell system a smoothed calibration was also prepared, results in which are referred to as *Munsell Renotation* (Newhall, Nickerson, and Judd, 1943).

REFERENCES

Burnham, R. W., *J. Opt. Soc. Amer.*, **49**, 254 (1959).
Burnham, R. W., Evans, R. M., and Newhall, S. M., *J. Opt. Soc. Amer.*, **42**, 597 (1952).
C.I.E., *Proc. 14th Session (Brussels)*, Vol. A, p. 95 (1960).
C.I.E., *Proc. 15th Session (Vienna)*, Vol. A, p. 113 (1964).
Crawford, B. H., *J. Opt. Soc. Amer.*, **49**, 1147 (1959).
Evans, R. M., *J. Opt Soc. Amer.*, **49**, 1049 (1959).
Hopkinson, R. G., *Nature*, **178**, 1065 (1956).
Hunt, R. W. G., *J. Opt. Soc. Amer.*, **40**, 362 (1950).
Hunt, R. W. G., *J. Opt. Soc. Amer.*, **42**, 190 (1952).
Hunt, R. W. G., *J. Photogr. Sci.*, **1**, 149 (1953).
Hunt, R. W. G., *J. Sci. Instrum.*, **31**, 122 (1954).
Hunt, R. W. G., *J. Opt. Soc. Amer.*, **55**, 1540 (1965).
Judd, D. B., *J. Opt. Soc. Amer.*, **30**, 2 (1940).
Judd, D. B., *J. Opt. Soc. Amer.*, **50**, 254 (1960).
Judd, D. B., and Wyszecki, G., *Colour in Business, Science, and Industry*, p. 295, Wiley, New York (1963).
Judd, D. B., MacAdam, D. L., and Wyszecki, G., *J. Opt. Soc. Amer.*, **54**, 1031 (1964).
Kelly, K. L., *J. Opt. Soc. Amer.*, **33**, 627 (1943).
Kelly, K. L., Gibson, K. S., and Nickerson, D., *J. Opt. Soc. Amer.*, **33**, 355 (1943).
MacAdam, D. L., *J. Opt. Soc. Amer.*, **27**, 294 (1937).
MacAdam, D. L., *J. Opt. Soc. Amer.*, **46**, 500 (1956).
MacAdam, D. L., *J. Soc. Mot. Pic. Tel. Eng.*, **65**, 455 (1956).
Newhall, S. M., Nickerson, D., and Judd, D. B., *J. Opt. Soc. Amer.*, **33**, 385 (1943).
Nimeroff, J., *J. Opt. Soc. Amer.*, **54**, 1365 (1964).
Padgham, C. A., and Saunders, J. E., *Trans. Illum. Eng. Soc.*, **31**, 122 (1966).
Schofield, R. K., *J. Sci. Instrum.*, **16**, 74 (1939).
Stevens, S. S., and Stevens, J. C., *J. Opt. Soc. Amer.*, **53**, 375 (1963).
Stiles, W. S., *Phys. Soc. Year Book*, p. 44 (1955).
Stiles, W. S., and Burch, J. M., *Optica Acta*, **6**, 1 (1958).
Winch, G. T., and Young, B. M., *G.E.C. Journal*, **18**, 88 (1951).
Wright, W. D., *Proc. Roy. Soc. B.*, **115**, 49 (1934).
Wright, W. D., *Proc. Phys. Soc.*, **53**, 99 (1941).
Wright, W. D., *Researches on Normal and Defective Colour Vision*, Kimpton, London, pp. 209–255 (1946).
Wyszecki, G., *J. Opt. Soc. Amer.*, **53**, 1318 (1963).
Wyszecki, G., and Wright, H., *J. Opt. Soc. Amer.*, **55**, 1166 (1965).

GENERAL REFERENCES

Hardy, A. C., *Handbook of Colorimetry*, The Technology Press, Cambridge, Massachusetts (1936).
Judd, D. B., and Wyszecki, G., *Colour in Business, Science, and Industry*, Wiley, New York (1963).
Murray, H. D., *Colour in Theory and Practice*, Chapman & Hall (1952).
Wright, W. D., *The Measurement of Colour*, Hilger and Watts (1964).

CHAPTER 8

Light Sources

8.1 Introduction

WE have already seen that the eye is able to *adapt* to illuminants of different colours. For example in tungsten light, which is deficient in blue light, the eye increases its blue sensitivity. In this way illuminants of different colours result in changes in colour rendering which are much reduced. It was also pointed out in Chapter 5 that cameras must similarly adapt to the colour of the illuminant, since the final picture is generally presented to the eye in such a way that the adaptation which takes place is much less than when the original is viewed. These variations in illuminant colour are of such importance in colour reproduction that we shall devote a short chapter to them.

8.2 Tungsten Lamps

The most important artificial illuminants are tungsten filament lamps, because of their extremely widespread use. The colour of the light they emit is affected by the colour of the glass used for the envelope, although this is generally very nearly colourless (usually very slightly greenish) and therefore has only a small effect. By far the most important factor determining the spectral energy distribution of the light emitted is the temperature at which the filament is operated, and this in turn depends on the resistance of the filament and the voltage applied to the lamp. As the temperature of the filament is raised from room temperature the colours listed in Table 8.1 are produced. The temperatures are listed both in degrees Centigrade or Celsius (°C) and degrees Kelvin (°K), since the latter figure (which exceeds the former by 273) is generally used for light sources. The temperatures assigned to the colour names are only approximate and the temperature at which the light becomes white depends on the state of adaptation of the observer, and also on the intensity of the light (Hurvich and Jameson, 1951). The maximum temperature obtainable with tungsten filaments is fixed by the melting point of tungsten, which is about 3700°K. However, modern tungsten lamps, which run at about 3000°K, give light of a colour which most people describe as white when they are fully adapted to it.

TABLE 8.1

TEMPERATURES OF HEATED OBJECTS

COLOUR	TEMPERATURE °C	TEMPERATURE °K
Extremely dull red	480	753
Very dark red	630	903
Dark red	750	1023
Cherry red	815	1088
Light cherry red	900	1173
Orange red	990	1263
Yellow	1150	1423
Yellow-white	1330	1603

The spectral energy distribution of the light emitted by certain incandescent sources can be defined very simply; these sources are known as *full radiators* or *black bodies*, and consist of heated enclosures with a small opening through which the light is emitted; this opening must be small in the sense that its area is a small fraction (e.g. one hundredth) of the area of the interior of the enclosure, like the door of a furnace, for example. For full radiators, the spectral energy distribution is given by *Planck's Radiation Law*:

$$E_\lambda = \frac{c_1}{\lambda^5} \cdot \frac{1}{e^{c_2/\lambda T} - 1}$$

where E_λ is the energy in watts radiated per square centimetre of surface per micron wavelength band at wavelength λ; λ is the wavelength in microns (one thousandth of a millimetre), T is the temperature in degrees Kelvin; $c_1 = 37,400$; $c_2 = 14,380$; and $e = 2 \cdot 718$. When the wavelength is short and the temperature not too high, $e^{c_2/\lambda T}$ becomes very large compared with one, and, to a close approximation:

$$E_\lambda = c_1/\lambda^5 e^{c_2/\lambda T}$$

This is known as *Wien's Radiation Law*, and for temperatures typical of those used in tungsten filament lamps and for wavelengths in the visible part of the spectrum it is accurate to about 1%.

Tungsten filament lamps are obviously not full radiators in the sense of being heated enclosures with small openings. But the energy distributions which they emit are very nearly identical to those emitted by full radiators of temperatures about 50° higher than those of the filaments, so that it has become customary to designate the colour of tungsten filament lamps by quoting these temperatures, which are referred to as *colour temperatures*. Thus a lamp of colour temperature 3000°K, for example, emits light of spectral energy distribution almost identical with that of a full radiator operating at this temperature; the actual filament temperature would be about 2950°K but this figure is of little interest and is not generally quoted.

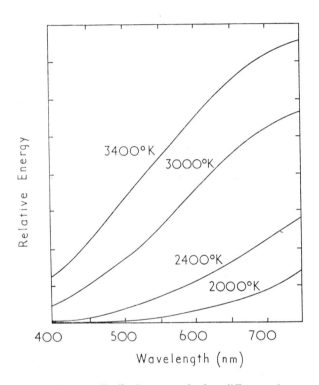

Fig. 8.1. Spectral energy distribution curves for four different colour temperatures.

In Fig. 8.1, spectral energy distributions for four different colour temperatures are shown (after Murray, 1952). The higher the colour temperature the greater is the efficiency of the lamp, because more visible light (as shown in the figure) and less infra-red light is emitted for a given wattage. Also, high colour temperatures correspond to bluer light and a reduction in the difference between the colour of the light from the lamp and that of daylight. For these reasons, lamps are made to operate at the highest possible colour

5A

temperatures. For lamps with thick filaments (about a fifth of a millimetre in diameter) colour temperatures of about 3400°K are possible, but with thin filaments (about a fiftieth of a millimetre in diameter) colour temperatures of only about 2500°K can be achieved owing to the fragility of the filament and the serious weakening resulting from any evaporation thereof. Thick filaments, of course, are of lower electrical resistance than thin filaments, so that they can only be used for low voltage or high wattage lamps. Thus for a lamp to operate at a colour temperature of 3000°K or over and have a reasonable life, the wattage must be 250 or more, if it is in the 200–250 volt range; but in the 12–24 volt range wattages as low as about 30 can be achieved at these colour temperatures. Conversely, for a given wattage, a low voltage lamp can be operated at a higher colour temperature (and hence at a greater efficiency) than a high voltage lamp. For these reasons, tungsten lamps used in motion-picture and television studios are generally of 100–120 volts and not 200–250 volts. In cine-projectors, where a highly efficient and compact source is required, voltages of 100–120, or even 6–12 are used; for not only are high voltage lamps less efficient, but compact filaments are difficult to make because of a tendency for arc discharges to occur from one filament to another, causing early lamp failure (Aldington, 1954).

Failure of tungsten filament lamps is most commonly caused by evaporation of tungsten from the filament: for various reasons this evaporation occurs more markedly at some points than at others so that the filament develops local 'waists' which are thinner than the rest. These waists then become hotter, because of the high resistance caused by the reduced diameter, and the tungsten therefore evaporates at an even greater rate, until finally a break occurs. The tungsten evaporated from the filament is deposited on the inside of the glass wall of the lamp, where it forms a grey or brownish deposit which absorbs light and therefore reduces the light-output.

In *tungsten-halogen* lamps (Zubler and Mosby, 1959; Strange and Stewart, 1963) the blackening caused by the evaporated tungsten is avoided by running the filament in an atmosphere of low-pressure iodine vapour, and constructing the envelope of the lamp of quartz so that its wall can be maintained above about 250°C in temperature (Levin and Westlund, 1966). When this is done, the tungsten combines with the iodine at the wall to form tungsten iodide:

$$W + I_2 \rightarrow WI_2$$

The tungsten iodide then returns to the neighbourhood of the filament, where, under the influence of its temperature of over 2000°C, the tungsten iodide then dissociates to form tungsten and iodine:

$$WI_2 \rightarrow W + I_2$$

The tungsten is then redeposited on the filament. Unfortunately the tungsten does not go preferentially to the hottest (and therefore thinnest) parts of the filament, so that lamp failure still occurs because of local filament breakage; but such lamps have their average life extended as a result of the iodine cycle, or can be run at a higher colour temperature than ordinary lamps for the same average life. The envelope of these lamps is made of quartz so as to withstand the high operating temperature, the temperature being maintained by making the envelope of the lamp very compact. The compactness of the lamp is an advantage in that it enables highly efficient light-collecting optical components to be used. Hence the tungsten-halogen lamp has the advantages that it does not blacken with use, and therefore is more efficient and less variable during its life; it can be run at a higher colour temperature, and is therefore more efficient; and it is compact, so that it is convenient and efficient when used with optical components. The iodine vapour does absorb slightly in the yellow-green part of the spectrum so that if too much iodine vapour is included the light has a purplish tinge (Studer and Van Beers, 1964).

In colour photography, when films are designed for use with tungsten light, the colour temperature is usually specified. The photographer frequently finds, however, that the lamps with which he is obliged to illuminate his scene are not of exactly the required colour temperature. But the colour temperature of tungsten lamps can be modified by means of filters, and if all the lamps illuminating a scene are of the same (but wrong) colour temperature, a very convenient method of correction is to put the appropriate filter over the camera lens. If the lamps vary appreciably in colour temperature amongst themselves, some or all of them must be filtered individually, either with or without a filter over the camera lens for general correction.

The colour temperatures of tungsten lamps can be conveniently measured by means of photoelectric colour temperature meters; these instruments compare the intensity of illumination through red and blue filters, and are calibrated in degrees Kelvin (Harding, 1952; Palmer, 1965).

8.3 Energy converting filters

When using filters for modifying the colour temperature of the light emitted by lamps, it is convenient to use the reciprocal of the colour temperature, rather than the colour temperature itself. In order to obtain numbers of convenient size, these reciprocals are multiplied by a million and the values thus obtained are called micro-reciprocal degrees, or *mireds*. Thus a colour temperature of 2000°K is equivalent to 500 mireds; 4000°K to 250 mireds. A filter which raised the colour temperature of the light emitted by a source from 2000°K to 4000°K would thus produce a change of −250 mireds. Now it so happens that such a filter *always* produces a change of −250 mireds no matter what the original colour temperature of the source. This is true for filters of all mired-shift values, whether positive or negative, to the same accuracy as that to which Wien's Radiation Law is true. This important property of *energy-converting filters* can be proved as follows.

Assuming that the temperatures of the sources and the wavelengths of the spectrum being considered are such that, to a reasonably good approximation, Wien's Radiation Law applies, we have:

$$E_\lambda = c_1/\lambda^5 e^{c_2/\lambda T}$$

Converting this to logarithms (to the base e), for two temperatures T and T' we have:

$$\log_e E_\lambda = \log_e c_1 - 5\log_e\lambda - \frac{c_2}{\lambda T}$$

$$\log_e E_\lambda' = \log_e c_1 - 5\log_e\lambda - \frac{c_2}{\lambda T'}$$

Therefore, by subtraction:

$$\log_e E_\lambda - \log_e E_\lambda' = \left(\frac{1}{T'} - \frac{1}{T}\right)\frac{c_2}{\lambda}$$

The expression $\log_e E_\lambda - \log_e E_\lambda'$ is the difference (in logarithmic units) between the two energy distributions and therefore represents the optical density (to the base e) which a filter must have at each wavelength in order to convert the energy distribution from that which is characteristic of a colour temperature T to that characteristic of a colour temperature T'. The way in which the density of this filter varies with wavelength is shown by the above equation to be simply inversely proportional to the wavelength λ, and directly proportional to:

$$\frac{1}{T'} - \frac{1}{T}$$

But this expression is simply one millionth of the mired shift, so that the nature of the filter depends only on the mired shift, and not on the individual colour temperatures T and T'.

The derivation of the spectral density curve required for a filter of a given mired shift, M, is then calculated as follows. The required density (D_e) to the base e is given by:

$$D_e = \left(\frac{1}{T'} - \frac{1}{T}\right)\frac{c_2}{\lambda}$$
$$= 10^{-6}M\, c_2/\lambda$$

But the density is usually evaluated to the base 10, so that on this basis the density D is given by:

$$D = 10^{-6}Mc_2/2.303\lambda$$

Inserting the value 14380 for c_2 we obtain:

$$D = 0.00624M(1/\lambda).$$

Hence if D is plotted against $1/\lambda$, a straight line is obtained, the slope, m, of which is given by:

$$m = 0.00624M$$

Conversely if a filter has a slope of m, the mired shift is given by:

$$M = (160.2)m$$

The slope m is that of the line when plotted against scales such that one unit of density on one axis is the same length as one unit of reciprocal microns on the other axis.

It will be noted that if M is positive, m is also positive, so that for a positive mired shift, that is, a lowering of colour temperature, density increases with reciprocal wavelength, and therefore decreases with wavelength. Conversely, for a negative mired shift, that is, an increase in colour temperature, density increases with wavelength.

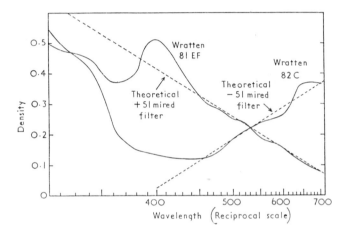

Fig. 8.2. Spectral density curves for two theoretical (dotted lines) and two actual (full lines) 'energy converting' filters.

In Fig. 8.2 the spectral densities of two Wratten filters, Numbers 81EF and 82C, are plotted against wavelength (on a reciprocal scale increasing from right to left). If these filters were true energy-converting filters, their spectral density curves would be straight lines on this graph. It is clear that over the major part of the visible spectrum the filters do have curves which approximate fairly closely to the theoretical requirements (indicated by the dotted lines); the discrepancies at the short wavelength end of the spectrum are quite large, but the wavelength scale is very extended in this region on the reciprocal scale, so that these shortcomings tend to be somewhat over-emphasized. In practice these two filters can be used as energy converting filters quite successfully, and similar filters, of both glass and gelatin, giving various mired shifts are commercially available.

137

8.4 Daylight

The most important—and the most variable—source of light is daylight. The sun, from which all phases of daylight are derived, is believed to have a temperature of millions of degrees at its centre, but its surface is much cooler and the colour temperature of the light which it emits is probably between 6000 and 7000°K. The exact determination of this figure is difficult because the light passes through the atmospheres of both the sun and the earth, which are neither neutral nor constant in their spectral absorptions (Moon, 1940; Taylor and Kerr, 1941; Jones and Condit, 1948; Hull, 1954). In Fig. 8.3 a

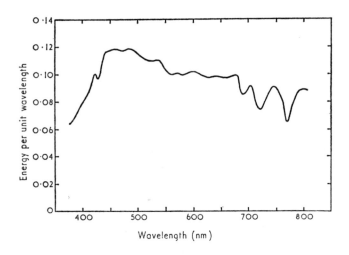

Fig. 8.3. A typical spectral energy distribution curve for sunlight as received on the earth's surface (MacAdam, 1958).

typical spectral energy distribution of sunlight as received on the earth's surface is shown as reported by MacAdam (MacAdam, 1958). The curve exhibits a number of undulations, some caused by absorption bands in the solar atmosphere (Fraunhofer lines) and others by absorptions in the terrestrial atmosphere (caused by oxygen and water vapour, for instance).

If the atmosphere is clear and cloudless, the total daylight consists of a mixture of the direct light from the sun together with the diffuse light scattered by the atmosphere. Because light of short wavelengths is scattered much more than light of long wavelengths, this diffuse sky-light consists mainly of blue light, and gives rise to the blueness of the clear sky. The diffuse light, however, is not only scattered downwards to the earth, but also outwards into space, so that there is a net loss of blue light in the combined sunlight and skylight incident on the earth. The sun's surface probably approximates closely in energy distribution to a full radiator; but, as seen from the earth's surface, because of the loss of blue light by scattering, and because of the absorptions in the atmospheres of both the earth and the sun, the departures from full radiation are considerable. In Fig. 8.4 are spectral energy distributions typical

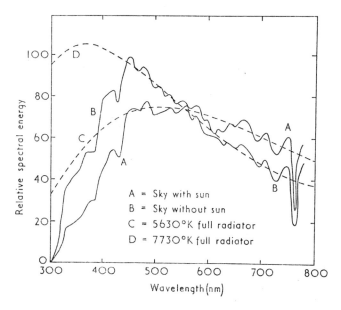

Fig. 8.4. Relative spectral energy distribution curves typical of daylight when the sun is shining and when the conditions are cloudy (Henderson and Hodgkiss, 1963 and 1964), together with those of full radiators of about the same colour temperatures.

of daylight when the sun is shining and when the conditions are cloudy (Henderson and Hodgkiss, 1963 and 1964). For comparison with the results for the sunny conditions the spectral energy distribution of a full radiator at 5630°K is shown by the broken line C, and it is seen that while the general distribution is similar there are some quite appreciable differences. The difference between the colour temperature to which the sunlight now approximates (5630°K) and that of the surface of the sun (6000–7000°K) is a measure of the loss of light of the shorter wavelengths by scattering into space. Compared with the full radiator, daylight is particularly deficient in energy at wavelengths below about 430 nm. For comparison with the results for the cloudy conditions the spectral energy distribution of a full radiator at 7730°K is shown by the broken line D.

When the weather is cloudy the spectral energy distribution of the daylight depends on the height of the clouds. If the clouds are low, then they simply act as a neutral diffusing and absorbing layer which mixes the blue skylight and direct sunlight incident upon them to produce a diffuse light of colour similar to that of the sun and sky together on a clear day. But if the top of the cloud layer is very high, the spectral energy distribution on the earth approximates to that of the sun outside the earth's atmosphere. The reason for

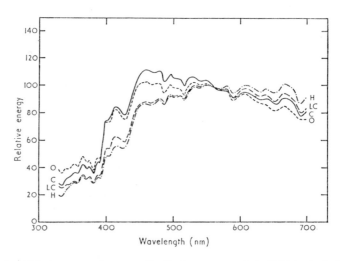

Fig. 8.5. Relative spectral energy distribution curves of daylight typical of various weather conditions as received on a nearly vertical surface facing towards the sun. O: Overcast; C: clear; LC: light cloud; H: hazy.

this is that a very high layer of cloud can catch much of the scattered blue light before it is lost to space and can reflect it back to earth again; that this is possible can be deduced from the fact that at altitudes of 40,000 feet the sky appears quite dark (Harding and Lambert, 1951), indicating that most of the blue light of the sky is scattered at lower altitudes. The colour temperature to which the spectral energy distribution for cloudy conditions most closely approximates is about 6500°K, and this in turn approximates to the estimated colour temperature of the sun outside the earth's atmosphere. Fig. 8.5 shows spectral energy distributions of daylight for various weather conditions (Condit and Grum, 1964). It has also been shown on theoretical grounds (Middleton, 1954) that the colour of the ground has an appreciable effect on the colour of cloudy daylight, making it greenish over grass, for instance.

The way in which the colour of the illumination changes as the sun sets depends on the weather conditions. If the sky is cloudless, the increased thickness of the atmosphere through which the rays of the sun must pass before reaching the earth's surface produces the familiar reddening of the light as shown by the spectral energy distribution curves of Fig. 8.6 (Condit and Grum, 1964). Thus colour photographs taken in low altitude sunlight often show a pronounced orange cast. But as sunset is approached the direct rays from the sun become much weaker so that the diffuse light, which is

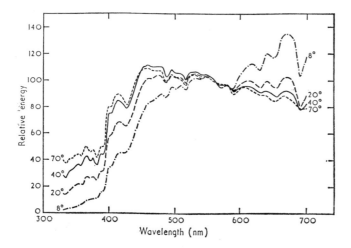

Fig. 8.6. Relative spectral energy distribution curves of daylight with clear sky for various solar altitudes, as received on a nearly vertical surface facing towards the sun.

very blue, becomes of more and more importance (see, for instance, Fig. 18 of the paper by Jones and Condit (Jones and Condit, 1948) where sunlight and skylight intensities, and their ratio, are plotted against the solar altitude). Hence the light becomes first redder, and then bluer. With cloud at medium heights, some reddening of the light may be expected at first, but this will soon give way to an increase in blueness as sunset is approached. With high cloud, little or no reddening of the light should occur before sunset. Pitt and Selwyn (1938) found that, except when the direct rays of the sun provided an important part of the general illumination, the colour of the light remained remarkably steady until the rapid increase in blueness took place at sunset. The total variation which can be produced by different phases of daylight are very considerable, as illustrated by Fig. 8.7, where the spectral energy distributions are shown for surfaces facing towards clear sun at a solar altitude of 8° and facing away from it at a solar altitude of 30° (Condit and Grum, 1964).

TABLE 8.2

Kodak Colour Correcting Filters required to correct the colour of various phases of daylight for colour photography. B: Sun behind camera. C: Sun in front of camera.

WEATHER	SUNNY		CLOUDY	
DIRECTION SOLAR ALTITUDE	B	C	B	C
10–15°	20B+5C	None	10B+5C	5B+5C
15–20°	10B	,,	10B	5C
20–30°	5B	5Y	5B	None
30–40°	None	10Y	None	,,
40–50°	,,	10Y	,,	,,
50–60°	,,	15Y	,,	5Y

In Table 8.2 are listed Kodak Colour Correcting Filters which can be used to correct various phases of daylight, so that, as far as colour photography is concerned, the results will always approximate to those which would occur in sunlight on a clear day when the solar altitude is 55°. It must be emphasized that these filter recommendations are only very approximate, and that on individual occasions the required filter may be very different, because of the particular weather conditions prevailing.

Photoelectric colour temperature meters can be used for assessing the relative blue-to-red balance of daylight, but should be calibrated in terms

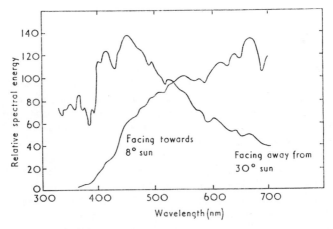

Fig. 8.7. Relative spectral energy distribution curves of an extremely bluish (facing away from 30° sun) and an extremely reddish (facing towards 8° sun) sample of daylight.

of a suitable range of correcting filters, since the colour temperature readings will be upset by the departures of the energy distribution of daylight from those of full radiators.

It should be noted that it may not always be desirable from the artistic point of view to correct the colour of lighting; some distortion in the final colour reproduction may well be useful in creating the right 'mood'; bluish when cloudy, yellowish in low altitude sunlight, for instance.

Standardized spectral energy distributions have been drawn up to represent daylight for correlated colour temperatures (this term is defined in Section 8.10) from 4000 to 25000°K (Judd, MacAdam and Wyszecki, 1964).

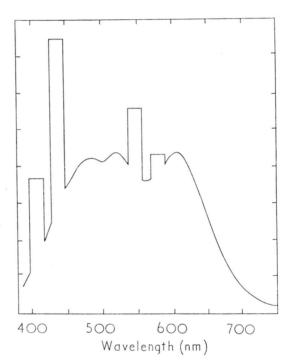

Fig. 8.8. Spectral energy distribution curve for a fluorescent lamp. The rectangular protuberances are caused by the lines of the mercury spectrum; the areas of these rectangles give a true representation of the amount of energy emitted at their mid-wavelengths, but their true shape is much higher and thinner than that which can conveniently be drawn on a diagram.

Wavelength (nm)

8.5 Fluorescent lamps

Fluorescent lamps have spectral energy distributions which are mixtures of that of the mercury vapour spectrum and of those of various fluorescent powders. A typical example is shown in Fig. 8.8. The sharp peaks in the spectral energy distribution are caused by the presence of the lines of the mercury vapour spectrum, and these, together with the relatively small amount of light in the far red part of the spectrum can result in a certain amount of distortion in the appearance of colours.

8.6 Xenon arcs

Another source providing a mixture of a continuous spectrum and emission at discrete lines is the Xenon arc (Beeson, Bocok, Castellain and Tuck, 1958; Uffers, 1958); a typical spectral energy distribution of this source is shown in Fig. 8.9; the exact energy distribution depends somewhat on the pressure of the Xenon gas in the lamp, but it is usually fairly similar to that of daylight having a correlated colour temperature of about 6000°K; however, the emission at the red and blue ends of the spectrum is usually rather higher so that the light is very slightly purplish compared to daylight.

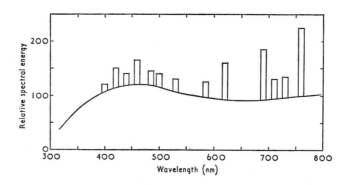

Fig. 8.9. Spectral energy distribution curve for Xenon arc, using the same convention for presenting spectral lines as in Fig. 8.8.

Xenon lamps are available for running continuously, or with very short pulses of power to give flashes of light of about 1/1000 of a second duration for flash photography. The continuously-run lamps can be used in professional motion-picture film projectors, for studio lighting, and for flood-lighting, and are particularly useful when light of near-daylight colour is required.

8.7 Carbon arcs

Carbon arcs, operating in air without any glass envelope, have long been used for projecting professional motion pictures. The light produced comes partly from the intensely hot craters of the carbon rods forming the arc, and partly from the combustion of gases between the arcs. The efficiency and colour of the emission are improved by incorporating additives, such as cerium, in the carbon rods, and a typical spectral energy distribution is as shown in Fig. 8.10 (a) (Dull and Kemp, 1956). Sometimes it is required to supplement studio tungsten lamps with arcs, and in this case arcs are required which emit light having a correlated colour temperature of about 3200°K. The carbon arc can be used for this purpose, too, by suitable choice of additives, a typical spectral energy distribution then being as shown in Fig. 8.10 (b) (Holloway, Plaskett, Dull, and Handley, 1955; Dull and Kemp, 1956).

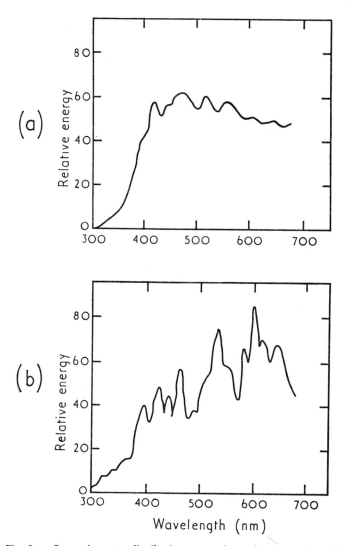

Fig. 8.10. Spectral energy distribution curves for carbon arcs. (a) White-flame arc giving light of approximately average daylight quality. (b) Yellow-flame arc giving light having a correlated colour temperature of about 3200°K.

8.8 Photographic flash-bulbs

The familiar photographic flash-bulb usually consists of a combustible metallic wire, such as aluminium wire, enclosed in a glass envelope containing oxygen. The light emitted is usually similar to that of a full radiator at about 3800°K for an aluminium filling, or about 4000°K for a zirconium filling. Flash-bulbs intended for use with films balanced for use in daylight are usually coated with a lacquer containing a blue dye so as to raise the effective colour temperature to around 5500°K.

TABLE 8.3

CORRELATED COLOUR TEMPERATURES OF COMMONLY USED LIGHT SOURCES

SOURCE	°K	M
Typical north-sky light	7500	133
Typical average daylight	6500	154
Artificial Daylight fluorescent lamps[1]	6500	154
Xenon (electronic flash or continuous)	6000	167
Typical sunlight plus skylight	5500	182
Blue flash-bulbs	5500	182
Carbon arc (for projectors)	5000	200
Cool White fluorescent lamps[2]	4300	233
Clear flash-bulbs	3800	263
White fluorescent lamps	3500	286
Photo-flood tungsten lamps	3400	294
Tungsten-halogen lamps	3300	303
Projection tungsten lamps	3200	312
Studio tungsten lamps	3200	312
Warm White fluorescent lamps	3000	333
Floodlighting tungsten lamps	3000	333
Domestic tungsten lamps (100 to 200 W.)	2900	345
Domestic tungsten lamps (40 to 60 W.)	2800	357

[1] Sometimes called North-light or Colour Matching Lamps.
[2] Sometimes called Daylight lamps.

8.9 The red-eye effect

It is sometimes found that, in colour photographs taken by means of flash-bulbs, the pupils of people's eyes are reproduced red instead of black. This effect is caused by light being reflected by the layers of the eye immediately behind the retina, and since these layers are reddish the reflection has this colour. It is not noticed in everyday life because the amount of light involved is small compared to the general level of illumination. But in flash photography, during the time of the exposure, the flash-bulb produces an illumination level far higher than the ambient light, and the optical system of the eye focusses the reflected light in a fairly narrow beam back towards the flash bulb, so that if the camera lens is close to it, it picks up the reddish light and records the pupils as red instead of black. The effect can only be entirely avoided by having the flash-bulb several inches away from the camera lens; but if the ambient lighting is kept high the trouble is alleviated because the pupils of the eyes are then small, thus reducing both the illumination level inside the eye, and the proportion of light reflected.

8.10 Correlated colour temperatures of commonly used light sources

Although colour temperature only defines the relative spectral energy distributions of full radiators (black bodies), it is common with other sources of whitish light to quote their *correlated colour temperature:* this is defined as the colour temperature of that full radiator which produces light most closely matching the particular source. These correlated colour temperatures then provide a useful indication of the relative bluishness or yellowishness of the sources. In Table 8.3 the correlated colour temperatures are given for typical examples of a number of sources commonly used in colour reproduction systems; the corresponding mired values, M, are also given. This mired scale is particularly useful because, over the range of mired values involved, it so happens that equal mired intervals are to a good approximation equivalent to equal colour differences.

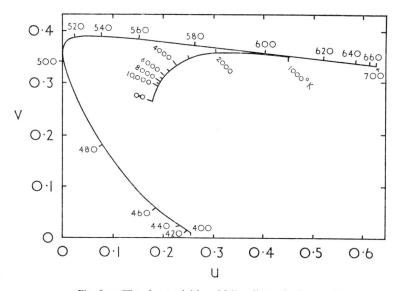

Fig. 8.11. The chromaticities of full radiators in the u, v triangle.

In Fig. 8.11 the chromaticities of full radiators at various colour temperatures are shown on the u,v chromaticity triangle by the curved line, which is known as the *full-radiator locus* (or the *black-body locus*). For sources which do not lie on the full-radiator locus, the correlated colour temperature is calculated as that colour temperature whose chromaticity lies closest to the chromaticity of the source in question; since the u,v triangle represents equal colour differences by approximately equal distances, this method of calculation gives results reasonably close to those which would be obtained by direct visual comparison by a normal observer. In Fig. 8.12 the part of the full-radiator locus covering the range of colour temperatures of greatest practical importance is shown on a larger scale, together with the chromaticities of some important illuminants.

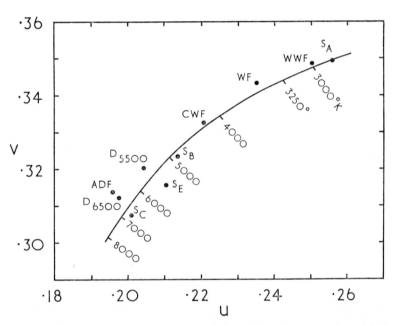

Fig. 8.12. The chromaticities of some important illuminants together with those of full radiators of similar correlated colour temperature. Fluorescent lamps are indicated thus: WWF, warm white; WF, white; CWF, cool white; ADF, artificial daylight.

REFERENCES

Aldington, J. N., *Trans. Illum. Eng. Soc.*, **19**, 319 (1954).
Beeson, E. J. G., Bocock, W. A., Castellain, A. P., and Tuck, F. A., *Brit. Kinematography*, **32**, 59 (1958).
Condit, H. R., and Grum, F., *J. Opt. Soc. Amer.*, **54**, 937 (1964).
Dull, R. B., and Kemp, J. G., *J. Soc. Mot. Pic. Tel. Eng.*, **65**, 432 (1956).
Harding, H. G. W., *J. Sci. Instrum.*, **29**, 145 (1952).

Harding, H. G. W., and Lambert, G. E. V., *Nature*, **167**, 436 (1951).
Henderson, S. T., and Hodgkiss, D., *Brit. J. Appl. Phys.*, **14**, 125 (1963).
Henderson, S. T., and Hodgkiss, D., *Brit. J. Appl. Phys.*, **15**, 947 (1964).
Holloway, F. P., Plaskett, C. A., Dull, R. B., and Handley, C. W., *J. Soc. Mot. Pic. Tel. Eng.*, **64**, 657 (1955).
Hull, J. N., *Trans. Illum. Eng. Soc.*, **19**, 21 (1954).
Hurvich, L. M., and Jameson, D., *J. Opt. Soc. Amer.*, **41**, 521, 528, and 787 (1951).
Jones, L. A., and Condit, H. R., *J. Opt. Soc. Amer.*, **38**, 123 (1948).
Judd, D. B., MacAdam, D. L., and Wyszecki, G., *J. Opt. Soc. Amer.*, **54**, 1031 (1964).
Levin, R. E., and Westlund, A. E., *J. Soc. Mot. Pic. Tel. Eng.*, **75**, 589 (1966).
MacAdam, D. L., *J. Opt. Soc. Amer.*, **48**, 832 (1958).
Middleton, W. E. K., *J. Opt. Soc. Amer.*, **44**, 793 (1954).
Moon, P., *J. Franklin Inst.*, **230**, 583 (1940).
Murray, H. D., *Colour in Theory and Practice*, Chapman & Hall, London, p. 205 (1952).
Palmer, D. A., N.P.L. Quarterly, page 2 (July to September, 1965).
Pitt, F. H. G., and Selwyn, E. W. H., *Phot. J.*, **78**, 115 (1938).
Strange, J. W., and Stewart, J., *Trans. Illum. Eng. Soc.*, **28**, 91 (1963).
Studer, F. J., and Van Beers, R. F., *J. Opt. Soc. Amer.*, **54**, 945 (1964).
Taylor, A. H., and Kerr, G. P., *J. Opt. Soc. Amer.*, **31**, 3 (1941).
Uffers, H., *J. Soc. Mot. Pic. Tel. Eng.*, **67**, 389 (1958).
Zubler, E. G., and Mosby, F. A., *Illum. Engr.*, **54**, 734 (1959).

GENERAL REFERENCES

Barrows, W. E., *Light, Photometry, and Illuminating Engineering*, McGraw Hill, New York (1951).
Edwards, E. F., and Burgin, R., *Phot. J.*, **106**, 319 (1966).
Moon, P., *The Scientific Basis of Illuminating Engineering*, McGraw Hill, New York (1936).
Murray, H. D., *Colour in Theory and Practice*, Chapman & Hall, London, (1952).
Stiles, W. S., and Wyszecki, G., *Colour Science*, Wiley, New York (1967).
Walsh, J. W. T., *Photometry*, Constable, London, (1953).

CHAPTER 9

Assessing the Final Result

9.1 Introduction

THE ultimate test of any colour reproduction is the opinion of the person who views it. But opinions differ, and, in cases where dissatisfaction is felt, the viewer often finds great difficulty in saying exactly why he does not like the sensations which he experiences when looking at the picture. Trained observers may feel more competent to name the faults in a reproduction, but training often makes an observer especially sensitive to certain faults which have been prevalent in his experience, while other faults, equally bad to a naïve (but less articulate) observer, he may overlook. A scientific approach to the problem, though difficult, has therefore to be attempted.

9.2 Comparative methods

If it is required to know simply by how much one colour reproduction of some given scene is better than another, a quantitative assessment can be made by recording the independent judgments of a number of observers. Thus if, out of 50 observers, 35 preferred reproduction A, 10 preferred reproduction B, and 5 rated reproductions A and B as being of equal merit, the distribution of the votes can be used as a quantitative measure of the subjective difference between A and B. Similar judgments can then be made between other reproductions, A and C, B and C, A and D, B and D, C and D, and so on, and an order of merit drawn up in which the number of times each reproduction was preferred provides its index of quality. This method of *paired comparisons* is a very powerful tool, and enables a very thorough comparison of a small number of alternative reproductions to be made. For a large number of reproductions, however, it becomes a very time-consuming and laborious undertaking, and in this case the *single-stimulus* method is more practicable.

In the *single-stimulus* method, the alternative reproductions are shown to the observers one at a time, and they are asked to rate them according to some given scale, such as: Acceptable, Doubtful, Not Acceptable; or Excellent, Good, Fair, Poor, Bad. In each case some number of marks is allocated arbitrarily to each category, such as 1, $\frac{1}{2}$, 0 for the first series, or 4, 3, 2, 1, 0, for the second series, and the total number of marks obtained by each reproduction from all the observers is expressed as a percentage of the total number of marks which it could have obtained if all observers rated it as high as possible. In this way, merit-percentages are obtained, which provide a quantitative assessment of the reproductions. One difficulty with the single-stimulus method is that the observers may tend to change their standards as the tests proceed, since each picture has to be judged against some mental standard in the observers' minds. But the effects of this difficulty can be greatly reduced by showing the reproductions in random order, and by varying the order for different panels of judges.

The above methods are useful when a number of existing reproductions have to be compared. But they are less useful in answering such questions as 'What are the main faults in this system of colour reproduction?' And they are quite powerless to predict *quantitatively* the changes which should be made in a system in order to improve it. This is the field in which colorimetry has to be used, although the difficulties are very considerable.

9.3 Exact colour reproduction

At first sight, it would seem that all that is required is for the tristimulus values of a number of original colours to be compared with those of the corresponding colours in the reproduction. But if neutral colours in an original scene are illuminated by daylight and are reproduced exactly as they are, the eye, if it is adapted to tungsten light for instance, will see the colours as being not neutral, but blue. And this is by no means an unusual situation, for it obtains whenever an outdoor scene is televised or photographed in colour and viewed in rooms lit by tungsten lamps.

But even if, for the moment, we restrict our considerations to the case where the taking and viewing illuminants result in the same visual adaptation, which implies that they are of the same colour (tungsten and tungsten, or daylight and daylight, for instance) and of the same intensities (so as to avoid changes in saturation with luminance as shown in Fig. 7.14), the comparison of original and reproduction tristimulus values poses a number of serious questions. If tristimulus values are plotted in a three-dimensional diagram, are the errors in colour reproduction to be represented merely as the distance between the points representing the original and the reproduction? If this were done using the 1931 C.I.E. system, the results could hardly be expected to be very valuable. For, from the visually equal steps shown in the chromaticity diagram of Fig. 7.9, it is clear that equal distances in the three-dimensional tristimulus plot would be visually more important near the Z-axis than near the Y-axis, for instance. It would seem to be more sensible, therefore, in this type of investigation to use a more nearly uniform system such as the U*V*W* system, whose chromaticity diagram is shown in Fig. 7.10 and for which the correlate of luminosity or lightness is derived as $W^* = 25Y^{\frac{1}{3}}-17$.

A measure of colour reproduction errors could then be obtained from a formula of the type:

$$e^2 = (U_o^*-U_r^*)^2+(V_o^*-V_r^*)^2+k(W_o^*-W_r^*)^2$$

where U_o^*, V_o^*, W_o^* refer to the original colour, U_r^*, V_r^*, W_r^* to the reproduction colour, k is a constant, and e is the error. Some decision has to be taken regarding the value of k, and this will clearly determine the relative weights given to discrepancies in chromaticity and luminance. The value of k might be chosen as a result of some practical tests on the importance of correct lightness in colour reproduction, or from more basic investigations such as that by Brown and MacAdam on the relative ability of the eye to discriminate small changes in chromaticity and luminance (Brown and MacAdam, 1949). These data have been used and compared with differences in equivalent neutral density for subtractive colour photography with interesting results (Evans, Hanson and Brewer, 1953, pages 538–541).

Fixing the value of k, however, is by no means the only difficulty. The u, v chromaticity diagram is not perfectly uniform in chromaticity differences, so that some discrepancies on this account must be expected; and are discrepancies in different directions in the u, y diagram equally important in colour reproductions, as our formula would indicate? It has been suggested in Chapter 5 that there are good reasons for believing that errors in saturation are less important than errors in hue. If this were the case, polar co-ordinates would have to be used in the u, v diagram so that the error formula might become:

$$e^2 = (\theta_o-\theta_r)^2+k_1(S_o-S_r)^2+k_2(W_o^*-W_r^*)^2$$

where, in the U^* V^* W^* solid, θ is a correlate of the hue (in terms of dominant wavelength, for instance), S a correlate of the saturation (in terms of purity multiplied by W^*, for instance) and k_1 and k_2 are constants. The values of both constants now require to be fixed, and the tacit assumption has been made that the hue and saturation errors are independent. But this cannot be true, for if the saturation were very small, so that the colours were practically grey, the hue error could be very large with impunity. The formula must, therefore, be modified thus:

$$e^2 = S^2(\theta_o-\theta_r)^2+k_1(S_o-S_r)^2+k_2(W_o^*-W_r^*)^2$$

where S is a correlate of the average saturation, $\frac{1}{2}(S_o+S_r)$. It has been suggested (Judd, Plaza and Balcom, 1950) that in such a formula the hue errors should be weighted about four times as heavily as the saturation errors, so that, if θ is measured in radians, we obtain:

$$e^2 = S^2(\theta_o-\theta_r)^2+\tfrac{1}{4}(S_o-S_r)^2+k(W_o^*-W_r^*)^2$$

The value of k is probably best determined empirically for the particular system under consideration. (As for example in a similar formula for evaluating colour granularity, Koch and Stultz, 1956.)

Such formulae must be regarded as extremely tentative, and the whole subject is controversial. Some writers have made use of the Munsell colour space in deriving formulae (Judd, Plaza, and Balcom, 1950), while others have denied that the error is zero when the luminance and chromaticity of the original and reproduction are the same (MacAdam, 1951). This last suggestion is most interesting, for it implies that even when the original and viewing illuminants are the same, in both colour and intensity, exact colour

TABLE 9.1

TYPICAL LEVELS OF ILLUMINATION MET WITH IN PRACTICE

TYPICAL DAYLIGHT ILLUMINATION LEVELS

Bright Sun	5000	–	10,000	foot-candles	
Hazy Sun	2500	–	5000	,,	,,
Cloudy Bright	1000	–	2500	,,	,,
Cloudy Dull	200	–	1000	,,	,,
Very Dull	10	–	200	,,	,,
Sunset	0.1	–	10	,,	,,
Full Moon	0.001	–	0.01	,,	,,
Star Light	0.00001	–	0.0001	,,	,,

TYPICAL ARTIFICIAL LIGHT ILLUMINATION LEVELS

Operating Theatre	500	–	1000	foot-candles	
Shop Windows	100	–	500	,,	,,
Drawing Offices	30	–	50	,,	,,
Offices	20	–	30	,,	,,
Living Rooms	5	–	20	,,	,,
Corridors	5	–	10	,,	,,
Good Street Lighting	2			,,	,,
Poor Street Lighting	0.01			,,	,,

reproduction is not required. This could occur if, for instance, we had become so accustomed to colours being desaturated in reproductions, that exact colour reproduction would appear to be too highly saturated. MacAdam does in fact show that the most preferred caucasian flesh colours in reproductions are less saturated than those of the originals. He also shows that a slight change of hue in the yellow direction is preferred; this may be because we prefer caucasian flesh tones in pictures to be sun-tanned rather than pink. (See Bartleson, 1959.)

Furthermore, as mentioned in Chapter 5, the fact that a colour reproduction is always limited in space, and therefore has some sort of an edge or border, almost certainly distorts the scale of luminances required in the picture; and the fact that most colour reproductions are flat, rather than three-dimensional (stereoscopic), means that an illusion of depth has to be created in other ways, notably by appropriate rendering of shadow densities (Evans, 1948). In both photography and television, whether colour or black and white, it is frequently preferable to lighten shadows which in the original scene appeared to the eye to be perfectly well lit; this is usually done in outdoor scenes by means of flash bulbs or large reflectors, and in studio work by careful control of the lighting (Evans and Klute, 1944). These and other effects call for distortions in the luminances of the reproduced colours (Breneman, 1962).

9.4 Adaptation and exact colour reproduction

So far, we have assumed that the state of adaptation of the eye is the same when the original and the reproduction are viewed. As has already been pointed out, however, original scenes are very often seen by observers adapted to daylight, and their reproductions by observers adapted to tungsten light, or some other artificial light. Moreover, there is frequently not only a large difference in the colour of the two adapting illuminants but also in their intensities. A range of typical intensities of illumination is shown in Table 9.1. An outdoor sunlit scene may be illuminated at about 5000 foot candles (see Appendix 2 for a list of units), whereas the reproduction is likely to be seen at an intensity of illumination of only about 20. The evidence of Fig. 7.14 and 7.16 suggests that this difference in illumination will call for an increase in the saturation of the colours in the reproduction. It is interesting to note that, in these circumstances, if an original colour lies on the spectral locus, it will be impossible to reproduce it at the same *apparent* saturation, for this would require a reproduction chromaticity lying outside the spectral locus. This is not an entirely academic case, for red, orange, and yellow colours whose chromaticities lie on the spectral locus do occur in nature.

How, then, can the effects of adaptation be allowed for in assessing correctness of colour reproduction? The problem is a difficult one, but there are three main ways of attacking it: by memory matching, by subjective scaling, and by binocular matching. In memory matching, an observer views the original scene for long enough to become properly adapted to the prevailing illumination and makes a careful mental note of some particular colour in it. He then views the reproduction for long enough to become properly adapted to its prevailing illumination, and makes a memory comparison between the original and the reproduction colours. At the illumination levels involved the time required for complete adaptation is generally about five minutes, and this lapse of time between seeing the two stimuli means that the method is not very precise. Moreover, as outlined above, it is only qualitative. It can be made quantitative, however, by idealizing the situation so that the 'original' consists of a small uniform area of colour surrounded by an adapting field, and the 'reproduction' consists of a small uniform area of mixed red, green and blue light, surrounded by its adapting field. The observer then alters the amounts of red, green and blue light in the 'reproduction' patch until they give him the same sensation as that which the 'original' patch produced. Again, the time which must elapse between seeing the two patches results in low precision.

In the subjective scaling method, the observer assigns numbers (or names) to the subjective attributes of the colour sensations he experiences when looking at both the original and the reproduction. Thus he might scale lightness from 0 to 100, saturation from zero for greys to some suitable maximum figure for maximum saturation, and hue by means of colour names, such as 'very slightly yellowish green'. Comparison of these assessments of the colours in the original and the reproduction could then indicate the nature of any errors in the reproduction. It has been shown that this type of judgment can be made satisfactorily for lightness (Stevens and Stevens, 1963; Breneman, 1962; Bartleson and Breneman, 1966) but its extension to saturation and hue awaits further research.

The binocular method was outlined in Chapter 7, with reference to Fig. 7.15. If one eye is adapted to the 'original' illumination, and the other to the 'reproduction' illumination, a direct comparison can be made between the sensation produced by the original colour and that of the reproduction. Alternatively, one eye can be kept in a constant, reference, state of adaptation, and the other eye used for viewing first the original and then the reproduction, each in its own proper conditions of adaptation: any differences between the two appearances can then be measured in terms of the changes required in stimuli presented to the reference eye in order to produce the same pairs of sensations. Such stimulus-changes, for broad ranges of colours, are related in a systematic way, and in several investigations attempts have been made to discover sets of transformation equations to represent the changes in a general way. Using linear transformation equations, discrepancies have generally been found which were not wholly ascribable to experimental error. The equations are, however, useful approximations and, for limited ranges of adapting and test colours, may be sufficiently correct for practical purposes. Burnham, Evans, and Newhall (1957) give the following transformation equations for adaptation by standard illuminants A and C at equal luminances, using the X, Y, Z co-ordinate system:

$$X_a = 0.9132X_c + 0.4220Y_c - 0.1988Z_c + 0.0024$$
$$Y_a = 0.0299X_c + 1.0215Y_c - 0.1020Z_c + 0.0025$$
$$Z_a = 0.0175X_c - 0.1378Y_c + 0.4708Z_c - 0.0019$$
$$X_c = 1.0972X_a - 0.4054Y_a + 0.3725Z_a - 0.0005$$
$$Y_c = -0.0296X_a + 0.9994Y_a + 0.2144Z_a - 0.0016$$
$$Z_c = -0.0776X_a + 0.3666Y_a + 2.1114Z_a + 0.0036$$

X_a, Y_a, Z_a are the tristimulus values of stimuli which, when viewed under adaptation to standard illuminant A, present the same appearance as stimuli having tristimulus values X_c, Y_c, Z_c, when viewed under adaptation to standard illuminant C, at the same luminance. Any difference in the luminances of the two adapting fields might make these particular equations inapplicable, but if the appropriate equations were available, then we would know the colours required in the reproduction in order to produce the same sensations as were experienced when the original was viewed. Any discrepancies from these required colours could then be evaluated by some formula such as that proposed earlier in the chapter:

$$e^2 = S'^2(\theta_o' - \theta_r)^2 + \tfrac{1}{4}(S_o' - S_r)^2 + k(W_o^{*\prime} - W_r^*)^2$$

where S_o', θ_o' and $W_o^{*\prime}$ are the purity, dominant wavelength, and luminance values which, in the reproduction adaptation, correspond to S_o, θ_o and W_o^*, the values in the original adaptation.

Any such formula, however, again presupposes that exact colour reproduction is what is required. We saw that, even when the adaptation of the original and reproduction were similar, there were good reasons for thinking that exact colour reproduction was not necessarily desirable; with different adaptation conditions, exact colour reproduction (even though evaluated so as to allow for the effects of adaptation) is even less likely to be the criterion for optimum quality.

In Fig. 9.1 some results are shown for a case where two very different adaptation conditions are involved (Hunt, 1965). The conditions of adaptation for the reference eye were the same as those used to obtain the results shown in Fig. 7.16 (1050 foot-lamberts at a colour temperature of 4000°K); the other eye viewed a colour chart first in bright sunlight (4000 foot-candles) and then in a dark room, with the light from a tungsten-light projector providing an illumination of 15 foot-candles on the area of the chart only. The tungsten projector condition was then equivalent to projecting a slide of the chart having perfect physical colour reproduction, except that by having the reproduction 'at the screen' instead of in the gate of the projector, complications caused by vignetting and flare were avoided.

It is clear from Fig. 9.1 that this 'perfect physical colour reproduction' does not, under its very different viewing conditions, reproduce the same sensations as those produced by the chart viewed in bright sunlight: the colours in the 'reproduction' appeared less saturated, more yellow, and darker. It is interesting to note, therefore, that colour films intended to provide transparencies of daylight scenes, for projection by tungsten light, are customarily made so as to reproduce a grey scale not grey, but slightly bluish; the need for this feature evidently stems from the yellowish appearance of screens when illuminated by tungsten projectors. Some influence of the colour of the adapting illuminant has also been observed in the case of reflecting prints (Bartleson, 1958). It is also interesting to note that the quality of projected colour transparencies rises markedly as the screen luminance is increased (Bartleson, 1965) an effect attributable no doubt to the fact that the lumino-

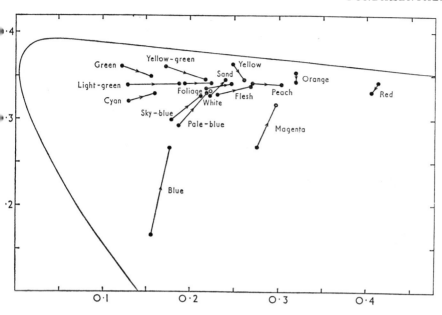

Fig. 9.1. Change in appearance of sixteen different test colours as the adapting
conditions were changed from bright sunlight at an illumination level of 4000 foot-
candles with typical out-door surround, to tungsten-projector light at 15 foot-candles
with a dark surround typical of those occurring when projecting slides in a darkened
room; the conditions of reference were 1050 foot-lamberts at 4000°K. The following
changes in apparent lightness (evaluated as $25Y^{\frac{1}{3}} - 17$) also occurred:

Colour	Apparent lightness	
	Bright sun	Tungsten projector
White	86	63
Yellow	78	74
Flesh	71	52
Sand	67	42
Orange	60	35
Light-green	60	31
Yellow-green	62	35
Peach	55	41
Sky-blue	55	31
Pale-blue	57	34
Foliage	52	27
Red	43	21
Magenta	39	18
Green	40	12
Cyan	29	8
Blue	27	9

sities and colour saturations of the original scene can only be produced at high screen luminances. It may indeed seem surprising that colour transparencies of sunlit scenes, when projected at about 15 foot-candles could ever look other than disappointing in view of their considerably reduced lightness and saturation. It may be, however, that just as an observer in a given viewing situation has quite a good idea of how light a white can look (and if it looks lighter than this it appears fluorescent or self-luminous, Evans, 1959), so perhaps observers have some idea of how saturated a colour can be expected to look at a given level of adapting luminance; if some such psychological effect were operating it would help to explain the subjectively satisfying results which can be obtained when colour transparencies of sunlit scenes are projected at screen illuminances as low as 15 foot-candles. Of course, as has already been noted, much better quality is achieved if the screen illuminance is raised, and an interesting confirmation of this fact has been noted in colour television. The introduction of sulphide phosphors in colour-television display tubes enabled pictures of higher luminance but somewhat lower colour saturation to be produced. It has been shown, however, (Matthews, 1963) that an increase of screen luminance from 16 to 33 foot-lamberts more than compensates for the loss of colour saturation which the sulphide phosphors cause.

As already mentioned, several objective studies have shown that the most desirable reproductions of certain well-known object colours, such as flesh, sky-blue, and grass-green, are different from typical values for the corresponding original subjects (MacAdam, 1951; Bartleson, 1959 and 1962). Some of these differences may, however, only be of such a nature as to achieve equality of colour *appearance* in the viewing situations for the original and reproduction. While the importance of colour preference in so aesthetic a realm as colour reproduction is not to be denied, it would seem unwise to assume that distortions of colour appearance are really necessary until full allowance has been made for the effects caused by the viewing conditions.

The quantitative assessment of colour appearance in reproductions is thus a complex and difficult task. But the confidence and consistency with which observers can make subjective assessments of colour fidelity in pictures encourages the hope that the problem is not an insoluble one. So although the above approach can at present only be tentative, it seems the only basic one, and, ultimately it should be capable of hacking a recognizable pathway through the forests of empiricism.

REFERENCES

Bartleson, C. J., *Phot. Sci. Eng.*, **2**, 32 (1958).
Bartleson, C. J., *Phot. Sci. Eng.*, **3**, 114 (1959).
Bartleson, C. J., *Phot. Sci. Eng.*, **9**, 174 (1965)
Bartleson, C. J., and Bray, C. P., *Phot. Sci. Eng.*, **6**, 19 (1962).
Bartleson, C. J., and Breneman, E. J., Private communication (1966).
Breneman, E. J., *Phot. Sci. Eng.*, **6**, 172 (1962).
Brown, W. R. J., and MacAdam, D. L., *J. Opt. Soc. Amer.*, **39**, 808 (1949).
Burnham, R. W., Evans, R. M., and Newhall, S. M., *J. Opt. Soc. Amer.*, **47**, 35 (1957).
Evans, R. M., *An Introduction to Colour*, Wiley, New York, pp. 140–146 (1948).
Evans, R. M., *J. Opt. Soc. Amer.*, **49**, 1049 (1959).
Evans, R. M., Hanson, W. T., and Brewer, W. L., *Principles of Colour Photography*, Wiley, New York (1963).
Evans, R. M., and Klute, J., *J. Opt. Soc. Amer.*, **34**, 533 (1944).
Hunt, R. W. G., *J. Opt. Soc. Amer.*, **55**, 1540 (1965).
Judd, D. B., Plaza, L., and Balcom, M. M., *Proc. I.R.E.*, **38**, 980 (1950).
Koch, D. A., and Stultz, K. F., *J. Opt. Soc. Amer.*, **46**, 832 (1956).
MacAdam, D. L., *J. Soc. Mot. Pic. Tel. Eng.*, **56**, 502 (1951).
Matthews, J. A., Private communication (1963).
Stevens, S. S., and Stevens, J. C., *J. Opt. Soc. Amer.*, **53**, 375 (1963).

GENERAL REFERENCES

Brewer, W. L., *J. Opt. Soc. Amer.*, **44**, 207 (1954).
Burnham, R. W., Evans, R. M., and Newhall, S. M., *J. Opt. Soc. Amer.*, **42**, 597 (1952).
Evans, R. M., *J. Opt. Soc. Amer.*, **33**, 579 (1943).
Hunt, R. W. G., *J. Opt. Soc. Amer.*, **40**, 362 (1950).
Hunt, R. W. G., *J. Opt. Soc. Amer.*, **42**, 190, (1952).
Hunt, R. W. G., *J. Opt. Soc. Amer.*, **43**, 479 (1953).
MacAdam, D. L., *J. Opt. Soc. Amer.*, **46**, 500 (1956).
MacAdam, D. L., *J. Soc. Mot. Pic. Tel. Eng.*, **65**, 455 (1956).
Winch, G. T., and Young, B. M., *G.E.C. Journal*, **18**, 88 (1951).
Wright, W. D., *Proc. Roy Soc. B.*, **115**, 49 (1934).
Wright, W. D., *Researches on Normal and Defective Colour Vision*, Kimpton, London, pp. 209–255 (1946).

PART TWO
COLOUR PHOTOGRAPHY

CHAPTER 10

Subtractive Methods in Colour Photography

1. Introduction – *2.* Relief-images – *3.* Colour-development – *4.* Integral tripacks – *5.* Processing with the couplers incorporated in the film – *6.* Reversal processing – *7.* Processing with the couplers in developers – *8.* The philosophy of colour negatives – *9.* Subtractive methods for amateur use – *10.* Subtractive methods for professional use – *11.* Subtractive methods for motion-picture use

10.1 Introduction

THE basic step in subtractive colour photography is the formation of cyan, magenta, and yellow dye-images. For the dyes to be present as *images*, it is necessary for their concentrations to vary from point to point in the picture-area in a manner that is appropriately dependent on the distribution of the colours of the scene. There are several ways of accomplishing this, but the one which has achieved the widest commercial success is known as *colour-development;* however, before describing this, it is convenient to consider the *relief-image* method, which has a considerable use in the professional motion picture industry, and is also used on a small scale for professional still photographs.

10.2 Relief-images

The principle of the *relief-image* method of producing dye-images is as follows. The thickness of a gelatin layer is made to vary from point to point in the picture according to the intensity of the exposure. On immersing such a layer in a solution of dye, more dye will be taken up by the areas where the gelatin is thick than where it is thin, and hence, a dye-image is obtained. The way in which a relief gelatin image is produced from a separation negative is shown in Fig. 10.1 which relates to the Kodak Dye Transfer Process.

Dye Transfer Matrix film, on which the positive dye images are produced, consists of an ordinary black-and-white emulsion coated on film base, except that the emulsion is unhardened, contains a yellow dye, and is not dye-sensitized (so that it is sensitive only to blue light). The emulsion is exposed through the base, and the yellow dye absorbs the blue light to which alone the emulsion is sensitive. Parts of the emulsion near to the base are easily exposed, because the light can reach them without having to traverse more than a very thin layer of dye. Parts of the emulsion further away from the base, however, can only be exposed with difficulty, for the light must traverse a comparatively thick layer of yellow dye before it can reach them. The exposure of this film,

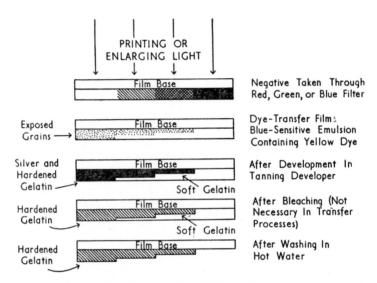

Fig. 10.1. Method of forming a gelatin relief-image from a separation negative.

therefore, occurs most easily near the base, and becomes progressively more and more difficult throughout the emulsion layer. Hence, when exposures of different intensities are made over the area of the film, the latent image formed will vary in depth according to the intensity of the exposure. Heavily exposed areas (such as that on the extreme left in the diagram) will exhibit latent image throughout practically the whole layer, but less intensely exposed areas will have a shallower latent image concentrated near the film base. The image is, therefore, an image in depth or a *relief-image*.

What is now required, is to remove all the gelatin which does not contain latent image and to leave the rest; we shall then have a gelatin relief-image which can be dyed the appropriate colour. Now gelatin, in its usual state, is soluble in hot water. But by suitable chemical treatment it can be hardened, or tanned, so that it becomes insoluble. If, therefore, we could harden all the gelatin around the latent image and leave the rest unchanged, by washing the film in hot water, we could remove the unwanted gelatin and leave the relief gelatin image adhering to the film base. The way in which this can be done is surprisingly simple.

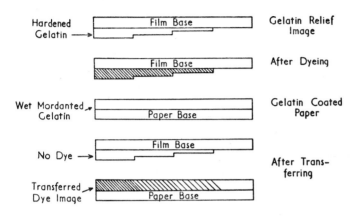

Hardened Gelatin ——▶   Film Base   Gelatin Relief Image

Film Base   After Dyeing

Wet Mordanted Gelatin   Paper Base   Gelatin Coated Paper

No Dye ——▶   Film Base   After Transferring

Transferred Dye Image   Paper Base

Fig. 10.2. Method of using a gelatin relief-image to transfer a dye-image to paper.

Amongst other ingredients, ordinary photographic developers contain a developing agent and sulphite. The reaction with an exposed silver bromide grain can then be represented thus:

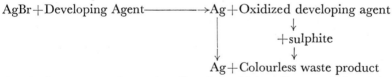

AgBr + Developing Agent ————▶ Ag + Oxidized developing agent
↓
+ sulphite
↓
Ag + Colourless waste product

The developing agent reduces the silver bromide to silver, and, by doing so, it becomes oxidized, whereupon it reacts immediately with the sulphite to form a colourless waste product. To harden the gelatin around the latent image and nowhere else, it is only necessary to use pyrogallol as the developing agent and greatly to reduce the amount of sulphite in the developer. The first part of the reaction then takes place as before, but the oxidized developer, having very little sulphite with which to react, proceeds to react with the gelatin, and in fact hardens it. We thus have:

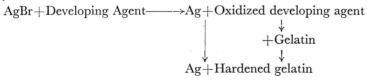

AgBr + Developing Agent ————▶ Ag + Oxidized developing agent
↓
+ Gelatin
↓
Ag + Hardened gelatin

165

The matrix film is, therefore, processed in a 'pyro' developer with very little sulphite, and then washed with hot water to leave a hardened gelatin relief-image. This relief-image is then dyed, and since the amount of dye absorbed is proportional to the thickness of the gelatin, the amount of dye present at each point will be proportional to the image exposure, as required. If three such dye-images are made using cyan, magenta, and yellow dyes, after bleaching away the silver, a subtractive colour photograph can be produced simply by superimposing the three images in register. If a paper print is required, it is possible to transfer the dye from the gelatin relief-image to a suitably prepared paper surface as in Fig. 10.2. It is in this way that the Kodak Dye Transfer Process works.

If a colour transparency or film is required the dye-image can be transferred on to a suitably prepared transparent support; this is the principle of the Technicolor process. In any transfer process, after the dye-image has been transferred, the relief image can be dyed again and a second transfer made on another piece of support. By doing this with each dye, a second copy of the colour photograph is made; and the process can be repeated, more or less indefinitely, so as to obtain a large number of copies. Incidentally, since in transfer processes the dye is always transferred from the gelatin relief image and viewed on another support, it is not necessary to remove the silver from the relief image.

10.3 Colour-development

The *colour-development* method of producing dye-images is simpler to operate than the relief-image method because it obviates the need for separate developing and dyeing stages. This method is very similar to the tanning development technique in that only a very little sulphite is present in the developer, but instead of letting the oxidized developer react with the gelatin of the emulsion, a coupler is present in the developer (or in the emulsion layer) and this reacts with the oxidized developing agent to form an insoluble dye.

We thus have:

$$AgBr + \text{Developing Agent} \longrightarrow Ag + \text{Oxidized developing agent}$$

$$\downarrow$$
$$+ \text{Coupler}$$
$$\downarrow$$
$$Ag + \text{Insoluble dye}$$

This reaction only works satisfactorily with some developing agents, notably paraphenylenediamine and some of its derivatives. It is clear that the dye is formed jointly from the coupler and the oxidized developer, and the colour of the dye formed is determined by the nature of the coupler and the developing agent, although they are themselves usually colourless. The amount of dye formed depends on the amount of oxidized developer available and this in turn depends on the amount of silver which has been developed; thus the amount of dye is related directly to the amount of exposure given at each point, and is therefore laid down as an image and not as a uniform layer. The reaction involving the oxidized developer is localized around silver halide grains containing latent image, so that, on colour development, blobs of insoluble dye are formed only around the silver grains developed by the developing agent, and hence the dye-image obtained reproduces in a somewhat blurred manner the granular nature of the silver image from which it is derived. If three such dye-images are produced, using cyan, magenta, and yellow dyes, by bleaching out the silver and superimposing the images in register, a subtractive colour photograph is obtained. Alternatively the dye images could be transferred to another support, but colour development processes cannot easily be used to give large numbers of copies as can the relief gelatin processes.

The great advantage of the colour development technique, however, is that it becomes possible to produce dye-images of different colours in different layers of a single film. Colour development is discussed further in Chapter 15.

Fig. 10.3. Sensitization of the layers in an integral tripack typical of those used for films of camera speed.

10.4 Integral tripacks

Any process of colour photography which involves taking three pictures one after the other clearly has the severe limitation that only 'still-life', or very slowly moving, scenes can be taken. In the mosaic and lenticular additive processes the three pictures were taken at the same time on neighbouring areas of film. In modern subtractive processes of colour photography the three pictures are taken on three emulsions coated one on top of the other, as shown in Fig. 10.3, an arrangement known as an *integral tripack*.

Photographic emulsions are naturally sensitive only to the blue part of the spectrum, and their sensitivity is extended to the green and red parts only by the addition of sensitizing dyes. An ordinary, unsensitized, emulsion usually constitutes the top layer in a tripack, and in it is produced a negative which provides the blue record of the scene, but in this case no blue filter is necessary because the emulsion itself responds only to blue light. The bottom layer of the film consists of an emulsion sensitized only to red light. It still has its natural sensitivity to blue light, of course, but this is rendered inoperative by means of a yellow filter layer immediately beneath the top layer. In this bottom layer, therefore, we produce a negative providing the red record of the scene; but once again no red filter is needed, because the yellow filter together with the red sensitizing of the emulsion make the layer sensitive only to red light. Between the yellow filter layer and the bottom layer is an emulsion sensitized to green light only. This sensitizing, together with the yellow filter layer, constitutes a layer sensitive to green light only, and therein we produce a negative providing the green record of the scene, but without using a green filter.

It will be clear that with such a three-layer film a single exposure suffices to record the three images required, one being effectively taken through a red filter, another through a green, and the third through a blue. It remains to process the film in such a way that cyan, magenta, and yellow dye-images are formed in these three layers respectively. There are two main methods of achieving this by colour development. In one method the couplers are incorporated in the film; in the other they are in three separate developers.

10.5 Processing with the couplers incorporated in the film

Fig. 10.4 shows in diagrammatic form the way in which an integral tripack material can be processed when the couplers are incorporated in the film. Each of the four large circles depicts a highly magnified cross-section of the three emulsion layers and the yellow filter layer. Each small triangle represents a silver halide crystal (or *grain*) and the triangles with dots in them indicate grains which have been exposed and contain latent image, while those without dots indicate grains which have not been exposed and do not contain latent image. It is thus clear, Fig. 10.4 (a), that in this example light has fallen on the right-hand part of the film but not on the left. The circles represent particles of couplers, those in the top (blue-sensitive) layer being capable of forming yellow dye, those in the bottom (red-sensitive) layer being capable of forming cyan dye, and those in the other (green-sensitive) emulsion layer being capable of forming magenta dye. The couplers are prevented from wandering away from their proper layers, either by attaching long molecular chains to them (used first by Agfa in 1936 (Koshofer, 1966)) or by dissolving them in oily solvents and then dispersing them in the form of minute oil globules (used first in Kodak materials (Mees, 1942)): when oil globules are used they are usually of about a tenth of the size of the silver halide grains. On immersing the material into a solution containing a suitable developing agent the situation becomes as shown in Fig. 10.4(b).

The developing agent converts the silver halide to silver (represented by the black triangles) wherever latent image was present, and, around each grain of silver thus formed, the oxidized developer reacts with coupler to produce dye: yellow (Y) in the top layer, cyan (C) in the bottom layer, and magenta (M) in the other emulsion layer. The dyes are deposited as very small 'clouds' of molecules or globules around each developed grain. It is now necessary to remove the unexposed silver halide from the film, for this would gradually darken as the film was viewed, and this *fixing* is carried out as in black-and-white films by means of a 'hypo' solution; but it is also necessary to remove the silver image, which otherwise would darken the result, and this is conveniently done by converting the silver back to silver halide by means of a suitable bleach, used prior to the fixing stage. The remainder of the process is therefore basically as shown in Fig. 10.4(c) where the bleach converts the silver to silver halide again, and Fig. 10.4(d) where all the silver halide is removed by the fixer. (In some processes the bleaching and fixing steps are combined in a single solution known as a *blix*.) The yellow filter layer generally also disappears

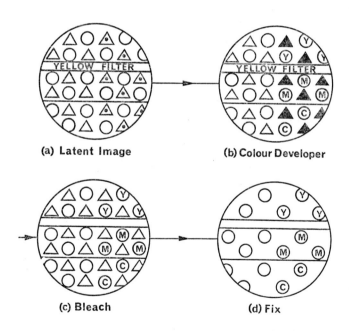

(a) Latent Image   (b) Colour Developer

(c) Bleach   (d) Fix

Fig. 10.4. Diagrammatic representations of highly magnified cross-sections of an integral tripack material with incorporated couplers being processed so as to give a negative image. △ : unexposed silver halide grain. ▲ : exposed silver halide grain. ▲ : developed grain of silver. ○: particle of coupler. Ⓨ : particle of yellow dye. Ⓜ : particle of magenta dye. Ⓒ: particle of cyan dye.

at the bleach stage. The unused coupler is harmless and is allowed to remain; in fact in some colour films the unused coupler is actually used to improve the accuracy of the final results, and in these cases it is usually coloured yellow or pink, but normally it is colourless.

The final result in Fig. 10.4 is that on the right-hand side of the film, where the light originally fell, all three dyes, cyan, magenta and yellow are produced (resulting in a dark area), whereas on the left-hand side, where no light fell, no dyes are produced (resulting in a light area). The result is thus a negative: light becoming dark, and dark becoming light. In addition, colours will be reversed; red becoming cyan, green becoming magenta, and blue becoming yellow, and *vice-versa*. That this is so can be seen by considering the following example. If the light falling on the film had been red, only the bottom layer would have been exposed; hence only cyan dye would have been formed. Conversely if the light falling on the film had been cyan (blue-green) only the blue and green sensitive layers would have been exposed, and hence only yellow and magenta dye would have been formed and the superimposition of these two dyes results in a red colour. To produce a colour positive from such a record, which is called a *colour negative*, it is only necessary to re-photograph or *print* the processed negative on to a similar piece of film or paper: once again, by the same arguments, both the tones and the colours will be reversed and the final result will be in its correct colours. Systems operating in this way include Kodacolor, Eastman Colour, Ilfocolor and Agfacolor.

10.6 Reversal processing

As in black-and-white photography, if a separate negative stage is not required, the film exposed in the camera can be *reversal processed* to give a positive image directly. The way in which this can be achieved is shown diagrammatically in Fig. 10.5 in which the symbols all have the same meaning as in Fig. 10.4. As in Fig. 10.4 light has fallen on the right-hand part of the film but not on the left, so that the latent image is present only on the right, Fig. 10.5(a). The film is then immersed in an ordinary black-and-white developer, which converts the exposed silver halide to silver, thereby oxidizing the developing agent; but being an ordinary black-and-white type developing agent its oxidized form does not react with the couplers and hence no dye is formed at this stage, Fig. 10.5(b). The next step is to re-expose the film uniformly to a strong white light so that latent image is formed in all the undeveloped silver halide, Fig. 10.5(c); the film then enters a colour developer which converts this silver halide to silver and the oxidized developer formed in the vicinity of this silver reacts with the couplers to form cyan, magenta, and yellow dye images as before, Fig. 10.5(d). The usual bleaching, Fig. 10.5(e), and fixing, Fig. 10.5(f), stages then remove all the silver, to give, now, all three dyes (a dark area) on the left hand part of the film where the light originally did not fall, and no dyes (a light area) on the right hand part of the film where

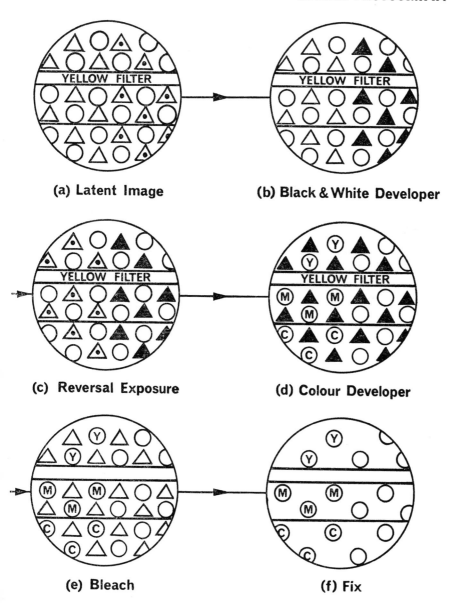

(a) Latent Image

(b) Black & White Developer

(c) Reversal Exposure

(d) Colour Developer

(e) Bleach

(f) Fix

Fig. 10.5. Same as Fig. 10.4 but showing the processing sequence necessary (reversal process) to obtain a positive image directly on the camera film.

the light originally did fall. The result is thus a positive, as required. That colours also come out correctly can be seen by the following example. If the right-hand side was exposed only to red light, only the bottom layer would have been exposed, so that, in the black-and-white developer, silver would only have been produced in the bottom layer. The reversal exposure would therefore produce latent image in the top two light-sensitive layers, but not in the bottom later. On colour development, yellow and magenta, but no cyan, dyes would therefore be formed and hence a red colour produced on the film in the area in which the red light originally exposed it. Films operating in this way include Ektachrome, Agfacolor Reversal (or Agfachrome), Ferraniacolor, Anscochrome, and Gevacolor.

10.7 Processing with the couplers in developers

In Fig. 10.6 a diagrammatic example is given of one way in which direct positive colour images can be obtained using the other main method of colour development; that in which the couplers are in three separate developing solutions. The symbols used are the same as before, and once again light has fallen on the right-hand part of the film and not on the left, Fig. 10.6(a). An ordinary black-and-white developer therefore produces silver images on the right-hand part, Fig. 10.6(b) as before. The film is then re-exposed uniformly, not to white light as in Fig. 10.5, but to red light from the bottom, Fig. 10.6(c). Since only the bottom layer is sensitive to red light, latent image is formed only in this layer so that, on immersing the film in a colour developer containing cyan-forming coupler, cyan dye is formed in the left-hand part of the bottom layer only, Fig. 10.6(d). The film is next exposed to blue light from the top and since the yellow filter layer protects the bottom two layers from all blue light, latent image is at this stage formed only in the top layer, Fig. 10.6(e), so that on immersing the film in a colour developer containing yellow-forming coupler, yellow dye is formed in the left-hand part of the top layer only, Fig. 10.6(f). It is now required to form magenta dye in the left hand part of the middle layer, and, since it is only in this part of the entire film that there is any silver halide left, use is made of a colour developer containing magenta-forming coupler and of such a character that development takes place even when the silver halide has not been exposed, Fig. 10.6(g). The final two stages are the usual bleaching, Fig. 10.6(h), and fixing, Fig. 10.6(i), steps. It will be seen that the final disposition of the dyes is the same in Fig. 10.6 as in Fig. 10.5, so that a positive has been achieved, and by the same arguments as used previously the colours as well as the tones are correctly reproduced.

This method of colour development cannot conveniently be used to obtain colour negative images because it is the reversal exposure step which provides the opportunity of enabling the colour developers to affect each layer in turn independently.

It will be appreciated from Fig. 10.6 that this type of process is of consider-

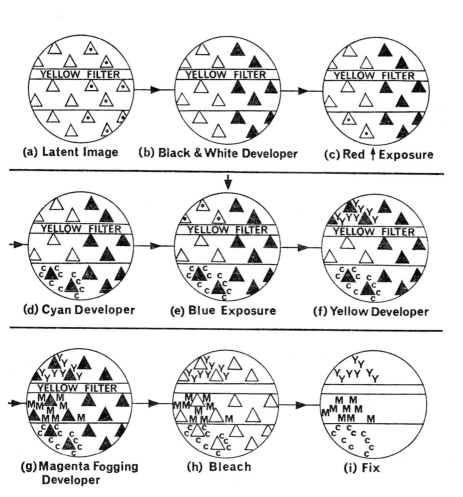

(a) Latent Image (b) Black & White Developer (c) Red ↑ Exposure

(d) Cyan Developer (e) Blue Exposure (f) Yellow Developer

(g) Magenta Fogging Developer (h) Bleach (i) Fix

Fig. 10.6. Same as Fig. 10.5 but using the method where the three couplers are in three different developers instead of in three layers of the tripack.

173

able complexity, and is, for this reason, only operated at a few large processing stations. In return for this complexity, however, the process can yield an extremely high resolving power, so that it can be used satisfactorily even for 8 mm. cinematography where the frame size is only 5 mm. × 3·7 mm., while for 35 mm. use its resolving power is usually ample. Examples of this type of process include Kodachrome (introduced in 1935), Kodachrome II (1961), Ilfochrome (1948, see Hornsby, 1950), Fujicolor, and Dynacolor. The original Kodachrome process, which was worked out by two musicians, Leopold Mannes and Leopold Godowsky (Davies, 1936; Matthews, 1955), was in fact rather different and involved a series of differential bleaching steps; the type of process shown in Fig. 10.6 was introduced in 1938.

10.8 The philosophy of colour negatives

A colour negative, fundamentally, consists merely of three negative images (exposed by red, green, and blue light) superimposed in register, but differing from one another in such a way that they can be distinguished from one another. Thus three black-and-white silver images superimposed would be of value if they could be stripped apart; this, incidentally, is a practicable form of colour negative and has been tried in the motion-picture industry (Capstaff, 1950). But, of course, there is no need to strip the images apart when they are differently coloured. Thus if one of them is a cyan image, another magenta, and the third yellow, when the colour negative is viewed by red light only the cyan image will be seen, and in green light only the magenta will be seen, and in blue light only the yellow will be seen (to a first approximation). It is customary, but not essential, to make the image which was exposed in the camera by red light a cyan image, that by green light a magenta image, and that by blue light, a yellow image. When this is the case the colour negative, as well as reversing all tones (blacks becoming whites and whites becoming blacks) reverses all colours too, so that reds become blue-greens, blue-greens become reds, greens become magentas, magentas become greens, blues become yellows, and yellows become blues; in other words every colour takes on the complementary hue. The important consideration, however, is not what the negative looks like in white light to the eye, but how efficiently it enables the three superimposed negatives to be distinguished at the printing stage. With the above arrangement, the printing material must produce a red-absorbing (cyan) image when exposed to red light, because light of this colour isolates the negative image which was made by red light in the camera. Similarly the printing material must produce a magenta image when exposed to green light, and a yellow image when exposed to blue light. A print on such a material will reverse not only the tones but also the colours of the negative to give correct tones and hues in the print.

    In principle, however, it would be just as good if, for instance, in the colour negative the image exposed by the red light in the camera were developed magenta, and that by green light were developed cyan. Then the printing material must be such that green light, which will isolate the negative exposed by red light in the camera, must produce a red-absorbing (cyan) dye. Similarly red light would have to produce a green-absorbing image on the printing material. Furthermore, again in principle, the lights used for printing the negative on to the printing material need not be red, green, and blue. They could, sometimes with advantage, be for instance infra-red, green, and ultra-violet. The only requirement is that the light forming the red-absorbing (cyan) image in the print must isolate the negative which was formed by red light in the camera; and similarly for the green and blue. The intermediate dyes used in the negative and the spectral content of the printing light are entirely a matter of convenience; and of course it is not essential to print with separate beams of, for instance, red, green, and blue light, since, by making the print material sensitive only in the required narrow bands of the spectrum, white light can be used instead. (In practice, however, something is sometimes gained in colour saturation in the print by using a printing light consisting of only narrow spectral bands specially chosen to coincide with the absorption peaks of the dyes used in the colour negative, if this more effectively isolates each negative image and reduces contamination from the other two.)

Some of these principles have found application in colour films used for professional motion picture and aerial survey work (see Sections 10.10 and 10.11).

10.9 Subtractive methods for amateur use

Both the negative-positive and the reversal versions of subtractive colour photography are widely used by amateur photographers. The colour transparency, so conveniently provided by reversal processing of the film used in the camera, gives results of excellent quality at remarkably low cost, and the system is used very widely indeed. The disadvantages of the colour transparency, however, are first that it requires equipment (and preferably a darkened room) for viewing, and secondly that reflection prints and duplicate transparencies cannot easily be made from original transparencies without some loss of quality.

For these reasons, the negative-positive systems are also widely used: they have the advantages that as many identical prints or transparencies as are required can be made from the same negative, and the printing operation enables corrections for exposure errors (in intensity and in colour) to be made, thus giving a system which can have excellent exposure latitude, and good flexibility as far as illuminant colour is concerned. The disadvantages of the negative-positive system are as follows: first, because of the use of both negative and positive materials and the necessity for the printing operation, the cost of making one picture from a scene is higher than in the case of reversal materials; if more than one picture is required the negative-positive system is usually cheaper, but most amateurs require only one of most of the pictures they expose. The second disadvantage of the negative-positive system is that the quality of the transparencies it produces is not usually quite as good as can be obtained on reversal film (but it is usually better than that obtained on copies of reversal-film transparencies).

The choice of system for amateur use therefore depends upon whether prints or transparencies are the prime requirement; whether only one, or more than one, copy is required; and whether the cheapest system is desirable. The history of the popular amateur colour transparency started with the introduction of 35 mm. Kodachrome film in 1936. The history of the colour negative also extends back to the 1930's, when it was introduced for use both in mosaic additive processes (Harrison and Spencer, 1937), and also in integral tripack subtractive materials (Berger, 1950; Koshofer, 1966). But it was not until the beginning of the next decade that a colour negative system intended mainly for amateur snapshot use was placed on the market in the form of Kodacolor in 1942 (Mees, 1942). At first, the unexposed areas of Kodacolor negatives were clear, as is the case for black-and-white negatives, but in 1944 a silver mask was introduced in order to improve colour reproduction (Evans, Hanson, and Brewer, 1953), and the negatives then took on an overall grey appearance. In 1949 the silver mask was removed and coloured couplers (see Chapter 13) were used, with the result that the negatives became orange in the unexposed areas; a further change to a slightly different orange colour was made in 1955 when the same film was sold for both daylight and clear flash use; this film possessed increased latitude so as to accommodate both types of illuminant without reducing the permissible margin of exposure error for the user. Subsequently, flash bulbs covered with blue filter material, so as to make the colour of the light emitted by them similar to that of daylight, became standard for most amateur colour photography. The problems involved in printing amateurs' colour negatives are discussed in Chapter 14.

10.10 Subtractive methods for professional use

Many of the same considerations apply in professional as in amateur subtractive colour photography, but generally speaking the emphasis in professional work is more on quality than on cost. For this reason reversal films in large formats (for example, 8×10 ins.) are quite commonly used in order to obtain extremely high definition and to facilitate retouching. Professionals also require more often to be able to process their own films and coupler-incorporated reversal films such as Ektachrome (introduced in 1946) are therefore needed.

The Dye Transfer system is important for professional users because, in spite of the high cost of operating it, its great flexibility, arising from the independent handling of the three coloured images, is often very useful.

Professional photographers sometimes need to give very long or very short exposure times and for this reason certain films are made specially for particular ranges of exposure times, since it is often impossible to make a film in which the contrasts of the three layers are equal at all exposure times. Thus Ektacolor Sheet Film type S, for instance, is intended for exposure times of 1/10 sec. and shorter, while Ektacolor Sheet Film type L is for times from 1/10 to 60 secs.

A particular branch of professional photography is aerial survey work, and special films have been made for this purpose. In one of these films the three layers, instead of being sensitive to the red, green, and blue parts of the spectrum and yielding cyan, magenta, and yellow images respectively, are made sensitive to the red, green, and infra-red parts of the spectrum yielding magenta, yellow, and cyan dyes respectively (Tarkington and Sorem, 1963). When this film records green vegetation whose coloration is caused by chlorophyll, on reversal processing, a red or magenta result is obtained because, in addition to its green reflection, chlorophyll reflects strongly in the infra-red; green paints, however, do not usually have this property and reproduce as blues. The film therefore distinguishes very sharply between vegetation and green paints: it was therefore introduced (in 1942) to overcome camouflage in aerial reconnaisance work. This type of film can also be used in aerial survey work to detect the distribution of certain types of trees in a forest (Spencer, 1947) and is also very valuable for recording under-water detail (Mott, 1966).

10.11 Subtractive methods for motion picture use

For amateur motion pictures, where the desire to have copies made is even smaller than in amateur still photography, the reversal types of film are used almost exclusively. But in professional motion picture work both reversal and negative camera films are used. Fig. 10.7 summarizes the different methods employed.

Since more than one copy is invariably required the direct use of reversal film is not possible. The next simplest system is the straight negative-positive combination, shown in Fig. 10.7(a), using, for instance, Eastman Colour Negative and Print Films, or Eastman Colour Negative Film with the Technicolor Process for the positive prints; this system gives the highest quality at the lowest cost (Hanson, 1952; Hanson and Kisner, 1953; Dundon and Zwick, 1959; Kisner, 1962).

It is interesting to note that in Eastman Colour Print Film the conventional order of the layers, shown in Fig. 10.3, is not followed. To obtain pictures of maximum sharpness it is desirable to have the magenta layer, whose image is the most strongly visible of the three, at the top, and the yellow layer, whose image is the least visible of the three, at the bottom. This can be done if emulsions can be made which are not sensitive to blue light. This is possible by using silver-chloride or silver-chloro-bromide emulsions, which have their natural sensitivity in the ultra-violet instead of in the blue. These emulsions cannot be used for camera films because of their rather low sensitivity, but for print films they are fast enough, and Eastman Colour Print Film has the magenta layer on top, the cyan layer in the middle, and the yellow layer at the bottom.

Although the system shown in Fig. 10.7(a) is used whenever possible, because of its quality and cost advantages, there are a number of reasons why extra stages are sometimes advisable between the camera film and the release print (Gale and Kisner, 1960). First, many motion picture productions require special effects, such as dissolves and wipes, and these require intermediate steps if they are to be carried out conveniently. Secondly, intermediate records are useful as an insurance against loss or damage to the original camera film. Thirdly, intermediate records are useful for exporting to foreign countries for local release-printing. Fourthly, intermediate records facilitate any change of size or format between the camera film and the release prints. Fifthly, in the case of a reversal camera original, cheaper prints can sometimes be made from an intermediate record than from the camera film.

Fig. 10.7(b) shows a system in which the colour negative is duplicated by printing it through red, green, and blue filters on to suitable black-and-white films. These black-and-white films used, at one time, to be printed on to a special *inter-negative* film having false colour sensitization, the blue layer giving the magenta image, the green layer the cyan image, and the red layer the yellow image (Anderson, Groet, Horton, and Zwick, 1953). This arrangement was chosen so that the magenta image (the most important for sharpness) was at the top, and the yellow image (the least important for sharpness) was at the bottom, of the tripack. This film was superseded, however, by an *intermediate* film having the conventional layer order (using absorbing dyes in the three layers to obtain good definition) known as Eastman Colour Intermediate Film (Bello, Groet, Hanson, Osborne, and Zwick, 1957). By making this intermediate film have a closely controlled contrast of 1.0, the system shown in Fig. 10.7(c) provides an alternative method which is much simpler to operate, because it avoids the necessity for printing three separate films in register; however, the use of four colour films in cascade makes it difficult to avoid some loss in quality.

Reversal camera films are usually used when, for reasons of economy or portability, a 16 mm. camera has to be employed. For the best quality in this system it has been convenient to use a camera film having a lower contrast than normal. Special films for operating the system of Fig. 10.7(d) have been made available, such as Ektachrome Commercial, Ektachrome E.R., and Ektachrome Reversal Print Films (Groet, Liberman, and Richey, 1959; Groet, Murray, and Osborne, 1960; Beilfuss, Thomas, and Zuidema, 1966) and Eastman Reversal Color Print Film (Thomas, Rees, and Lovick, 1965; Wall and Zuidema, 1966). Release prints can be made more cheaply, however, from a negative than from a reversal film, and so if the number of copies required is sufficient, it becomes more economical as well as more flexible, to use an inter-negative film, such as Eastman Colour Internegative

Film as shown in Fig. 10.4(e): this film is of low contrast and has conventional layer order and sensitizing (Zwick, Bello, and Osborne, 1956) and is printed on to ordinary Eastman Colour Print Film. All the negative, intermediate, and inter-negative films mentioned employ coloured couplers: the function of coloured

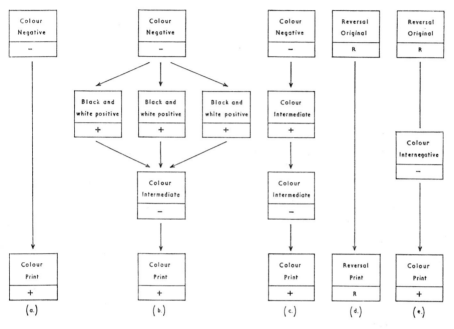

Fig. 10.7. Different methods of producing release prints in colour in professional motion picture work. Films bearing the following different types of image are indicated thus:

    — Negative image
    + Positive image printed from a negative
    R Positive image obtained by reversal processing.

couplers will be explained more fully later (see Section 13.3), but in these films they provide a means of correcting for the unwanted absorptions of cyan and magenta dyes, their use being particularly important in all systems where the dyes are used in several successive stages.

REFERENCES

Anderson, C., Groet, N. H., Horton, C. H., and Zwick, D., *J. Soc. Mot. Pic. Tel. Eng.*, **60,** 217 (1953).
Beilfuss, H. R., Thomas, D. S., and Zuidema, J. W., *J. Soc. Mot. Pic. Tel. Eng.*, **75,** 344 (1966).
Bello, H. J., Groet, N. H., Hanson, W. T., Osborne, C. E., and Zwick, D., *J. Soc. Mot. Pic. Tel. Eng.*, **66,** 205 (1957).
Berger, H., *Agfacolor*, W. Girardet, Wuppertal-Elberfeld, p. 32 (1950).
Capstaff, J. G., *J. Soc. Mot. Pic. Tel. Eng.*, **54,** 445 (1950).
Collins, R. B., *Phot. J.*, **100,** 173 (1960).
Davies, E. R., *Phot. J.*, **76,** 248 (1936).
Dundon, M. L., and Zwick, D., *J. Soc. Mot. Pic. Tel. Eng.*, **68,** 735 (1959).
Evans, R. M., Hanson, W. T., and Brewer, W. L., *Principles of Colour Photography*, Wiley, New York, p. 307 (1953).
Gale, R. O., and Kisner, W. I., *J. Soc. Mot. Pic. Tel. Eng.*, **69,** 874 (1960).
Groet, N. H., Liberman, M., and Richey, F., *J. Soc. Mot. Pic. Tel. Eng.*, **68,** 8 (1959).
Groet, N. H., Murray, T. J., and Osborne, C. E., *J. Soc. Mot. Pic. Tel. Eng.*, **69,** 815 (1960).
Hanson, W. T., *J. Soc. Mot. Pic. Tel. Eng.*, **58,** 223 (1952).
Hanson, W. T., and Kisner, W. I., *J. Soc. Mot. Pic. Tel. Eng.*, **61,** 667 (1953).
Harrison, G. B., and Spencer, D. A., *Phot. J.*, **77,** 250 (1937).
Hornsby, K. M., *Brit. J. Photog.*, **97,** 132 (1950).
Koshofer, G., *Brit. J. Photogr.*, **113,** 644 (1966).
Kisner, W. I., *J. Soc. Mot. Pic. Tel. Eng.*, **71,** 776 and 779 (1962).
Matthews, G. E., *P.S.A. Journal*, **21,** 33 (1955).
Mees, C. E. K., *Phot. J.*, **82,** 300 (1942).
Mott, P. G., *Photogrammetric Record*, **5,** 221 (1966).
Spencer, D. A., *J. Roy. Soc. Arts*, **95,** 675 (1947).
Tarkington, R. G., and Sorem, A. L., *Photogramm. Engng.*, **29,** 88 (1963).
Thomas, D. S., Rees, H. L., and Lovick, R. C., *J. Soc. Mot. Pic. Tel. Eng.*, **74,** 671 (1965).
Wall, C. M., and Zuidema, J. W., *J. Soc. Mot. Pic. Tel. Eng.*, **75,** 345 (1966).
Zwick, D., Bello, H. J., and Osborne, C. E., *J. Soc. Mot. Pic. Tel. Eng.*, **65,** 426 (1956).

GENERAL REFERENCES

Berger, H., *Agfacolor*, W. Girardet Wuppertal-Elberfeld (1950).
Bomback, E. S., *Manual of Colour Photography*, Fountain Press, London, (1964).
Cornwell-Clyne, A., *Colour Cinematography*, Chapman & Hall, London (1951).
Koshofer, G., *Brit. J. Photog.*, **112,** 780 (1965); **113,** 562, 606, 644, 738, 824, 920 (1966), and **114,** 128 (1967).
Evans, R. M., *Eye, Film, and Camera in Colour Photography*, Wiley, New York (1959).
Evans, R. M., Hanson, W. T., and Brewer, W. L., *Principles of Colour Photography*, Chapman & Hall (1953).
Mees, C. E. K., *From Dry Plates to Ektachrome Film*, Chapter 17, Ziff-Davis, New York, (1961).

CHAPTER 11

Reflection Prints in Colour

1. Introduction – *2.* Direct reflection-print systems – *3.* Reversal-reversal systems – *4.* Negative-positive systems – *5.* Inter-negative systems – *6.* Basic difficulties in reflection prints – *7.* Effect of surround – *8.* Inter-reflections in the image layer – *9.* Luminance ranges – *10.* Luminance levels

11.1 Introduction

ALTHOUGH in cinematography the transparency is the ultimate requirement, in still photography reflection prints are usually preferred. Transparencies can justifiably claim the advantages of being inexpensive and of providing excellent photographic quality, but they suffer from the disadvantage of being inconvenient to view: a projector must be provided, a room must be darkened, a screen has to be set up, and a source of electricity provided; none of this is necessary for reflection prints.

11.2 Direct reflection-print systems

At first sight it might seem that the simplest way of producing reflection prints would be just to coat a reversal tripack material, such as 'Kodachrome' or 'Ektachrome', on a paper support instead of on the usual transparent film base, and to use it in the camera. But this suffers from a number of serious difficulties. Such a system gives laterally reversed, or mirror-image, pictures of the real world. This could be overcome by using a prism in front of the camera lens, but this is inconvenient in practice. In the 'Polacolor' process the image, immediately after development, is soluble, and this enables it to transfer to a receiving sheet, placed in contact with it, where it becomes insoluble again. Since the receiving sheet is placed face to face with the material exposed in the camera, the transferred image is laterally reversed with respect to the camera image, and is therefore correct with respect to the original scene. (Incidentally, the 'Polacolor' system is one of the few commercially successful systems of colour photography which do not depend on paraphenylenediamine colour developers: see Section 15.10.) The development and transference of the image take place actually in the camera and the user can see the completed print within one minute of making the exposure.

But whether by prism or by transfer, two disadvantages of direct reflection-print systems may be noted. First, no enlargement occurs, so that a compromise choice has to be made between large cameras and small prints; secondly, accurate determination of exposure is necessary because the tolerances for image density and colour balance are smaller for reflection prints (which can be compared with other objects in the field of view surrounding them) than for transparencies projected in a dark room.

11.3 Reversal-reversal systems

If the production of reflection prints directly in the camera presents difficulties, it might be thought that the most attractive alternative would be to provide means whereby reflection prints could be made from transparencies. An enlarging stage could easily be incorporated so as to produce large prints from small cameras; correction for variations in the density or colour of the transparenceis could be provided and so as to produce prints of correct exposure and colour balance; and lateral reversal is of course avoided merely by turning the transparency over before printing it. Selection of those transparencies from which prints are especially wanted is rendered easy by virtue of the fact that colour transparencies consist of positive, and not negative, images. It is not surprising, therefore, that the first colour reflection prints offered to the public on a wide commercial scale used colour transparencies as intermediates, both in the U.S.A. (in 1941) and in England (in 1954). It is interesting to note that some of these prints have been made by processes in which the dye images, instead of being formed in the layers by colour development, are formed by image-wise destruction of dyes which are already present in the layers: the 'Ilford Colour Prints' introduced in 1954 were of this type, and the 'Cilchrome' prints announced in 1964 also use this system; the chemical basis of these systems is described in Section 15.10. Papers on which positive transparencies can be printed directly to give positive images are known as *reversal colour papers* and the system as the *reversal-reversal* system. Several such papers are commercially available, and print services depending on this system are offered by some photographic manufacturers and by some photo-finishing laboratories.

11.4 Negative-positive systems

There are, however, several advantages in using *negatives* instead of positives as camera films when requiring reflection prints. Since colour negatives reverse all the tones and colours of the original scene, they are obviously not intended to depict its appearance, and hence their characteristics can be adjusted solely to obtain the highest quality, at the greatest convenience, on the final print. Thus negative materials can be made of low contrast (a high contrast print material being used to give the required overall contrast to the system);

and their low contrast enables them to possess good exposure latitude without over-exposure resulting in very high densities (which tend to be difficult to print). They can also incorporate couplers which are coloured, to correct for the unwanted absorptions of the dyes in the system (see Section 13.3). Finally negative photographic materials are, at least in principle, inherently easier to manufacture and process than reversal materials. Colour negative films are therefore widely used as camera materials when reflection prints are required.

11.5 Inter-negative systems

Another method of making prints which, like the reversal-reversal system, employs a transparency as the starting point is the *inter-negative* system. In this system, a colour negative is made from the transparency and this is then printed on to the same type of colour paper as is used for the ordinary negative-positive system.

The inter-negative stage provides an opportunity for introducing colour correction and this is important because the use of cyan, magenta, and yellow dye-sets three times (in the transparency, in the inter-negative, and in the print material) means that the effects of their deficiencies, such as unwanted absorptions, are much more noticeable: the use of coloured couplers at some stage in the system is therefore desirable, and they can be incorporated in the inter-negative film.

Furthermore, by making the inter-negative film have a higher contrast at the high-exposure end of its scale than at its low-exposure end, some correction can also be made for the tendency for transparencies printed on to paper to reproduce light parts of the picture at too low a contrast relative to dark parts. This tendency arises from a combination of the fact that photographic papers cannot be made without the contrast falling at the low densities where the light tones of the picture are reproduced, and the fact that transparencies are made so that the light tones are reproduced at lower contrast than the dark tones because this results in more pleasing pictures on projection: the occurrence of this contrast difference between light and dark tones *twice* in the system usually requires some correction (see Section 12.16).

Thus the inter-negative system offers more scope for colour and tone correction than the reversal-reversal system, but the necessity for producing the inter-negative makes it more expensive (unless the cost of the inter-negative can be spread over more than one print), it is more complicated to operate, and it may involve loss of definition unless special precautions are taken.

11.6 Basic difficulties in reflection prints

Whether made by a direct, a reversal-reversal, a negative-positive, or an inter-negative system, for reflection prints in colour to be successful, three difficulties additional to those inherent in transparencies have to be accommodated. These difficulties are: the effect of the surround; the effect of inter-reflections in the image layer; and the limited tone range caused by light reflected by the top-most surface of the prints.

11.7 Effect of surround

The first difficulty is that when a reflection print is viewed, other objects in the field of view provide a reference framework of lightness and colour balance against which any deviations in these respects in the print are easily noticed. But when a transparency is projected in a dark room the viewer has little or no such reference framework and hence variations in the lightness and colour balance of transparencies often pass undetected. The tolerances in density and colour balance when making reflection prints to a given standard of acceptability are therefore smaller than in the case of transparencies, and special printing techniques are required: these have been successfully established and will be described in Chapter 14.

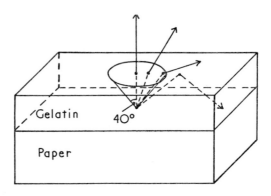

Fig. 11.1. Gelatin has a refractive index of 1.5, so that only light reaching its surface within a cone of semi-angle 40° is able to escape, the rest being totally internally reflected.

11.8 Inter-reflections in the image layer

The second difficulty encountered in making reflection prints arises from the fact that the dyes composing the image are situated in a layer which is bounded at one side by the diffusing paper surface, and at the other by the gelatin-air interface. This means that the light by which the images in a reflection print are viewed passes not just once each way through the image layer, but, on the average, several times. The reason for this can be seen from Fig.

11.1. Gelatin, which is used as the vehicle for photographic emulsions, has a refractive index of about 1.5. This means that light reflected from the paper base beneath the gelatin can only escape from the gelatin if it emerges within an angle of about 40° from the perpendicular to the gelatin surface. Light reflected outside this cone is totally internally reflected back on to the paper where it is rediffused for a second attempt at escaping. Light reflected at the critical angle, which for gelatin is about 40°, emerges along the actual surface of the gelatin. The paper reflects light in all directions, and the fraction of the rays which emerge at the first attempt is less than half the total, actually only 38.6 per cent (Williams and Clapper, 1953). Thus 38.6 per cent of the incident rays emerge at the first attempt, the rest travelling back to the paper and up again, thus traversing the layer four times instead of twice and magnifying the density by a factor of two. Again only 38.6 per cent of the rays escape, and the remainder have to traverse the layer a further twice, six times in all, before another attempt is made, and so on. It is clear, therefore, that reflection densities are not simply equal to twice the transmission densities but to more than twice. The magnitude of the increase in density, however, is dependent on the transmission density of the layer; for if the density is very high the contributions of the rays which have traversed the layer four or more times will be quite small, but, if the density is low, rays which have traversed four, six, or even eight or more times will still have a noticeable effect. Suppose, for instance, the layer transmitted only one-tenth of the light, so that its trans-

mission density was 1.0 (optical density is defined as $\log \frac{1}{T}$ where T is the trans-

mittance). The light which had passed twice through the layer would be reduced to only one-hundredth of its original intensity, equivalent to a density of the layer of 2.0; but light which had passed four times through the layer would be reduced to one ten-thousandth, which is fairly negligible compared to a hundredth. But if the layer had a transmission density of only 0.15, then the intensities would be reduced by effective densities of 0.3 after two passes, 0.6 after four, 0.9 after six, and so on, and the corresponding intensities of one-half, one-quarter, one-eighth, and so on, do not fall quickly to a negligible proportion of the total reflection. The result, therefore, is that low transmission densities are magnified by factors considerably in excess of the simple doubling which might be expected, but that as the density of the layer increases the increase in the factor gradually reduces. This shown in Fig. 11.2.

This behaviour of absorptions in reflection print layers has two important consequences in colour reflection prints. In the first place, it means that, in areas intended to be white, very great care must be taken to minimize any traces of residual dyes, because, as can be seen from Fig. 11.2 very low transmission densities are magnified by factors as large as five or more. Secondly, because the unwanted absorptions of cyan, magenta, and yellow dyes are of lower density than the wanted absorptions, they will be increased in density more than the wanted absorptions; this means that the unwanted absorptions have a stronger effect in reflection than in transmission materials. The effect also results in an effective broadening of the spectral absorption curve of a dye as shown in Fig. 11.3 (Evans, Hanson, and Brewer, 1953). Once again low densities have been raised by a greater factor than high densities so that although the required peak density is obtained in a reflection image by having slightly less than half the amount of dye present, as compared with the amount required in a transmission image, the absorptions at wavelengths off the peak are increased more and hence the effective absorption of the dye becomes broader. Reflection prints, therefore, even if possessing dyes chemically identical to those used in transmission materials, have colorants which are broader in their absorption

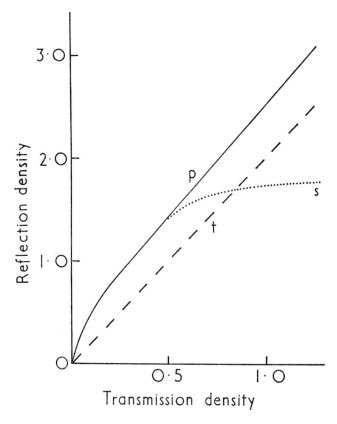

Fig. 11.2. Reflection density plotted as a function of transmission density: (p) when the dye layer is in optical contact with a diffusely reflecting white layer, as in a reflection print; (t) when the optical contact is broken and the reflection density is simply twice the transmission density; (s) the way in which surface reflections modify curve p in typical room viewing conditions.

bands and worse in their unwanted absorptions, and these effects tend to reduce colour saturation and lightness.

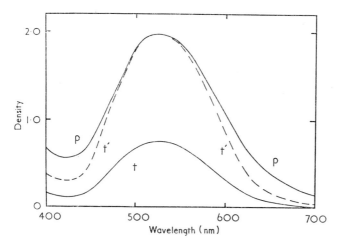

Fig. 11.3. Spectral absorption curves of the same dye (t) in a transparency material; (p) in a reflection print material; and (t'), curve (t) multiplied by 2.61 to make the peak density equal to that of curve (p). Curve (p) is broader and has higher unwanted absorptions than curve (t').

11.9 Luminance ranges

The third difficulty encountered in reflection prints arises from the existence of the top-most surface of the image layer; this surface inevitably reflects some light, and this light, because it has not traversed the image layer, simply acts as a whitish flare desaturating the picture, its greatest apparent effect being in dark areas. Of even more importance than the desaturating effect, however, is the limitation which this surface reflection has on the range of tones which can be reproduced in reflection prints.

Jones and Condit (1941) have shown that the range of luminances in outdoor scenes varies from about 1.45 to 2.8 log units, with an average of 2.2 log units (that is, from 28 to 1 to 630 to 1 with an average of 158 to 1, in arithmetic units). Transparency materials usually have maximum densities of over 3.0, corresponding to a tone-range of 1000 to 1, and this suggests that they should in theory be able to handle the maximum luminance range of outdoor scenes satisfactorily. However, measurements of typical maximum and minimum luminances actually present in projected pictures shows the range to be only about 2.1 log units or 126 to 1 (Estes, 1953; Hunt, 1965a). The difference is made up of several factors. First, transparency films all exhibit some absorption in fully exposed areas and this 'stain' often amounts to 0.2 or more log units.

Secondly, it is impossible to make photographic materials with characteristics which remain linear at the ends of their exposure scales, so that for whites to be reproduced with adequate tonal modulation their density has to be higher than that of the stain; this can account for a further loss of 0.2 or more log units. Thirdly, if the maximum density of a slide is about 3.0, a fairly typical figure, and the luminance caused by ambient light is 3.0 log units less than the open-gate screen luminance at the same point (a figure representative of good projection conditions), then the minimum luminance for a black would be equal to twice that of the ambient luminance, or 0.3 log units above that corresponding to the maximum density of the film. Fourthly, because of vignetting in camera lenses and fall-off in the luminance provided by projectors towards the corners of the picture, typical maximum luminances in pictures are further reduced by about 0.2 log units, because only in some cases will they occur in the centre of the picture where the maximum luminance is available. These factors, amounting to 0.9 log units, reduce the tone range from the 3.0 log units of the maximum density of the films to 2.1 log units in picture elements on the screen.

But, when similar measurements are made on the range of tones available between typical maximum and minimum luminances in reflection prints viewed in average conditions, a very different picture emerges.

It is possible to make colour photographic papers which, when processed to give highly glossy surfaces, possess blacks which when measured in good reflection densitometers have maximum densities of 2.4 or more. However, as with colour transparencies, this figure is reduced by a number of factors. First, the minimum density or 'stain' of colour photographic papers usually amounts to about 0.1 log unit; secondly another 0.1 log unit is normally lost because of the need for reproducing whites at a high enough density for adequate tonal modulation to be achieved; thirdly another loss of about 0.1 often occurs as a result of failure of the blacks always to achieve the maximum possible density, either because of less favourable surface characteristics, or because the exposure given to the area in question was too great (a situation more likely to be attributable to flare in the camera or the printer than to high luminance in the black of the original scene). Vignetting is usually only a small factor in negative-positive print systems because the negative tends to have light corners and this helps to correct fall-off of luminance towards the corners of the picture on enlargement: in reversal-reversal systems vignetting may add a further important loss. The factors so far considered amount to a total loss of range of about 0.3 log units, so that it might be expected that 2.1 log units should remain, as was found in transparencies.

Plate 4. Portrait by statue. The difficulty of accommodating very dark subject matter on a reflection print is illustrated by the loss of detail of the girl's hair in the shadow regions. *From an Ektachrome transparency by Jack M. Oakley.*

But measurements show that the actual tones perceivable usually run from 0.3 to a maximum of only 1.75 giving a range of only about 1.45 log units (Hunt, 1965a). A further large loss of 0.65 has therefore occurred, and this is the result of the light reflected from the topmost surface of the print. Similar results for black-and-white photographic papers have also been reported (Carnahan, 1955).

The reason why a black, which a densitometer can measure as having a maximum density of 2.40, appears to have a maximum density of only about 1.75 when seen under typical viewing conditions in a room can be explained by reference to Fig. 11.4. The top half of the figure illustrates the situation in the densitometer. The print is illuminated by a beam of light perpendicular to the surface and the reflection from the glossy top surface of the print is mainly back along the same path; the photocell, which views the print from an angle of 45° therefore picks up only the light reflected diffusely by the print after traversing the image layer. The area of the inside of the densitometer which is specularly reflected along the direction of the photocell is arranged to be of extremely low luminance; hence the effect of the light reflected by the topmost surface of the paper is virtually eliminated. The lower half of the figure illustrates the conditions when the print is viewed in a room: although most of the light may come from one (or a few) directions, as indicated by the heavy vertical arrow, some light will fall on the print from all other directions since the room, in general, has significant luminances in all its parts. Hence, no matter where the eye is placed, specular reflection of the light coming from some part of the room will enter the eye and prevent it from seeing the true maximum density of the paper. It is found that 1.75 represents about the maximum density that can be seen in ordinary rooms, and the effect of this on the relationship between reflection and transmission densities is shown by the dotted line in Fig. 11.2. The value of 1.75 is not affected by the maximum density evaluated in a densitometer, provided this figure is not less than about 2.0. (It should not be construed from this that the maximum densities of papers are unimportant so long as they are above 2.0: changes in the maximum amount of dye available in a colour print can affect the rendering of saturated colours by virtue of changes in the sloping sides of its spectral absorption curve, even though the appearance of blacks as viewed in rooms is unaltered.) The figure of 1.75 applies to rooms with rather directional light sources, such as are provided by tungsten lamps: in diffusely lit rooms, it may be only about 1.50. In highly unusual viewing situations, such as viewing the print by a shaft of sunlight in a coal-cellar, or, more realistically, holding prints in a

---

Plate 5. Chemical Plant. The white tank has to be reproduced at a density appreciably darker than that of the clear paper, in order to achieve adequate modulation of the tones; in this case the roundness of the object can only be conveyed by reproducing density variations corresponding to variations in illumination on its white surface. *From an Ektacolor reflection print by W. G. Gaskins.*

beam from a projector shining in an otherwise dark room, figures higher than 1.75, and even approaching the densitometer figure, may be achieved.

For ordinary conditions the range of luminances available in reflection colour prints can therefore be taken as 1.75 minus 0.30 (to allow for the three losses of 0.10 mentioned earlier), or a range of no more than 1.45 log units, or 28 to 1. This range is clearly much less than that available in projected transparencies (2.1 log units or 126 to 1) or in average out-door scenes (2.2 log units or 158 to 1) and hence appreciable 'crushing' of whites or blacks or both must often take place in reflection prints. When photographing scenes with the intention of producing colour reflection prints the successful photographer is therefore careful to compose or arrange the scene so as to

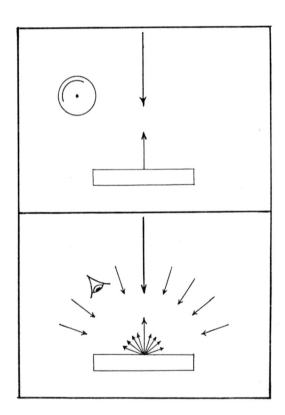

Fig. 11.4. Top: when illuminated perpendicularly, no specular reflection from a reflecting sample reaches a photo-cell placed at 45°. Bottom: when viewed in a light room, no matter where the eye is placed, some specularly reflected light is seen, and this limits the maximum density which can be seen on reflection prints in typical viewing conditions.

keep all important subject matter within a limited luminance range; in general this means that heavy shadows must not be allowed to fall on important parts of the scene. Even when this is done, difficulties remain with some types of scene: for instance, in wedding pictures, while a transparency will handle the white of the bride's dress, and the black of the bridegroom's suit without difficulty, in a reflection print it is not easy to avoid either loss of detail in the former by bleached-out highlights or in the latter by blocked-up shadows.

In Plate 1 (page 41) the shadows on the girl's face, and in the interior of the barge, were artificially lightened by using *fill-in flash*; that is, a (blue-coated) flash-bulb was fired at the time of the exposure from a position near the camera. Similar results can also be obtained by using white or metallic reflectors suitably placed. In these ways the lighting can be adjusted to suit the final reproduction medium. If a transparency intended for projection in a dark room was required, the lighting used in the case of Plate 1 would be too flat.

Plate 4 (page 189) provides an example of the difficulty of reproducing dark subject matter in reflection prints. Plate 5 (page 190) illustrates how whites have to be reproduced with some density in reflection prints in order to obtain adequate tonal modulation. In Plate 6 (page 207) specular highlights are reproduced by contrast with darker adjacent areas.

11.10 Luminance levels

The apparent-brightness, or luminosity, of any given luminance depends markedly on the adaptation conditions of the observer's eye. Thus the motor-car headlamp which dazzles painfully after dark, appears to be a very modest source in bright sunlight: the luminance has remained constant, but the luminosity has changed enormously.

In comparing the luminance ranges available in colour transparencies and prints, some attention must also be paid, therefore, to the absolute luminances involved and to the adaptation conditions. Projectors which provide about 10 foot-candles on the screen produce whites of luminances comparable with those on reflection prints illuminated at about 5 foot-candles: these levels are roughly equivalent to those obtained with average domestic projectors and average tungsten-lit rooms in houses. Projectors giving 50 foot-candles are sometimes used and are probably becoming more common, and living rooms lit at considerably more than 5 foot-candles are certainly encountered; but to consider the luminance of the whites in the two cases as typical seems broadly justifiable. What then of the luminosities? In the case of the projected slide the surround is dark and this has the effect of increasing the luminosity, or 'subtracting grey' from the picture, whereas no such effect usually occurs when viewing prints. The result is that the whites on projected transparencies look much whiter than those on reflection prints; moreover, as we have seen, the transparencies also have a greater luminance range, and this is usually sufficient to make the blacks look blacker as well. The advantage here, therefore, lies entirely with the transparency, the whites are whiter and the blacks blacker. But if colour reflection prints are viewed in bright sunlight the illumination level can reach 4000 foot-candles, and this leaves even a powerful projector far behind. But what happens to the luminosity? Some indication can be obtained by using the binocular matching technique (as described in Section 7.8), some results of which will now be described (Hunt, 1965a).

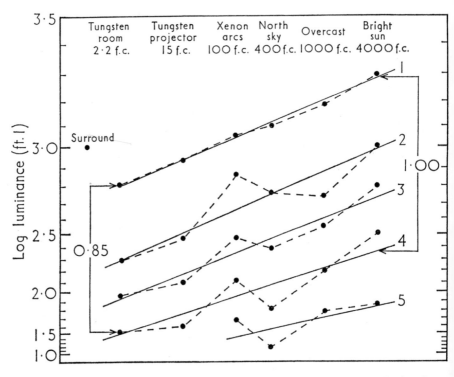

Fig. 11.5. Log luminance (of a 1½° central spot in a 15° surround of 1050 foot-lamberts) necessary to produce the same luminosity as that of a white (1) and four grey (2, 3, 4, 5) samples seen under the conditions shown. The reflectances of the white and the greys were: (1) 85.0, (2) 21.5, (3) 13.3, (4) 5.3, (5) 1.7%. If the visual contrast represented by the spacing between lines 1 and 4 for the bright sun conditions is regarded as unity, that for the tungsten room condition is about 0.85 (on this Munsell value type of scale with the surround being set at Munsell value 6).

In the instrument used, the observer's left eye had an unobstructed view of the scene, while his right eye viewed a white field of 15° subtense, and 1050 foot-lamberts luminance with a centre spot of subtense 1½° which could be adjusted in colour and luminance to produce a wide range of luminosities. A wide range of luminosities seen by the left eye could therefore be matched by the centre spot in the right eye, and the luminance of the centre spot necessary to do this was used as a measure of the luminosities seen in the left eye. Observations of this type were made on a white, and four grey, squares of a chart containing a neutral scale of six squares, and eighteen coloured squares. The results are plotted in Fig. 11.5. The luminances of the central spot seen by the right eye are plotted on a log scale which has been spaced so as to represent Munsell value intervals uniformly. The luminance corresponding to the right-eye surround luminance has been set arbitrarily at the point on the scale representing Munsell value 6. The dots marked 1 all refer to the white square on the chart, those marked 2, 3, 4, 5 refer to progressively darker greys. The left-eye viewing conditions used are marked along the top and the results obtained for each are plotted vertically below them. The spacing of the viewing conditions along the abscissa is entirely arbitrary (except that they are progressive in luminance level) and has been chosen so that approximately linear results are obtained for the white points. The condition marked 'tungsten projector, 15 foot-candles', consisted of the chart illuminated in a dark room by means of a tungsten projector the size of whose projected beams exactly covered the chart area and no more, so that the viewing conditions were closely analogous to projecting a transparency. It is seen that although the point labelled 1 for the tungsten projector at 15 foot-candles is higher than that for tungsten room lighting at 2.2 foot-candles, it is lower than those for Xenon arcs at 100 foot-candles, north sky at 400 foot-candles, overcast sky at 1000 foot-candles, and bright sun at 4000 foot-candles. Since, in these last four viewing conditions, the chart was seen in an average environment, and not surrounded by a very low luminance as in the case of projected pictures, it is clear that a substantial increase in the luminance of whites can produce a greater increase in luminosity, when measured in this manner, than occurs as the result of a dark surround. Thus, according to these results, even prints viewed in a room well-lit by daylight (100 foot-candles) should appear to have whites of greater luminosity than those of projected transparencies at about 15 foot-lamberts. It is therefore to be concluded that prints viewed in good indoor daylight have whiter whites than those of projected transparencies. Thus, although the range of luminances in the prints remains a restriction, their appearance should be greatly improved by viewing them under conditions of high illumination, and this is borne out in practice.

It is interesting to note in Fig. 11.5 that the spacing of the points representing the white and grey squares is roughly similar for most of the six viewing conditions, and, if the Munsell value scale as set is appropriate for these observations, this suggests that the contrast of the grey scale does not alter markedly over this range, although of course the luminosity varies. There is, however, some evidence for a slight fall in visual contrast as the luminance level falls, a tendency also reported by others (Breneman, 1962; Stevens, 1961) but it must be remembered that if the surround were allocated a different value on the Munsell scale the spacing of the points would be affected. The figure shows a tendency for the darkest grey (5) to become rather indistinguishable from black as the illumination level drops to 2.2 foot-candles, and, although this accords with one's general visual impression, the accuracy of binocular matching with a surround field of high luminance becomes very low as black is approached, and the position of the points is not very reliable; in fact the darkest grey (5) could not be measured at all under the two lowest illumination levels. Luminosity-scaling investigations have shown that dark greys tend to remain fairly constant in appearance, but that blacks actually *increase* in luminosity as the illumination level falls (Stevens, 1961).

It has been shown (Hunt, 1952 and 1965b) that not only does luminosity increase with illumination level but substantial increases in colour saturation also take place; this is a further reason why the appearance of colour photographs is improved by viewing them at high levels of illumination. It thus becomes at least debatable, and no longer a foregone conclusion, whether a projected transparency at 10 foot-candles, or a reflection print at 100 foot-candles, is to be preferred. Other factors peculiarly deleterious to reflection prints, such as the degradation of dye colour caused by inter-reflections, or the noticeability of stain as such, or the ability to detect quite small departures from optimum in density or colour balance, may give victory to the transparency; but as far as luminosity of the whites is concerned the advantage should be with the print, and if the subject matter is carefully handled the restricted luminance range need not have a serious effect. This was illustrated at the 1964/65 World's Fair at New York (Bartleson, Reese, Macbeth, and James, 1964), where a group of reflection prints displayed under very high levels of illumination appeared as attractive as transparencies; however, in this case the print was illuminated at a higher level than the surround so that some 'subtraction of grey' by virtue of simultaneous contrast increased the luminosity of the whites above that normally associated with the luminance level used.

REFERENCES

Bartleson, C. J., Reese, W. B., Macbeth, N., and James, J. E., *Illum. Eng.*, **59,** 375 (1964).
Breneman, E. J., *Phot. Sci. Eng.*, **6,** 172 (1962).
Carnahan, W. H., *Phot. Eng.*, **6,** 237 (1955).
Estes, R. L., *J. Soc. Mot. Pic. Tel. Eng.*, **61,** 257 (1953).
Evans, R. M., Hanson, W. T., and Brewer, W. L., *Principles of Colour Photography*, p. 365, Wiley, New York; Chapman & Hall, London (1953).
Hunt, R. W. G., *J. Opt. Soc. Amer.*, **42,** 190 (1952).
Hunt, R. W. G., *J. Phot. Sci.*, **13,** 108 (1965a).
Hunt, R. W. G., *J. Opt. Soc. Amer.*, **55,** 1540 (1965b).
Jones, L. A., and Condit, H. R., *J. Opt. Soc. Amer.*, **31,** 651 (1941).
Stevens, S. S., *Science*, **133,** 80 (1961).
Williams, F. C., and Clapper, F. R., *J. Opt. Soc. Amer.*, **43,** 595 (1953).

CHAPTER 12

Quantitative Colour Photography

12.1 Introduction

MANY colour films are successfully exposed without any measurement being made of the illumination levels of the scenes, and even when such measurements are made they are often restricted to the response of an exposure meter to the integrated light reflected by each scene as a whole. Appraisal of the final picture is often by visual inspection without any measurements being made at all.

But even in amateur colour photography measurement plays a very important, even if largely hidden, part in the success or otherwise of the results. Thus, when the final picture is in the form of a reflection print, measurements of the transmittance of the negatives, inter-negatives, or transparencies from which the prints are made, form a vital part of the printing operation, as will be discussed in Chapter 14; and even when transparencies are produced directly on a reversal film without any printing stage, a very great deal of measurement will have been made by the manufacturer on samples of film cut from the same batch of material as is being used by the customer, and the conditions in which the film is processed will normally be the subject of further extensive measurements.

In professional photography, more elaborate measurements are often made on the scene itself, including, for instance, determining the luminance of an average white (or the maximum and minimum luminances), as well as, or instead of, determining the average luminance of the scene as a whole; and if intermediate stages are used, involving black-and-white separations, inter-negative or intermediate films, or masking techniques (to be described in Chapter 13), then measurement is usually essential.

If photographic steps are used in conjunction with other media, such as television or half-tone printing, measurement is indispensable in the experimental and setting-up stages, otherwise it becomes virtually impossible to obtain a clear picture of the contribution of each part of the system to the virtues or deficiencies of the final result, and improvements cannot then be systematically sought.

Finally, in some scientific and technical investigations it may be desirable to use colour photography to obtain quantitative results of certain phenomena, and of course measurement is then involved.

There are thus many reasons why an understanding of the science of photographic measurement as applied to colour photography should be acquired. The measurement of the sensitivity of photographic materials is called *sensitometry*. Sensitometry is carried out in absolute terms by photographic manufacturers who are naturally greatly concerned with the photographic 'speeds' of their materials, but in many instances of applied colour photography the interest is confined to relative results, and in these cases measurements in absolute terms are not required and simpler techniques can often be adopted. The evaluation of the photographic records obtained in sensitometry is called *densitometry*, because, as the name implies, this usually involves measuring *density* (defined as $\log(1/T)$ where T is the transmittance or reflectance of the area being measured).

Sensitometry consists essentially of the three basic steps of all photographic systems, exposure, processing, and evaluation; but each step has to be carried out under closely controlled conditions to obtain consistent results. It is important, however, to see that the controlled conditions are still typical of the actual conditions of use of the material, or the results, though consistent, may not be relevant.

12.2 Sensitometric pictures

Sensitometric exposures are intended to illuminate the photographic material with known amounts of light, the purpose being either to determine the absolute sensitivity of the material, or to calibrate it in relative terms for some particular application. The difficulty of maintaining any real scene constant in luminance at all points means that some artificial 'picture' must be used in practice. This could be a suitable black-and-white or colour photograph, and this type of test object is sometimes used. If the photograph is a transparency it can be printed on to the photographic material under test by placing it in contact and illuminating it with a uniform controlled light source. But if the size of the image required on the test film is different from that of the original, a projection system must be used and the original can then be either a transparency or a reflection print; transparencies are generally used because of their greater tone range and because of the greater difficulty of keeping a reflection print clean. Instruments for forming images of photographs on to test films for sensitometric purposes are known as *camera sensitometers;* they are mainly used for rather special purposes: thus graininess and sharpness can be evaluated by forming an image greatly reduced in size on to the test film, and then magnifying it again; or if large numbers of identical pictures are required for a test programme it is often convenient to expose them on a camera sensitometer.

12.3 Sensitometric wedges

Using a picture of a scene as a test object, however, has the disadvantage that the identification of individual areas for measurement is rather complicated; and using a projected image for exposing the test-material has the disadvantage that vignetting and flare, caused by the lens, introduce uncertainties into the calibration, unless this is carried out by direct photometry of the image itself, which may be difficult to do with sufficient accuracy. For general purposes, therefore, a very much simplified 'scene' is usually used: this consists of either a stepped or continuous *wedge*. This is a strip of transparent material the transmittance of which varies along its length either in steps, or continuously, in a known manner. The test-material is exposed by contact-printing such a wedge on to it, the instrument in which this is done being called a *sensitometer;* the exposure given at each point is then identified either by the number of the step along the wedge (if it is stepped) or the distance along the wedge (if it is continuous).

For convenience, sensitometric wedges should have, for any one step or position, exactly the same transmittance at all wavelengths of the visible spectrum; in other words, they should be constructed of non-selective neutral material. Such material is not easy to find, and some sensitometers, instead of using wedges, use rotating drums which vary the exposure *time*, instead of the illumination, along the strip of test-material: however, changes in time and illumination, although approximately, are not exactly, inter-changeable on photographic materials (a phenomenon known as *reciprocity failure*), so that such variable-time exposures are usually only suitable for purely relative work, like checking processing uniformity. For general work, non-selective neutral wedges are required, and these are available commercially either as black-and-white photographic (silver) wedges or as colloidal graphite (carbon) wedges. Whenever photographic silver wedges or test-objects are made up, the neutrality of the image should be carefully checked, because preferential scattering at certain wavelengths can cause appreciable coloration.

The size of the steps on a step-wedge is largely a matter of convenience, but very small steps are difficult to evaluate and are affected by local development-exhaustion effects (edge-effects); a step-length of o.4 in. is widely used, with the width being either the same or extending right across the film. Transmittance increments from one step to the next are convenient if they are in the ratio of the square root of two, so that the exposure is doubled or halved for every two steps.

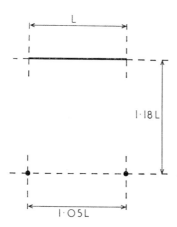

Fig. 12.1. Arrangement of two 'point-source' lights so as to give illumination, along a wedge of length *L*, uniform to within ±o.1 per cent.

12.4 Uniformity of illumination

In camera sensitometers the vignetting of the lens may have to be counteracted by illuminating the test object more strongly at the edges than at the centre, but in contact sensitometers very uniform illumination of the picture or wedge is desirable so that for calibration purposes any residual non-uniformities can be ignored. This means in practice that the light should be uniform to within about ±1 per cent. If a single source, small enough to be considered a 'point source' is used, it must be about 4½ times the length of the wedge away to provide ±1 per cent uniformity; thus if the wedge had 21 steps, each o.4 inches long, the total length of the wedge would be 8.4 inches and the distance of the lamp nearly 40 inches. However, it has been pointed out that if two 'point-source' lamps are used, much better uniformity can be obtained with the lamps much closer. Thus a uniformity of ±o.1 per cent is attained with the lamps 1.18 times the length of the wedge (about 11 inches for an 8.4 inch wedge) away from the plane of the wedge; in this case, as shown in Fig. 12.1, the lamps have to be equidistant from the centre of the wedge and separated by a distance equal to 1.05 times the length of the wedge (Marriage, 1955). This two-lamp arrangement thus enables a much more compact sensitometer to be built with better uniformity: one problem is that unequal ageing of the lamps would cause serious deterioration of the uniformity, but, because the lamps are now so much closer, the illuminance of the test-material is greatly increased, and hence the lamps can be under-run and good stability achieved.

12.5 Exposure time

The time for which the photographic material is exposed should be as near as possible the same as that used in the conditions which the sensitometer is supposed to simulate, unless it is known that the difference in exposure time does not involve reciprocity failure, or that the effects of any reciprocity failure are negligible in the application concerned. If enlarging on to photographic paper is the application, then exposure times of between about 1 and 30 seconds are involved: these can conveniently be given by switching tungsten filament lamps on and off by means of an electronic timing switch; the lamps of course must be run at constant voltage and a constant-voltage transformer is usually adequate for this purpose. With camera films, typical exposure times are usually much shorter and some sort of shutter must be used: for these short exposure times, usually in the range 1/50 to 1/500 second, the illuminance on the film has to be quite high in order to give an adequate exposure. In one convenient form of sensitometer, this is achieved by using a single lamp and a slit which are moved uniformly together along the strip; narrow slits can then be used to give very short exposure times, and short lamp-to-film distances to give high levels of illumination. Exposure times in the range from 1/1000 to 1/10,000 sec. are usually given in practice by means of electronic flash equipment, and in these cases it is therefore appropriate to use a carefully controlled version of this type of source in the sensitometer, no shutter being necessary.

12.6 Light sources for sensitometry

Except for the very short exposure times just mentioned, tungsten lamps are the most convenient source for sensitometry because of their ease of control and good stability if under-run. When the application which is being simulated also uses tungsten lamps, then they are clearly desirable in the sensitometer because their spectral energy distribution is also correct. If the source used in the application is daylight, however, the tungsten lamps must be filtered to simulate the spectral energy distribution of daylight, and this can be conveniently done with an appropriate thickness of a blue glass, such as one of the two shown in Fig. 12.2; it may also be desirable to add a heat-absorbing glass in order to reduce the amount of far-red and infra-red light, which the tungsten lamps emit relatively copiously and which, as can be seen from Fig. 12.2, the blue glasses do not absorb very fully. Gelatin filters may not be suitable for use in sensitometers because of inadequate permanence under the strong illuminances involved. It should be noted, however, that some glasses change colour appreciably with temperature and these should be avoided in sensitometers.

12.7 Transmission colour of lenses

Photographic lenses do not transmit all wavelengths equally freely, because of absorptions in the glasses and because of the effects of the anti-reflection coatings on the surfaces of the components; the effect of this on the colour of the light reaching photographic materials in practice is quite large (Williams and Grum, 1960), and may need simulating in sensitometers by the incorporation of suitable filters in the light beam. A British Standard was drawn up to provide tolerances within which the transmission colour of photographic camera lenses should lie (British Standard 3824 : 1964), but some lenses of earlier manufacture lie well outside its limits.

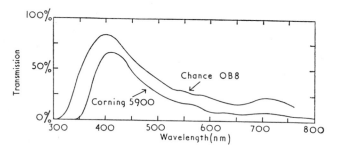

Fig. 12.2. Spectral transmission curves of two blue glasses, useful for simulating daylight with tungsten filament lamps.

12.8 Selective exposure of layers

If it is required to expose the layers of a colour material separately, this can usually be achieved by using narrow-cut red, green, and blue filters. Much can sometimes be learned by exposing the layers both separately, to give coloured wedges, and together, in the proportions to give a grey wedge, and then comparing the results; this technique is useful in evaluating *inter-image* effects (see Section 13.4).

12.9 Latent image changes

A variable which needs to be remembered in sensitometric work is the change in the latent image with time: this is not usually a large factor, but it may often occur in the form of a fairly rapid change in the first two or three days, followed by a fairly slow drift. For the highest accuracy it is thus advisable either always to process the material within an hour or so of exposing it, or to allow a few days for ageing at room temperature, followed by cold storage until processing. The former method is more convenient for general purposes, but the latter is useful when large numbers of strips are exposed at one time for subsequent use as process-control checks.

12.10 Controlled processing

Because of the inherent variability of the processing step in photographic systems, special precautions usually have to be taken when processing any material on which measurements are to be made; but care is necessary to ensure that the special precautions do not make the process untypical of those used in practice.

The factors affecting consistency of processing include the chemical compositions of the solutions, the temperatures of the baths, the time spent by the material in each bath, and the nature of the agitation of each solution over the surface of the material; developers usually require much more critical control than the other solutions.

Photographic baths alter with use, or 'season', on account of the chemical interactions between the materials and the solutions. One way of standardizing the chemical composition of the baths is therefore to make them up from fresh ingredients, or to draw fresh supplies from a large bulk mix for each process; but if this is done, it must be remembered that although good consistency may be obtained, the process will differ from a normal process unless the formulation of the solutions allows for the seasoning effects which occur in practice. Control of the solutions by chemical analysis may be used, but this is expensive and cannot guard against every possible type of variation: useful results, however, can be obtained by using on every occasion a strip from a 'check' or 'control' material similar to the test-material, to detect any processing variations.

Controlling the times in, and temperatures of, the solutions does not present any very great technical difficulties, but scrupulous care in watching these two factors is well repaid.

The agitation of the solution over the surface of the photographic material greatly affects the rate at which the exhausted products are removed and replaced by fresh supplies, and this in turn affects the rate of the reaction, especially in developers. The difficulty of exactly reproducing practical agitation conditions in special sensitometric processing devices is a strong argument for using practical agitation conditions whenever possible. The following methods of agitation are commonly used: recirculation of the solution through the tank by forcing it out through a pump and back again; gas-burst agitation, by releasing, once every few seconds, a burst of gas at the bottom of the tank and letting it rise to the top (nitrogen is generally used in developers because it has no chemical effect on them); the solutions may be sprayed on to the material from suitable nozzles, or they may be moved across the surface of the material mechanically by means of drums, paddles, vanes, or brushes; and for separate sheets or short lengths of film (but not for continuous lengths of motion-picture film or still films joined together) agitation may be effected by lifting the material out of the solution and letting it drain off at prescribed intervals (the lift-and-drain method); or, if a single sheet is being processed in a dish, a rocking motion may be used provided that regular patterns in the liquid are avoided; finally, processing may be carried out with zero agitation by coating the solutions on the material in viscous layers (Edgecombe and Seeley, 1963).

Sometimes, for instance when the couplers are in three separate developers as in Kodachrome, the process is too complicated to duplicate in a rigidly controlled version for sensitometric purposes; in these cases processing variations either have to be averaged out by processing a number of duplicate strips on different occasions, or allowed for by processing with the test material a control-strip exposed on a film of known properties. Although these procedures are somewhat cumbersome they do have the merit that the process used for the sensitometric material is the actual practical process itself.

The use of control materials introduces some further possible complications. It is, of course, necessary that such materials be very uniform themselves from one piece to another, and it is therefore essential that all the control material be from the same parent roll of the same batch. The sensitivity of photographic materials varies slowly with time so that a control material cannot be regarded as invariant over long periods; however, the rate of change can usually be greatly reduced by keeping the material at low temperature, and for the most critical work temperatures as low as zero degrees Fahrenheit (minus 18° Centigrade) are used (but it is essential to allow the material to reach room temperature before it is unpacked for use, otherwise condensation and local temperature variations will occur). Finally, it is possible for a control material to indicate that a process is on standard when one fault has cancelled out another, for instance a developer having a high temperature and a low concentration of developing agent: under these conditions the test-material may not give the same result as in a standard process, although the control material apparently indicates that all is well. To avoid these *film-process interactions*, careful control of the process is therefore still necessary even when control-strips are used, and for very critical work several processings should be used and the results averaged.

It might appear from the above discussion that controlled processing is an almost impossible undertaking. It is certainly true that to obtain the highest accuracy very great precautions have to be taken, and photographic manufacturers and large scale processing stations generally use both chemical analysis and frequent control-strips to keep their processes on standard; useful, though less accurate results, can still be obtained, however, by less elaborate means by using control-strips with reasonable care and common-sense.

When colour photographic materials are being used to record phenomena for subsequent colour measurement, an even better method than the use of separate control strips is to expose a sensitometric wedge (or other convenient series of controlled patches) on a part of the same piece of film as is being used to record the pictures: differences in processing between the picture and the calibrating exposures are then minimized. On roll-films or 35 mm. films, part of each film can be used for the wedge and the rest for a series of pictures; on sheet films, part of each sheet must be reserved for the wedge. Alternatively it is possible sometimes to introduce the wedge or a series of patches in the scenes themselves, but, if this is done, due allowance must be made for vignetting in the camera and for any non-uniformity of illumination on the wedge or patches in the scene.

12.11 Visual evaluation

The evaluation of the processed material can be carried out in various ways, some of which are highly sophisticated. The simplest method of all, visual inspection, should not be overlooked, however, because the eye is a very good detector of *differences* in transmittance or reflectance, even though not so precise as an absolute detector. Thus any important differences between a test-material and a control can usually be seen unless they involve changes in blue transmittance seen at low luminances, the eye being rather insensitive even to differences in these conditions. Visual inspection is also very useful in the detection of any streaks or marks on the processed material, such local blemishes being capable of producing most peculiar looking measurements unless they are avoided. Finally visual inspection can usually (but not always) be relied upon to act as a useful check on results obtained by other means.

12.12 Logarithmic scales

It was mentioned in Section 12.3 on sensitometric wedges that the transmittances of successive steps on stepped-wedges used for exposing photographic materials usually bore a constant ratio to one another: the reason for the increment being a constant ratio (the transmittances being for example 4, 8, 16, 32, 64, etc.) and not a constant arithmetic difference (4, 19, 34, 49, 64, etc.) are twofold: first, a ratio sequence of transmittances appears much more uniformly spaced to the eye than an arithmetic sequence; and secondly, when alterations

---

Plate 6. Machine operator. The very bright reflections in the metal require careful handling for successful reproduction in a reflection print. The illusion of sparkle can only be created by contrast with dark surrounding areas. When such a reproduction is being copied by photographic methods with masking, a highlight mask may be required to avoid loss of contrast in the bright reflections. *From an Ektacolor reflection print by Prudence Cuming.*

are made to the level of the exposure given to a photographic material (by altering the lens aperture, or the scene illuminance, for instance) all the illuminance levels on the photographic material are multiplied by a common factor, and on a ratio sequence this corresponds to the same shift, in terms of number of steps, along the wedge for all parts of the scene. It has therefore become universal practice to evaluate sensitometric results in terms of variations in the logarithm of the exposure (log E), for which a ratio sequence is spaced at equal intervals, instead of in terms of the exposure (E) itself. For similar reasons, instead of using the transmittance or reflectance, T, of photographic materials, a logarithmic function is used, but in this case although log T, the *opacity*, could be used, it has long been the practice to use *density*, which is defined as log $1/T$, or log $100/T$ if T is expressed as percentage transmittance or reflectance. The logarithms used are all in cases to the base 10, so that a difference in log exposure of one unit, for instance, represents a tenfold change in exposure, and a transmittance of one per cent, for example, is equivalent to a density of 2.0.

It is customary to plot density against log exposure to represent the tone-reproduction characteristics of photographic materials and the curves thus obtained are known as the *characteristic curves*, or *H and D curves*, after Hurter and Driffield, who first used this form of representation. The slope of the characteristic curve is related to the visual *contrast* of the image, and the slope of the straight line tangential to a straight part of a characteristic curve is known as the *gamma* (γ). In a photographic system involving more than one material, the overall gamma of the system is approximately equal to the product of the gammas of the individual parts, but the exact relationships are affected by flare and stray-light considerations.

12.13 Densitometers

Much ingenuity has been expended on the design of instruments for measuring density, and many different types have emerged. But modern instruments are usually in one of the three forms shown in Fig. 12.3. The top type represents a simple visual instrument; the middle type, a photo-electric instrument, working on the substitution principle; and the bottom type, a direct-reading photo-electric instrument.

In the visual instrument, beams from the transmission and comparison lamps are arranged to illuminate the two halves of a comparison field. (When reflection samples are measured, the two reflection lamps are used instead of

---

Plate 7. Colour derivation. By using masks of high contrast and varying their sharpness in a process where the three images can be handled separately, results can be obtained which resemble paintings although only photographic techniques are used. In this case the reproduction has been made from an Ektachrome transparency using the Kodak Dye Transfer Process. The technique was pioneered by R. M. Evans.

the transmission lamp.) The sample is then put in one beam, and the position of a continuously varying neutral wedge, situated in the other beam, is adjusted until the two halves of the field appear to match. The density of the sample is then related to the position of the wedge, which can be read by means of an appropriate scale mounted with it. Any lack of symmetry in the two beams can be allowed for by moving the transmission lamp (or the reflection lamps) so that with a sample of zero density in the instrument a reading of zero is obtained on the wedge, a procedure known as *zeroing*. When a reflection sample is being measured, the zeroing should, in theory, be carried out using a perfect diffuser: a surface of freshly smoked magnesium oxide is a good approximation to a perfect diffuser, but because of its fragility specially calibrated white tiles are often used instead.

Visual densitometers are usually simple, fairly inexpensive, and contain little that can go wrong, but they have three disadvantages. First, accurate visual matching is a tiring occupation and fatigue soon sets in if there is much work to do. Secondly, the time taken to make a large number of observations is rather long. Thirdly, the precision obtainable is sometimes less than desirable in the arrangement of Fig. 12.3(a) it is clear that the higher the density of the sample, the lower will be the luminance of the matching field and hence the worse the precision of matching; the only way to work at constant luminance would be to put the wedge into the same beam as the sample and to adjust it so that the combined density was always equal to some very large fixed density in the other beam; but this is very wasteful of light, with the result that rather low luminance, and hence low precision, usually results for low densities as well as for high densities.

However, when photo-electric cells are used, the sensitivity problems are usually greatly eased, and this method of working becomes possible, as shown in Fig. 12.3(b). One beam of light from the lamp passes through the wedge and the sample on to the photocell; the other beam passes through the zeroing wedge (which is used for zeroing and for providing a density similar to that of the wedge and sample), and then on to the photocell by means of an intermittent device such as a rotating sector mirror, which intersects the first beam. If the illuminance on the photocell provided by the two beams is different, as the sector rotates, a variation in current will be produced which can be amplified as an a.c. signal; but if the two beams provide equal illuminances on the photocell no a.c. current will be produced. The wedge is adjusted in position, either manually or by means of a servo-mechanism, until no a.c. current is produced, and the density of the sample can then be read from the position of the wedge (Hercock and Sheldrick, 1956; Neale 1956; Harvey, 1956). Substitution photo-electric densitometers of this type are usually easy to use, and give quick and accurate results; they are, however, more complicated and more expensive than visual instruments, and, in common with visual instruments, they depend for their accuracy on the calibration and constancy of their measuring wedges.

The third type of densitometer is a rather simpler photo-electric instrument, as shown in Fig. 12.3(c). Light from the lamp passes through the sample and on to a photocell, the output of which is amplified and then measured on an electric meter. Clearly this is a very simple arrangement, but it is usually advisable to add a sector to chop the light, so that the photo-cell produces an a.c. signal, which is easier to amplify than a d.c. signal. It is also necessary for either the meter or the amplifier to have a logarithmic output so that

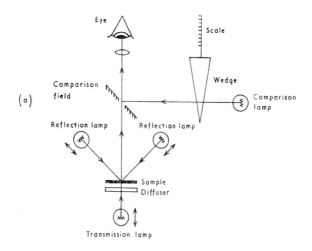

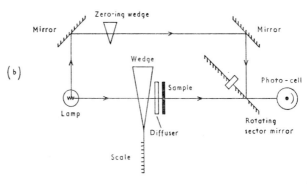

Fig. 12.3. Arrangements for three different types of densitometer: (a) visual instrument; (b) substitution type of photo-electric instrument; (c) direct-reading photo-electric instrument.

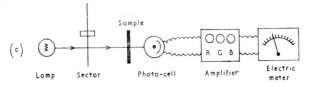

a linear scale of density, and not transmittance, results. This third type of densitometer is particularly useful for colour work, because the zeroing adjustment can conveniently consist of a gain control in the amplifier, and this can be triplicated so that three zeros, R, G, B, for reading through red, green, and blue filters can be set up simultaneously, thus enabling the three density readings to be made in succession on each area of the material without having to move it from the measuring position; alternatively zeroing can be carried out by means of three separate aperture adjustments mounted with the red, green, and blue filters. Densitometers of this type depend for their accuracy on the characteristics of the amplifier and meter, but one advantage of this is that all three readings are dealt with similarly, whereas in instruments using wedges any slight lack of neutrality in the wedge has different effects on the three readings. Commercially available densitometers of this type include the Eastman Electronic Densitometer Type 31A (MacLeish, 1953), the MacBeth Quantalog Colour Densitometers, the Baldwin Colour Densitometer, and the Photo-Laboratories Densitometer (*Photo Finisher*, 1966). Some of these instruments can measure both transmission and reflection densities, but others are designed specially for one or the other (Watt, 1956).

12.14 Specular and diffuse densities

Black-and-white densities composed of the usual photographic silver deposits not only absorb, but also scatter the light, and therefore the exact density of a silver image depends on the geometry of the illuminating and viewing optics (Powell, 1956). In Fig. 12.4 are illustrated some practical situations which are affected by this phenomenon. In Fig. 12.4(a) the situation for projection, or enlargement without any diffusion, is shown: most of the light which is scattered by the film will be lost, and the image has the highest possible density, termed *specular density*. In Fig. 12.4(b) a diffuser has been added to the enlarger, and now some of the light which leaves the diffuser at oblique angles, and which would therefore normally miss the objective lens, will be scattered by the image into it, and the density is thus reduced. Since the amount of diffusion tends to decrease with density and must clearly be zero with no sample in the beam, the effect of the diffusion is to lower contrast rather than just to reduce density all over; this reduced type of density is termed *diffuse density*. In Fig. 12.4(c) the situation obtaining when a film is viewed on an illuminated opal is shown, and since the geometry is rather similar to that of Fig. 12.4(b) the density is once again diffuse. In Fig. 12.4(d) a rather different situation is shown: here a directional source is used, so one might expect the density to be specular; but the receiver, in this case a piece of paper or a print film being printed by contact, picks up all the light and hence the diffused light is not lost: it can be shown in fact that the densities in cases (c) and (d) are very similar so that once again the density is diffuse. Finally in Fig. 12.4(e) contact printing by means of a diffuse source is used so that both the illuminating and 'viewing' are diffuse, a situation giving densities a little higher than diffuse, but not as high as specular, and termed *doubly-diffuse density*.

Standards have been drawn up defining the geometry of the illuminating and viewing arrangements for specular, diffuse, and doubly-diffuse densitometry (American Standards Association, 1959) but practical conditions may not exactly duplicate any of the three standards, so that calibration of images in their practical environments is necessary for the highest accuracy with silver images. With the dye-images of colour photographic materials the diffu-

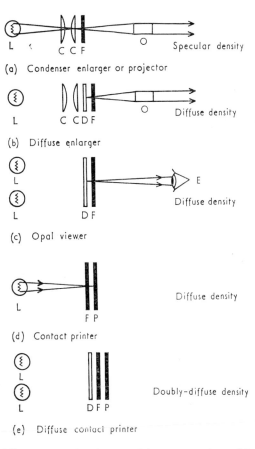

Fig. 12.4. Five different types of optical conditions commonly used in photography, together with the type of density to which each approximates. L = lamp. C = condenser lens. F = film. O = objective lens. D = diffuser. E = eye. P = printing paper or film.

sion is generally quite low, so that the effects of illuminating and viewing geometry are fairly small; diffuse density is therefore generally used for colour materials even when they are intended for enlarging or projecting without diffusion: it should be remembered, however, that in these conditions the practical densities may be a little higher than those measured.

In Fig. 12.3(a) and (b) the sample is illuminated diffusely and viewed specularly; in Fig. 12.3(c) the sample is illuminated specularly and viewed diffusely; thus in both cases diffuse-density is read. The specular beams in these instruments are usually confined to within about $\pm 10°$ from the optical axis; diffuse illumination is usually provided by an opal glass, and diffuse collection (as in Fig. 12.3(c)) by placing the photocell close to the sample.

12.15 Printing densities

When the transmission or reflection densities of black-and-white silver images are measured, it is ideal to illuminate the samples with light having a spectral energy distribution similar to that used in the practical situation, and to use a detector having a spectral sensitivity similar to that of the detector normally used with the material. However, silver images are usually fairly non-selective, so that it is often possible to use almost *any* light source and detector. The only serious exception to this in practice arises when a yellowish silver image is to be printed on an unsensitized printing material; in this case the visual density, or that recorded photo-electrically with a broad spectral band, gives results of lower density than that 'seen' by the print-material, and a detector whose spectral sensitivity approximates that of the print material (having sensitivity only in the blue and ultra-violet parts of the spectrum) has to be used: densities measured in this way are known as *printing densities*, or sometimes *actinic densities*.

When densities are measured on colour films whose function is to be printed on to other colour films or papers, then once again printing densities have to be measured; but this time, because the three layers of the colour print material have three different spectral sensitivities, three printing densities have to be measured. The simplest way of doing this is to measure the densities through three filters whose spectral transmissions, when combined with the spectral sensitivity of the detector, simulate the effective spectral sensitivities of the three layers. An exact match in sensitivity at all wavelengths is usually very difficult to achieve, and is unnecessary in practice: the main consideration is that the three contrasts measured by the densitometer should be similar to those 'seen' by the print-material. The densitometer curves (full lines) of Fig. 12.5(c) were obtained by multiplying, wavelength by wavelength, the spectral energy distribution of the source (as seen through any heat-absorbing or other filters) by the spectral sensitivity of the detector to obtain the relative response curve of Fig. 12.5(a), and then multiplying at each wavelength by the spectral transmittances of the filters whose spectral density curves are given in Fig. 12.5(b). These filters are widely used for evaluating both motion-picture

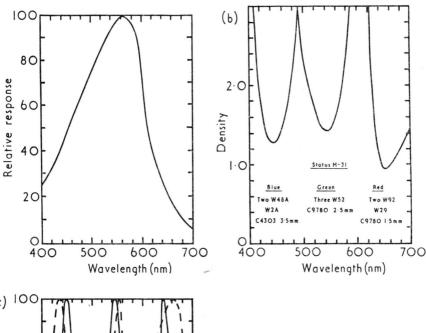

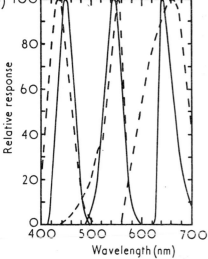

Fig. 12.5. (a) Relative spectral response of Eastman Electronic Densitometer Type 31A, obtained by multiplying at each wavelength the spectral lamp output (as seen through its optical system) by the spectral sensitivity of its detector. (b) Spectral densities of Status M-31 red, green, and blue filters. W = Wratten gelatin filters. C = Corning glass filters. (c) Full line: relative response of the densitometer through the Status M-31 filters. Broken line: relative sensitivities of the three layers of a typical colour photographic print material. (Note: the filter curves in (b) are broader than the densitometer response curves in (c) because the density scale of the former is logarithmic, but the response scale of the latter is linear.)

and still colour negative films and are known as Status M-31 filters (Miller and Powers, 1963). Although, strictly speaking, these filters should only be used with instruments having the spectral response curve shown in Fig. 12.5(a), each filter transmits a sufficiently narrow band of light for their use with instruments having somewhat different spectral responses to make only small differences to the results.

Since films are usually illuminated with white light when they are being printed, the colour filters in a densitometer should ideally be placed *after* the white light has passed through the sample; if this is done, and if the spectral energy distributions of the white light in the densitometer and in the printer are similar, the correct density readings should be recorded even if the sample fluoresces or scatters to different extents at different wavelengths (assuming that the geometry of the densitometer results in densities of the correct diffusion being read). In practice, however, as far as films are concerned, fluorescence is very unlikely and scattering is low, so that the filters can usually be either before or after the sample, and the spectral energy curve of the light source (as seen through any filters used) and the spectral sensitivity curve of the detector can be lumped together in a single response curve as has been done in Fig. 12.5(a). (With reflection prints, however, fluorescence may occur.)

Printing densities are nearly always used for colour negative films. In materials incorporating coloured couplers, such as Kodacolor negative film and Eastman Colour Negative film, the printing densities have quite high minimum values because of the absorption of green and blue light by the coloured couplers. Typical sets of curves, showing printing densities plotted against log exposure, for materials incorporating coloured couplers are shown in Fig. 12.6. The films intended for camera use generally have gammas of about 0.65 as shown in Figs. 12.6(a) and (b); the curves of the two films represented in these figures are similar except that those for films intended for amateur use (Fig. 12.6(b)) are longer than those intended for professional use (Fig. 12.6(a)) so as to provide the larger margin for error in exposure level (good *exposure latitude*) desirable in a product intended for amateur snapshots. Fig. 12.6(c) shows curves representative of an intermediate film (such as Eastman Colour Intermediate film) with a gamma closely equal to 1.0 so that when Eastman Colour Negative is printed on to it a positive of gamma 0.65 is obtained, which when printed on to the Intermediate film again (as shown in Fig. 10.7(c)) yields a duplicate negative of gamma 0.65. In Fig. 12.7 the characteristic curves of a reversal film are shown, and since in reversal films high exposures give low densities the curves now slope downwards, instead of upwards as is the case for negative materials. The curves of Fig. 12.7 relate to the type of reversal film (such as Ektachrome Commercial film) whose primary purpose is to serve as an original for making duplicates: this film therefore has fairly straight characteristic curves and a contrast of about 1.0.

Films of the type shown in Fig. 12.7 are usually printed either on to an inter-negative film having a contrast of about 0.65 with characteristic curves

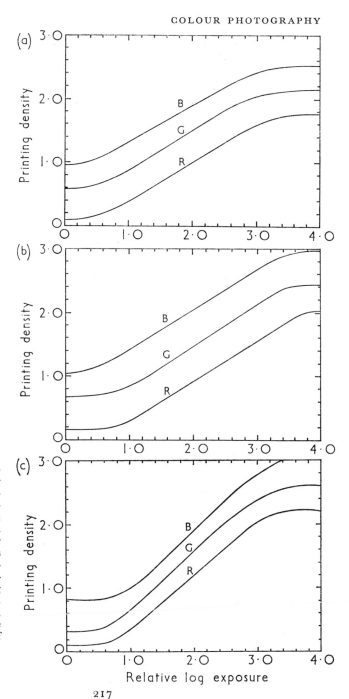

Fig. 12.6. Typical characteristic curves for colour negative films: (a) for professional use (such as Eastman Colour Negative); (b) for amateur use (such as Kodacolor); (c) for intermediate use (such as Eastman Colour Intermediate). Printing densities are plotted against log exposure for each colour. The high blue and green minimum densities are caused by the colours of the coloured couplers.

similar to those shown in Fig. 12.6(a), or on to a reversal film with characteristic curves suitable for producing pictures for projection (to be discussed in the next section).

12.16 Integral densities

The Status M filters used for measuring colour printing densities are rather dense, and for general use one of the two sets of red, green, and blue filters whose spectral density curves are shown in Fig. 12.8 is often employed; these sets of filters are sometimes referred to as Status A-31 (figure 5 of Brewer, Goddard, and Powers, 1955) and Status D-31, the latter set consisting of Wratten Filters, numbers 92, 93, and 94 (Miller and Powers, 1963). One problem with the

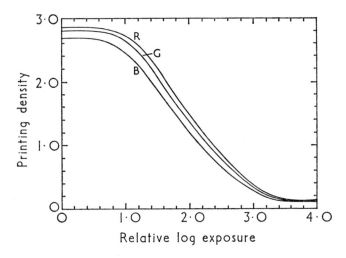

Fig. 12.7. Typical characteristic curves for a reversal film (such as Ektachrome Commercial film) designed primarily as an original for making duplicates.

use of gelatin filters, such as the Status D-31 set, is that they all tend to transmit very freely in the far-red and infra-red parts of the spectrum, and, since this is also true of the image-dyes used in colour photography, even a very small sensitivity of the photo-cell in this spectral region can completely falsify the results. It is therefore *essential* to absorb all the far-red and infra-red light with glass or interference filters (this is the function of the glass components in the A-31 and M-31 sets of filters). Absorption of the infra-red and far-red light is also advisable in colour tele-cine equipment: in this case the sensitivity of the photo-electric devices used is frequently greater than that of the eye in these regions of the spectrum and differences in the infra-red and far-red transmission of different types of film may then produce gross differences in colour balance and red-image contrast (Kozanowski, 1964).

Arbitrary sets of filters such as sets A-31 and D-31, do not generate spectral response curves corresponding to any specific application, but they are entirely satisfactory for tests where comparison of the results is restricted to any one set of image dyes. For general control and test work on individual colour products they are therefore quite suitable. The densities which they read are generally referred to as *integral densities* because each filter measures the total (or integrated) effect of the absorptions of all the dyes having any density in its spectral transmission band.

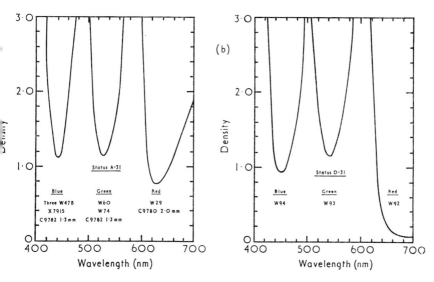

Fig. 12.8. Spectral density curves of filters typical of those used for measuring Integral Densities: (a) Status A-31; (b) Status D-31. W = Wratten gelatin filter. C = Corning glass filter. X = Experimental gelatin filter.

The colour corresponding to equal values of red, green, and blue integral densities is generally nearly grey for most practical illuminants, and for most colour photographic materials; but exact equality of densities does not necessarily correspond exactly to a grey for *any* illuminant, and it would be unlikely so to correspond for a *particular* illuminant used in practice, unless the filters were specially chosen to fulfil this condition for the particular dye-set and illuminant involved.

In Fig. 12.9 are shown typical sets of characteristic curves of red, green, and blue integral density plotted against log exposure for a reversal (a) and two print (b) and (c) materials, when the colour of the exposing light is such that most exposure levels are reproduced so as to appear grey in the viewing conditions typical of those used in practice for each material. When the viewing conditions consist of projection by tungsten light in a darkened room, the light from the projector appears yellowish (Hunt, 1965), and therefore to obtain results which appear grey the reproduction on the film has to be slightly bluish; this is why the curves of Fig. 12.9(a), which relate to materials intended for tungsten-light projection, are not even approximately coincident, the blue densities being lower than, and the red densities higher than, the green densities, in order to produce the bluish result required. The curves of Fig. 12.9(b) refer to a material intended for projection by arc-light, and since this is a whiter source than a tungsten lamp, the curves are now approximately coincident, and the greys are reproduced approximately grey on the film. The curves of Fig. 12.9(c) refer to a reflection print material, and again the curves are approximately coincident, and greys are reproduced as near-greys on the paper.

It will be noticed that the curves of Figs. 12.9(a), (b), and (c) are not straight: in addition to the usual 'toe' and 'shoulder' regions at the lowest and highest density levels respectively, the curves exhibit gradually increasing contrast as the densities increase. It is found that these changes in contrast produce more pleasant pictures than are obtained on materials with straight characteristic curves: the high contrast at high density improves the visibility of shadow detail by helping to offset the effect of flare in the camera and in the viewing situation, while the lower contrast at low density prevents 'harshness' in light subject-matter and increases the permissible margin for error in achieving the correct exposure level.

For the reversal film of Fig. 12.9(a) intended for projection in a dark room, the contrast at a density level of 1.0 (corresponding roughly to a medium grey) is about 1.4, and this is found in practice (for black-and-white as well as for colour (Clark, 1953)) to result in pleasing pictures: a contrast of 1.0 is too low because dark areas then appear too light as a result of the lightening effect of the dark surround (Bartleson and Breneman, 1966). The curves of Fig. 12.9(b) refer to a colour print film intended for use with a negative film of contrast about 0.65; the contrast at density 1.0 is therefore much higher, in this case about 2.4, so that the combination yields the required result, which in this case is about 1.6 at density 1.0; this is higher than that for the reversal film shown in Fig. 12.9(a) because this negative-positive system is designed specially for professional motion-picture use, where it is usually possible to keep the lighting-contrast fairly low; and the combination of low lighting-contrast and high photographic-contrast results in a useful gain in colour saturation.

In Fig. 12.9(c) similar curves are shown for a colour paper designed for making reflection prints from a low contrast negative film. A medium grey in a reflection print is usually reproduced at a density of about 0.5, and the contrast of the paper at this level is about 1.6, which, when combined with the negative contrast of 0.65 yields an overall contrast of about 1.0; this figure

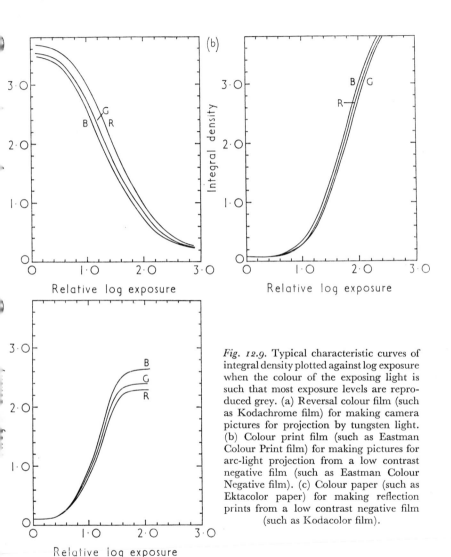

Fig. 12.9. Typical characteristic curves of integral density plotted against log exposure when the colour of the exposing light is such that most exposure levels are reproduced grey. (a) Reversal colour film (such as Kodachrome film) for making camera pictures for projection by tungsten light. (b) Colour print film (such as Eastman Colour Print film) for making pictures for arc-light projection from a low contrast negative film (such as Eastman Colour Negative film). (c) Colour paper (such as Ektacolor paper) for making reflection prints from a low contrast negative film (such as Kodacolor film).

is lower than that of transparency systems because the dark areas are not (usually) lightened by a dark surround (Bartleson and Breneman, 1966).

The changes in contrast with density which occur in films of the type depicted in Fig. 12.9(a) should be corrected if they are to be employed, not for projection, but as originals from which duplicate transparencies or reflection prints are to be made, using materials having the same type of contrast variations; if correction is not made, the contrast changes occur twice in the system and the shadows are too contrasty and the high-lights too flat. Fig. 12.10 shows curves for an inter-negative film which provides the correction necessary when a negative, made from a transparency with curves as in Fig. 12.9(a), is to be printed on to a paper with curves as in Fig. 12.9(c). The contrast varies from about 0.3 in the region where transparency shadows are recorded, up to about 1.0 where the transparency highlights are recorded, so that a negative of contrast about 0.65 can be produced from a transparency with contrast varying from over 2.0 in the shadows to only about 0.65 in the high-lights.

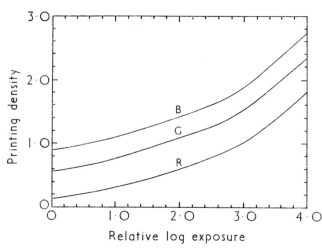

Fig. 12.10. Characteristic curves of an inter-negative film, with contrast increasing with exposure level so as to counteract the contrast variation in films of the type shown in Fig. 12.9(a).

12.17 Some effects of curve shape

One of the principal uses of densitometry is to record the shape of the density versus log-exposure curve for the purpose of seeing how the tone reproduction varies with density level. A full evaluation, however, requires the inclusion of proper allowances for camera flare and viewing flare for these are nearly always different, respectively, from sensitometric flare, and stray light in the densitometer; and if the system under study includes any printing stages, whether by contact or by projection, the effect of the printing flare must also be included.

In colour photography a very important aspect of densitometric evaluations is the extent to which a grey scale is reproduced as grey at all densities, and integral and printing densities are widely used for assessing this.

The fact that photographic characteristic curves are never straight at all densities introduces a complication which is illustrated in Fig. 12.11. Suppose for simplicity that, for some reversal colour film and its usual exposing illuminant, the integral densities are such that a scale of greys in its usual viewing illumination is represented by the three curves lying on top of one another, as shown in Fig. 12.11(a). If this film is then exposed in a light of different colour, say a bluer colour, a result similar to that shown in Fig. 12.11(b) might be obtained, the blue curve having shifted along the log exposure axis relative to the other two. This condition can be corrected by placing a yellow filter over the camera lens to give the result in Fig. 12.11(c) in which the blue curve has been moved along the log exposure axis and the three curves are once again superimposed; but it cannot be corrected by placing a yellow filter over the lens of the projector (or over the transparency itself)

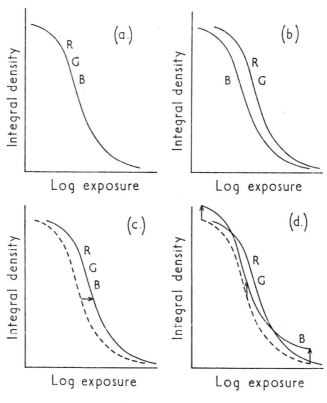

Fig. 12.11 The characteristic curves of a typical reversal film (a) when exposed to light of the correct colour; (b) when exposed to light of a bluer colour; (c) when the blue exposing light is corrected by placing a yellow filter over the camera lens; (d) when attempting unsuccessfully to correct the blue exposing light by placing the yellow filter over the projection lens or over the transparency.

223

because this moves the blue curve, not horizontally along the log-exposure axis, but vertically along the density axis as shown in Fig. 12.11 (d). If the curves were straight, then either vertical or horizontal shifts could be used to super-impose the curves, but, because of the curvature, the vertical shift causes over-correction at low densities and under-correction at higher densities (with over-correction at very high densities, although this is usually of no importance in reversal films); the consequent shift in colour balance, from yellow through grey to blue, results in very unpleasant picture quality. It is for this reason that when a reversal film is used in an illuminant other than that for which it is designed, a correcting filter should be used over the *camera* lens if the best results are to be obtained. Conversely, films with straight characteristic curves should be used if it is known that a wide range of taking-illuminant colour must be accommodated without the possibility of using corrective filters over the camera lens; for with films having straight characteristic curves correction can be achieved by viewing them through correcting filters. It is interesting also to note that in these cases a considerable measure of correction can also be supplied by the eye adapting to the overall colour of the pictures, and this correction is extremely rapid, as illustrated by the ease with which observers discount the colour of the resultant screen illuminant in the two-colour projections demonstrated by Land (Land, 1959). But, if the characteristic curves of the film are not straight, the colour bias varies with density level and does not have the character of an illuminant change *in the picture*, and there-fore cannot be discounted visually to the same extent.

12.18 Colorimetric densities

When comparison of results involving more than one set of image dyes is necessary colorimetric measurements have to be made, and these can be carried out on a densitometer if it is fitted with suitable filters. Thus if the combination of the spectral energy distribution of the densitometer lamp (with any filters being used), the spectral transmittances of the three measuring filters, and the spectral sensitivity of the detector, were such as to duplicate the distribution curves

$$E_{A\lambda}\bar{x}_\lambda \qquad E_{A\lambda}\bar{y}_\lambda \qquad E_{A\lambda}\bar{z}_\lambda$$

where $E_{A\lambda}$ represents the spectral energy distribution of standard illuminant A, then the three densities measured would be equal to:

$$\log (1/X_A)+k_x \qquad \log (1/Y_A)+k_y \qquad \log(1/Z_A)+k_z$$

where k_x, k_y, and k_z, are zeroing constants, and X_A, Y_A, and Z_A are the tristimulus values in the C.I.E. XYZ system when the sample is illuminated with standard illuminant A. Other functions can be used similarly: thus if the densitometer duplicated the distribution curves

$$E_{c\lambda}\bar{u}_\lambda \qquad E_{c\lambda}\bar{v}_\lambda \qquad E_{c\lambda}\bar{w}_\lambda$$

where $E_{c\lambda}$ represents the spectral energy distribution of standard illuminant C, then the three densities measured would be equal to:

$$\log{(1/U_c)}+k_u \qquad \log{(1/V_c)}+k_v \qquad \log{(1/W_c)}+k_w$$

where k_u, k_v, k_w are zeroing constants and U_c, V_c, W_c are the tristimulus values for Standard Illuminant in the C.I.E. UVW system. Readings of these types are known as *colorimetric densities*.

Colorimetric densities enable samples of different dye sets to be compared, and when the tristimulus values derived from them are in the same ratio as those for the illuminant being considered, then the sample is exactly grey whatever set of image dyes is being used. This is also true of densitometers which duplicate any linear combination of distribution curves, and such instruments can also be used to detect metameric pairs composed of different dye sets, and their results can be converted to standard colorimetric systems (for the same illuminants) by linear transformations.

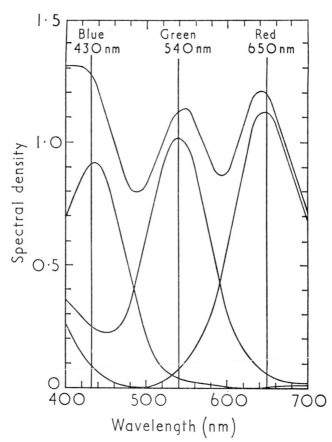

Fig. 12.12. Spectral density curve for a grey which is neutral to 4000°K light, together with the spectral density curves of the three dyes of which it is formed in a typical colour film. The three vertical lines indicate wavelengths which would be suitable to use for measuring spectral densities on such a film.

12.19 Spectral densities

If integral densities are measured using filters transmitting such a narrow band of wavelengths that the evaluation takes place effectively at one wavelength only for each of the red, green, and blue readings, the results are known as *spectral densities* or *monochromatic densities*. Such densities are important theoretically because for most dyes the transmission densities then become exactly *additive*: that is, the total red density of an image consisting of successive layers of cyan, magenta, and yellow dyes is equal to the sum of the red densities of the three dyes separately; and similar additivity occurs for the green densities, and for the blue densities. For most dyes, spectral transmission densities also obey a *proportionality rule*, in that, for any one dye, a given variation in the amount present alters all spectral densities by the same factor: thus if the red density is increased by 50 per cent, for instance, the green and blue densities will also be increased by 50 per cent.

12.20 Analytical densities

If the interest centres not so much on the total effect of the three dye images together, but on the contribution of each separately, then *analytical densities* are used. In the case of transmission densities these can be derived from *spectral* densities by solving three simultaneous equations. This is because, from the proportionality rule, it follows that, if the density of the cyan dye at the chosen red wavelength is C_R, then the densities at the green and blue wavelengths will be $k_1 C_R$ and $k_2 C_R$ where k_1 and k_2 are constants. Similarly if the magenta dye has density M_G at the green wavelength, then the other two densities will be $k_3 M_G$ and $k_4 M_G$; and if the yellow dye has density Y_B at the blue wavelength, the other two densities will be $k_5 Y_B$ and $k_6 Y_B$ where k_3, k_4, k_5, k_6 are constants. Because of the additivity property, the integral transmission spectral densities, I_R, I_G, I_B will therefore be equal to:

$$I_R = C_R + k_3 M_G + k_5 Y_B + r_s$$
$$I_G = k_1 C_R + M_G + k_6 Y_B + g_s$$
$$I_B = k_2 C_R + k_4 M_G + Y_B + b_s$$

where r_s, g_s, b_s are constants to allow for the presence of any constant 'stain' density which does not vary with the concentrations of the three image dyes. The above equations can be solved for the anlytical densities C_R, M_G, Y_B, if the constants are known. To find the values of the constants it is necessary to have available a sample of each dye on its own and to measure the ratios of the major absorption to the minor absorptions (Pinney and Voglesong, 1962) and thus find k_1, k_2, k_3, k_4, k_5, and k_6; r_s, g_s, and b_s are found by measuring a suitable area free of image dyes.

Fig. 12.12 shows a transmission spectral-density curve for a neutral grey typical of those in colour photographic films, together with the spectral density curves of the three individual dyes forming the neutral shown. Wavelengths suitable for measuring spectral densities on this material are shown, and it can be seen from the figure how the spectral integral densities are made up from the spectral analytical densities. It is often convenient to multiply the spectral analytical densities, C_R, M_G, Y_B by three factors so that when some chosen grey sample is measured, the modified spectral analytical densities have particular values. For instance, the chosen sample may be such that when viewed by an illuminant of colour temperature 4000°K it is exactly grey and has a visual density of 1.0 (in other words its tristimulus values are all exactly one-tenth of those of the 4000°K illuminant); the multiplying factors are then usually chosen so that the three spectral analytical densities are all equal to 1.0 for this sample. When this is done, equal values of the spectral analytical densities at other density levels also correspond quite closely to exact greys (under the same 4000°K illuminant) for most reasonable dye sets, and the density values then approximate to *equivalent neutral densities:* the equivalent neutral density of any particular amount of dye is defined as the visual density which results when the other two dyes are added in quantities just sufficient to produce a neutral grey.

It has been assumed throughout the above discussion that the analytical densities have been calculated from truly monochromatic integral densities. If, instead, the integral densities are measured through typical densitometer filters such as those shown in Fig. 12.8, the additivity and proportionality properties of the densities become only approximations, but the errors are not usually serious except for high densities; hence analytical densities are in fact usually obtained from non-spectral integral densities.

12.21 Integral reflection densities

All surfaces reflect some light from their topmost layers, and in the case of photographic reflection prints this light is unaffected by the image dyes; reflection densitometers are therefore usually designed so as to minimize the amount of this light picked up by the detector. Since most surfaces have some gloss, the detector is placed well away from the position corresponding to the mirror image of the light source (where the surface-reflection is at its maximum) and one of the two arrangements shown in Fig. 12.13 is generally used: either the light strikes the sample normally with the detector viewing it from 45°, or the light is incident at 45° with the detector viewing normally. In one instrument an ellipsoidal mirror collects light at 45° in all directions round the normal illuminating beam, thus giving a high efficiency (Watt, 1956). Like transmission densitometry, reflection densitometry is also the subject of standards: in these standards the two beams of light are confined to directions within ±5° of the nominal 45° and perpendicular directions (American Standards Association, 1958). The insides of reflection densitometers are usually very thoroughly blackened in order to prevent stray light from limiting the maximum densities which can be read.

12.22 Analytical reflection densities

Because of the effects of multiple reflections of the light between the diffusing base and the under-side of the top-most layer of reflection print materials, the additivity and proportionality properties of dyes do not apply even to monochromatic integral reflection densities. Analytical reflection densities can, however, be determined by using a calibration curve to convert from integral reflection to integral transmission density, then calculating the analytical transmission density, and finally using the calibrating curve again to convert from transmission analytical to reflection analytical density (Pinney and

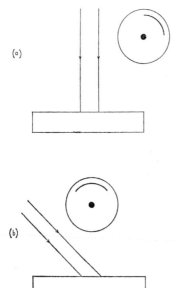

(a)

(b)

Fig. 12.13. Two alternative arrangements which can be used for reflection densitometry.

Voglesong, 1962). At high densities the calibration curve depends on the surface gloss of the sample and the stray-light behaviour of the reflection densitometer used for the measurements, but a typical curve is shown in Fig. 12.14. At low densities, multiple internal reflections cause reflection density to increase rapidly with transmission density; at medium densities, multiple internal reflections become progressively less important as the density increases, so that the rate of change of reflection density with respect to transmission density approaches the value of 2.0 (or 2.13 if one of the beams is incident on the layer at 45° and the other at 90° (Williams and Clapper, 1953)) which would be expected on account of the light having to pass twice through the layer in a reflection material. But at high densities the surface-reflection becomes more and more important so that the rate of change drops below 2.0, and finally flattens out to a maximum value which is usually well below twice the maximum transmission value (see Section 11.8).

For reflection densities between about 0.8 and 1.8 the curve of Fig. 12.14 is often approximately linear, and, for densities within this range, reflection analytical densities can be calculated to a good approximation by the same type of equations as are used for transmission work (described in Section 12.20), the constants in the equations then being evaluated specially for the reflection situation (Onley, 1960).

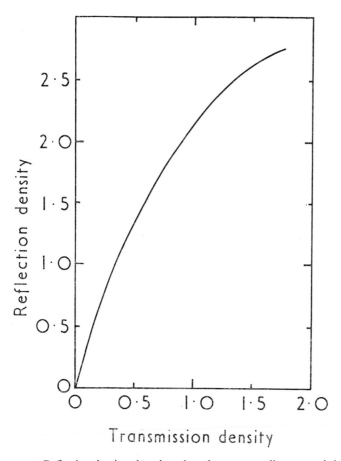

Fig. 12.14. Reflection density plotted against the corresponding transmission density of the image layer for a typical glossy paper and a reflection densitometer capable of reading high densities.

12.23 Exposure densities

When the performance of camera films is being considered, the log-exposures given to the red-, green-, and blue-sensitive layers by various parts of the scene (sometimes referred to as *actinic exposures*) are of considerable importance.

It is often convenient to consider these log exposures relative to those given by some standard type of object in the scene, such as a perfectly reflecting, perfectly diffusing white; differences in log exposure from those given by the standard are called *exposure densities*: thus an object giving a red log exposure of o.3 less than the standard, for instance, would have a red exposure density of o.3; an object having a green log exposure greater than the standard by o.1, say, would have a green exposure density of −o.1. If a reflection densitometer is fitted with filters so that its spectral sensitivities duplicate those of the film in question, then the exposure densities of reflection samples can be measured directly; otherwise, they can be calculated from a knowledge of the spectral characteristics of the light source, sample, and lens transmission colour. In neither case are the effects of atmospheric haze and lens-flare automatically allowed for; these may be important in some circumstances. so that it may be necessary to measure exposure densities in actual scenes or cameras using a photoelectric photometer or tele-photometer incorporating appropriate filters.

12.24 Scales of equal visual increments

One of the reasons for using scales of log exposure and density, instead of exposure and transmittance, is that the former scales represent more nearly uniform visual steps. It has been shown, however, that, for reflecting samples, a more uniform scale still is that of Munsell value, which is defined by the empirical formula

$$R = 1.2219V - 0.23111V^2 + 0.23951V^3 - 0.021009V^4 + 0.0008404V^5$$

where R is the reflectance and V is the Munsell value (Newhall, Nickerson, and Judd, 1943). In Fig. 12.15 Munsell value is plotted against reflection density (log $1/R$). It is clear that, as compared to the Munsell value scale, reflection density over-emphasizes high densities relative to low densities; and in reflection print work it is found in practice that a given density difference tends to be more important at low than at medium or high densities. It might, therefore, be more useful to plot Munsell value against log exposure for reflection materials; it would not be appropriate to use a Munsell value scale for the *exposure* axis, because original scenes usually include variations in illumination level over their area, and the eye is able to discount such variations to a considerable extent (Evans, 1943), whereas the Munsell value scale applies to conditions of uniform illumination.

With projected transparencies it is also found that a given density difference is more important visually at low than at medium or high densities, so that a scale more like the Munsell scale might be useful here as well.

The definition of Munsell value by the above formula is rather complicated, and for most applications the scale of W^*, which is given by $25Y^{\frac{1}{3}}-17$ (where Y is the percentage reflectance, see Section 7.6) can be used instead.

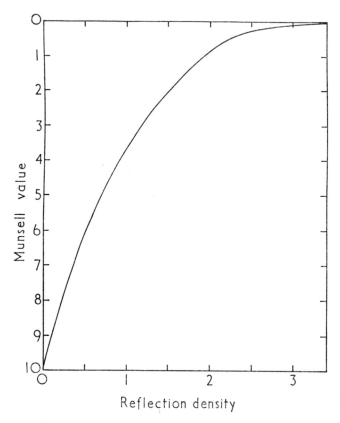

Fig. *12.15.* Munsell Value plotted against reflection density. (The reflection density is presumed to be measured against Magnesium Oxide as zero, but Munsell Value 10 refers to a perfect diffuser; taking the reflectance of Magnesium Oxide as 98 per cent, zero density thus corresponds to a Munsell Value of 9.90.)

12.25 Tri-linear plots

Colour balance is such an important variable in colour photography that it is often helpful to consider it separately from overall density level. This is often done by plotting density differences on triangular graph paper. An example of a *tri-linear plot* of this type is given in Fig. 14.1 where a green-red printing-density difference is plotted against a blue-red printing-density difference. Tri-linear plots are also used for integral, analytical, colorimetric, and exposure densities.

REFERENCES

American Standards Association, A.S.A. Standard PH2.17 (1958).
American Standards Association, A.S.A. Standard PH2.19 (1959).
Bartleson, C. J., and Breneman, E. J., private communication (1966).
Brewer, W. L., Goddard, M. C., and Powers, S. A., *J. Soc. Mot. Pic. Tel. Eng.*, **64**, 561 (1955).
British Standard 3824 : 1964, Specification for Colour Transmission of Photographic Lenses.
Clark, L. D., *J. Soc. Mot. Pic. Tel. Eng.*, **61**, 241 (1953).
Edgecombe, L. I., and Seeley, G. M., *J. Soc. Mot. Pic. Tel. Eng.*, **72**, 691 (1963).
Evans, R. M., *J. Opt. Soc. Amer.*, **33**, 579 (1943).
Harvey, E. A., *J. Phot. Sci.*, **4**, 130 (1956).
Hercock, R. J., and Sheldrick, G. E. A., *J. Phot. Sci.*, **4**, 113 (1956).
Hunt, R. W. G., *J. Opt. Soc. Amer.*, **55**, 1540 (1965).
Kozanowski, H. N., *J. Soc. Mot. Pic. Tel. Eng.*, **73**, 939 (1966).
Land, E. H., *Proc. Nat. Acad. Sci.*, **45**, 115 and 636 (1959).
MacLeish, K. G., *J. Soc. Mot. Pic. Tel. Eng.*, **60**, 696 (1953).
Marriage, A., *Science and Applications of Photography*, Royal Photographic Society, London, p. 220 (1955).
Miller, O. E., and Powers, S. A., *J. Soc. Mot. Pic. Tel. Eng.*, **72**, 695 (1963).
Neale, D. M., *J. Phot. Sci.*, **4**, 126 (1956).
Newhall, S. M., Nickerson, D., and Judd, D. B., *J. Opt. Soc. Amer.*, **33**, 385 (1943).
Onley, J. W., *J. Opt. Soc. Amer.*, **50**, 177 (1960).
Pinney, J. E., and Voglesong, W. F., *Phot. Sci. Eng.*, **6**, 367 (1962).
Photo Finisher, **3**, 69 (January, 1966).
Powell, P. G., *J. Phot. Sci.*, **4**, 120 (1956).
Watt, P. B., *J. Phot. Sci.*, **4**, 116 (1956).
Williams, F. C., and Clapper, F. R., *J. Opt. Soc. Amer.*, **43**, 595 (1953).
Williams, F. C., and Grum, F., *Phot. Sci. Eng.*, **4**, 113 (1960).

GENERAL REFERENCES

Brewer, W. L., Goddard, M. C., and Powers, S. A., *J. Soc. Mot. Pic. Tel. Eng.*, **64**, 561 (1965).
Duerr, H. H., *J. Soc. Mot. Pic. Tel. Eng.*, **54**, 653 (1950).
Evans, R. M., Hanson, W. T., and Brewer, W. L., *Principles of Colour Photography*, Wiley, New York (1953), Chapters XI, XII, and XIII.
Mees, C. E. K., and James, T. H., *The Theory of the Photographic Process*, 3rd Edition, Chapter 21, Macmillan, New York (1966).
Society of Motion Picture and Television Engineers, *Principles of Colour Sensitometry*, Society of Motion Picture and Television Engineers, New York (1963).
Syke, G., *J. Phot. Sci.*, **4**, 131 (1956).
Williams, F. C., *J. Opt. Soc. Amer.*, **40**, 104 (1950).
Williams, F. C., *J. Soc. Mot. Pic. Tel. Eng.*, **56**, 1 (1951).

CHAPTER 13

Masking and Coloured Couplers

1. Introduction – *2.* Contrast masking – *3.* Coloured couplers – *4.* Inter-image effects – *5.* Masking when making separations – *6.* Masking for exact colour reproduction – *7.* Masking for approximate colour reproduction – *8.* Calculation of mask contrasts – *9.* Simplified procedures – *10.* Special films for masking – *11.* Non-linear masks – *12.* Patches for setting up masking procedures

13.1 Introduction

IN earlier chapters we have seen that all forms of trichromatic colour reproduction introduce errors, and that such pictures do not therefore represent all the colours as they were in the original scene. But we have also seen that the mental standards by which colour in pictures is usually judged are rather imprecise, so that the tolerances are quite large, and, as a result, the errors are often unnoticeable. In certain circumstances, however, the errors can mount up to the point where they are very serious. This is particularly the case where a trichromatic colour reproduction is itself copied by trichromatic means; in particular, in the case of subtractive colour photographs, the unwanted absorptions of the cyan, magenta, and yellow dyes result in dark blues and greens, and in the copy these colours are darkened again, sometimes even to the point where the colour almost vanishes and gives way to black. Furthermore, in reflection prints, as was explained in Chapter 11, there is often a serious problem in accommodating the scene within the limited range of tones normally available on reflecting surfaces such as paper. To provide partial solutions to these problems, recourse is often had to a technique known as *masking;* the principles of masking will now be described, both in general terms and in the form of the use of *coloured couplers* which provide a particularly important method of masking. The analogous technique of *electronic masking* in colour television is discussed in Section 20.4.

13.2 Contrast masking

From 1944 to 1949, before the advent of coloured couplers, the Kodacolor system for amateur reflection prints used a negative having dye-image

233

contrasts of about 1.0, together with a high contrast paper; the high over-all contrast resulted in the system giving colours of high saturation. But the contrast was so high that severe loss of highlight and shadow detail would have been caused, but for the effect of an extra layer in the film which acted as a *mask*. This extra layer was developed in the colour negative as a low contrast positive black-and-white image. The effect of this was to cover light areas of the colour negative with dark deposits of silver, but to leave the dark areas unaltered. The overall contrast of the negative was thus reduced, but without any loss in the saturation of the colours in the negative because the three *colour* layers of the negative still operated at the same high contrasts. At the printing stage a slightly longer exposure was then given, thus enabling burnt-out highlights to be avoided, while the black-and-white mask image present in the negative prevented the shadow areas from becoming blocked up.

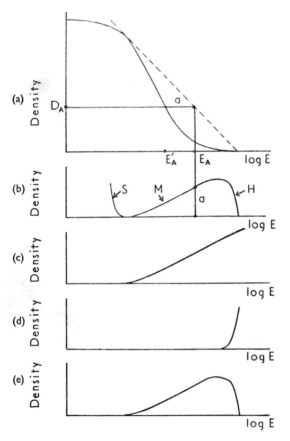

Fig. 13.1. Use of contrast correcting masks in reversal copying. Characteristic curves of (a) the copying material, (b) the ideal mask to correct it, (c) the nearest approximation to the ideal, using a single mask only, (d) the highlight mask required, and (e) the mask made from the original when the latter was bound up with the highlight mask.

The introduction of coloured couplers in the Kodacolor system enabled a lower overall contrast to be used, so that the black-and-white mask layer became unnecessary and was abandoned. But the principle involved is of wide interest, particularly when copies of colour photographs have to be made, as when, for instance, a colour print or a colour transparency has to be made from an existing colour transparency.

In Fig. 13.1 the problem is presented in graphical form for the case of making a duplicate transparency from an original transparency, both the original and the duplicate being positives. In Fig. 13.1(a) the characteristic curve (density plotted against log exposure) of a typical reversal colour photographic process is shown (full line). The slope of this curve at the higher densities is usually greater than 45° in order to obtain increased colour saturation and better rendering of shadows when projecting with typical levels of ambient lighting and projection-lens flare. But, if the tones of the original transparency are to be reproduced without distortion, a material of contrast 1.0 (characteristic curve at 45°) is required; this is shown by the broken line. Hence, if a material having the characteristic curve shown by the full line were used for making the copy the tones would be distorted. The object of contrast masking is to avoid this distortion. The method is to make a low contrast negative by contact-printing the original transparency on a suitable black-and-white plate or film. After processing, this negative, or mask as it is called, is bound up with the original transparency and reduces its contrast, much as did the masking layer in the old Kodacolor negative film.

In Fig. 13.1(b) the characteristic curve required by the mask in order to achieve complete tone correction is shown. This curve is constructed by plotting the horizontal distance a of the broken line from the full curve in Fig. 13.1(a), as a density in Fig. 13.1(b) against the log exposure on the broken line. The reason for this construction is that, since the exposure E_A should result in the density D_A (as indicated by the broken line) it is necessary to reduce the exposure to E_A' in order that the full curve should give the density D_A. This is achieved by arranging that all parts of the original which, unmasked, would print at E_A, when masked print at E_A'. Thus all these parts of the original require an increase in density a equal to the difference in exposure between E_A and E_A'. The same argument applies to all values of E_A, and hence the required characteristic curve for the mask is obtained by plotting a against E_A. This curve, shown in Fig. 13.1(b), exhibits first a positive, then a negative, and then another positive characteristic. The reason for this is not far to seek. The central portion of the full curve of Fig. 13.1(a) is of contrast higher than 1.0, and therefore requires negative masking in order to reduce the contrast. The toe and shoulder of the full curve of Fig. 13.1(a), however, are of contrasts lower than 1.0 and therefore require positive masking in order to increase the contrast.

There is no photographic material which has the characteristic shown in Fig. 13.1(b). But the function of the initial positive part, S, of the curve is to correct the tone rendering of the darkest shadow detail which is usually of little importance in the picture and therefore can remain uncorrected without much loss of quality. The negative part, M, of the curve can be obtained fairly easily from a suitable low contrast negative material, as shown in Fig. 13.1(c). A significant improvement usually results from using such a negative mask alone, ignoring both the positive portions S and H of the ideal mask. But such a mask results in a flattening of the highlights in the copy which sometimes robs it of much of the brilliance and sparkle of the original transparency. For certain subjects a marked improvement is therefore gained by making a mask having the positive portion H in addition to the negative portion M. This can only be done by using a rather more complicated procedure, which will be described in a moment, involving the use of a *highlight mask*. But when a highlight mask is not used, the flattening of the highlights in the copy can be reduced by over-exposing the mask, M, so that the highlights of the original transparency fall in the shoulder region of the characteristic curve of the mask material. In this way the highlights, although reduced in contrast by the low contrast of the copying material, are not appreciably *further* reduced in contrast by the mask, M. This technique of using a mask which *shoulders* is very useful. For full correction of the contrast of the highlights, however, a separate highlight mask may have to be made.

A highlight mask is made by contact printing the transparency on to a very high contrast black-and-white negative material (Fig. 13.1(d)) using an exposure sufficiently short for only the highlight detail to be recorded. This negative mask is then bound up with the transparency when the latter is used to make the negative mask on the material having the characteristic of Fig. 13.1(c). This mask, being a negative, reverses the negative curve of the highlight mask into a positive curve as shown in Fig. 13.1(e). Having made the negative mask in this way, the highlight mask is then discarded, and the mask having the characteristic of Fig. 13.1(e) is bound up in register with the original transparency, before it is printed on the material characterized by the full line of Fig. 13.1(a). This technique is somewhat laborious but in cases where copies of the highest quality are required it is well worth while.

As mentioned at the beginning of this chapter, in copies, the unwanted absorptions of the cyan and magenta dyes take their toll twice, and blues and greens are often badly darkened. Some reduction in this darkening can be achieved by making the negative mask, M, through a red, orange, or yellow filter; such a mask will have a greater density in areas of red, orange, or yellow, than in areas of green and blue, and hence, in the masked original, blues and greens are lightened relative to reds, oranges and yellows; thus, in the copy, the blues and greens are lighter than they would be if the negative mask had been made without a filter. This technique is often well-while adopting. In the old Kodacolor process the black-and-white mask layer was situated above the cyan and magenta layers, but below the yellow layer of the negative.

The mask layer was sensitive to blue light only, and hence by exposing it with white light through the base the unwanted blue absorptions of the cyan and magenta dyes were printed on to it; the mask was therefore equivalent to a low contrast positive image of the scene made through a yellow filter (Neblette, 1962).

Another useful feature often used in masking was first suggested by Yule (Yule, 1944). Exact registration of the mask when bound up with the original is obviously difficult, and if not perfectly achieved results in halos appearing around any well-defined edges. Yule suggested that the masks should be deliberately made *unsharp* by printing them with a thin spacer between the transparency and the mask material. This not only helps to obscure slight lack of registration of the masks, but also improves the reproduction of fine detail. A negative mask reduces contrast, but fine detail is seen more clearly if reproduced at high contrast; by having the mask unsharp the fine detail is not resolved by the mask and hence, when it is bound up with the original transparency, it does not reduce the contrast of fine detail, but only of large areas. An example of unsharp masking is given in Plate 13 (page 468).

The use of unsharp masks, highlight masks, and negative masks of contrast high enough to provide severe over-correction of tones, together with various other techniques, has enabled Evans (Evans, 1951) to obtain with the Kodak Dye Transfer system, reproductions which resemble paintings rather than photographs, although photographic techniques are used throughout. These reproductions have been called *Colour Derivations* and have aroused considerable interest. An example is shown in Plate 7 (page 208).

13.3 Coloured couplers

The black-and-white mask used in the old Kodacolor film enabled the saturation of colours to be increased by raising the contrast of the system without spoiling the tone reproduction, with some correction for the unwanted absorptions of the magenta and cyan dyes. However, a more elegant method of correcting for these unwanted absorptions was introduced in 1949 (1948 in the case of Ektacolor film for professional use): the colour-forming couplers were themselves coloured, and in such a way that, as a dye was formed, the transmission of light in the regions of unwanted absorption remained constant. The negatives now became orange in the unexposed areas. The use of these *coloured couplers* in colour negative films is very extensive, and the principles involved will now be described. A colour negative, consisting as it usually does of three superimposed negative dye-images, is dependent for its success on the ability of the three dyes to make the three negative images easily distinguishable; it is therefore most important that the three dyes absorb only in three well-separated parts of the spectrum. But, if cyan, magenta, and yellow dyes are used, their spectral transmission curves will be similar to those shown in Fig. 4.1, having unwanted absorptions in the green and blue parts of the spectrum. Unfortunately, this type of defect is not confined to cyan, magenta, and yellow dyes; almost all dyes have subsidiary absorptions on the short wavelength side of their main absorption band, so that even if the three dyes were an infra-red absorber, a magenta, and an ultra-violet absorber, for instance, the same difficulty is present. It is the virtue of coloured couplers that they overcome the effects of these unwanted absorptions in a remarkably elegant fashion (Hanson, 1950). The credit for their introduction must be shared by the Research Laboratories of the Eastman Kodak Company and the Ansco Corporation who filed the first patents on the subject on the very same day! In the case of the former company, Dr. W. T. Hanson conceived the idea from first principles, its successful realization coming only after intensive research; in the case of the latter company the fortuitous discovery of a coupler which happened to be coloured in a beneficial way led to the same discovery.

The principle on which coloured couplers work is shown diagrammatically in Fig. 13.2. Suppose that, in the colour negative, the magenta dye, at its maximum concentration, m, has red, green and blue transmittances of 100 per cent, 5 per cent, and 50 per cent respectively, as shown in Fig. 13.2(a) by line A. It is thus assumed, for the sake of simplicity, that it is an ideal magenta dye except for a uniform unwanted absorption in the blue. The lines, B, C, D, E, and F, show what the transmittances would be at concentrations $\frac{3}{4}m$, $\frac{1}{2}m$ $\frac{1}{4}m$, $\frac{1}{8}m$, and zero, respectively. It will be supposed that this magenta dye is formed by the colour-development of a suitable coupler in one of the layers of a colour film. Let the concentration of the coupler before development be c. Then the concentrations of the coupler remaining after producing the dye-concentrations A, B, C, D, E, and F will be: zero, $\frac{1}{4}c$, $\frac{1}{2}c$, $\frac{3}{4}c$, $\frac{7}{8}c$, and c respectively.

Suppose, now, that the coupler, instead of being colourless, was *yellow*, having red, green, and blue transmittances (at concentration c) of 100 per cent, 100 per cent, and 50 per cent, respectively. As it is colour developed to form the magenta dye, its yellow colour in the layer gradually becomes less and less as it is used up, and its transmission curves for the same levels A, B, C, D, E, and F discussed above would be as shown in Fig. 13.2(b). The full transmission curves for the layer are given by combining the appropriate pairs of curves from Fig. 13.2(a) and (b) and these are shown in Fig. 13.2(c). It is seen that the transmittance in the blue region remains constant. When there is no magenta dye, the coupler alone has a transmittance of 50 per cent; when all the coupler has been used, it no longer absorbs at all, but the magenta dye has a transmittance of 50 per cent. At all intermediate stages the blue transmittance of the coupler multiplied by the blue transmittance of the magenta dye is also equal to 50 per cent. (This is because if, at any intermediate stage, the fraction of coupler used is n, the transmittance of the coupler is $(50/100)^n$, and the transmittance of the dye is $(50/100)^{1-n}$, giving a transmittance of the combination of $(50/100)^n \times (50/100)^{1-n}$ which is equal to $50/100$.)

Clearly with this system, the effect of light on this layer results in variations in the green transmission of that layer, but has no effect on the values of the red and blue transmissions which are fixed at 100 per cent and 50 per cent respectively. The low value of the constant blue transmission can be easily compensated by doubling the blue content of the light used for printing. Thus, the magenta dye and its yellow coupler together form an arrangement by means of which only light in the green part of the spectrum is modulated; hence, from the photographic point of view, the unwanted blue absorption of the magenta dye has been eliminated.

A pink coupler, which forms a cyan dye in another layer, can similarly eliminate the effects of the unwanted green and blue absorptions of that dye.

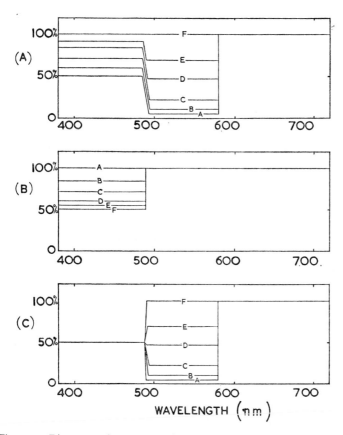

Fig. 13.2. Diagrammatic representation of the way in which a magenta-forming coloured coupler works. (a) Transmission curves of magenta dye at different concentrations. (b) Transmission curves of coloured coupler. (c) Combined transmission curves of the dye and the coupler.

The way in which this takes place is shown in Fig. 13.3. In Fig. 13.3(a), for the sake of simplicity, we have shown the transmission curves of a cyan dye which is ideal except for two uniform unwanted absorptions in the green and blue regions. The line A refers to the dye at maximum concentration, the red, green, and blue transmittances being 5 per cent, 30 per cent, and 40 per cent respectively. The other lines are analogous to those of Fig. 13.2(a). Suppose that the coupler is of a pink colour, having, at maximum concentration, red, green, and blue transmittances of 100 per cent, 30 per cent, and 40 per cent respectively, as shown in Fig. 13.3(b); when this coupler is present with the cyan dye which it forms on colour development, the red-sensitive layer will have the transmission curves shown in Fig. 13.3(c) for the different concentrations. Again it is seen that, where there were varying unwanted absorptions, they are now constant. Hence, by increasing the green content of the printing light by a factor of $3\frac{1}{3}$, and the blue by a factor of $2\frac{1}{2}$, the net result of the effect of light on this layer is merely to modulate the red transmission of the layer.

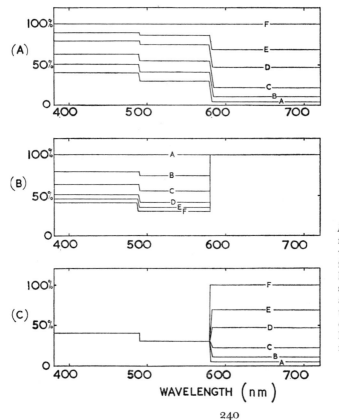

Fig. 13.3. Diagrammatic representation of the way in which a cyan-forming coloured coupler works. (a) Transmission curves of cyan dye at different concentrations. (b) Transmission curves of coloured coupler. (c) Combined transmission curves of the dye and the coupler.

When actual dyes and coloured couplers are used the transmissions shown as constant in Figs. 13.2(c) and 13.3(c) are only approximately constant, but this scarcely impairs the degree of improvement resulting. In fact, by allowing these transmissions to rise, by using couplers of deeper colours, the unwanted absorptions of the cyan and magenta dyes used in the print as well as those in the negative can also be, to some extent, compensated. Fig. 13.4 shows curves relating to an actual film; in this case the unwanted blue absorption of a magenta dye has been compensated by using a coloured coupler diluted with an uncoloured coupler. These types of curve can be replotted so as to allow for the increased printing exposure given in the regions of the spectrum where coloured couplers absorb, to obtain *equivalent-dyes* for each coloured coupler system (Sant, 1961; Watson, 1966).

The introduction of coloured couplers in colour photography was a major step forward in its technological development, and has resulted in the widespread use of colour negatives, not only for amateur reflection prints, but also for the production of professional motion pictures in colour, for which the positive prints are made either by a dye imbibition process such as Technicolor, or by direct printing on to three-layer colour positive stock.

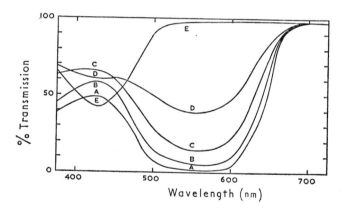

Fig. 13.4. Spectral transmission curves for a yellow coloured-coupler (curve E) and the magenta dye formed from a mixture of this coupler with an uncoloured coupler (curve A). Curves B, C, and D represent intermediate degrees of dye-forming reaction.

13.4 Inter-image effects

Coloured couplers can, unfortunately, only be used in materials designed to be printed or otherwise duplicated. The presence of the coloured couplers in light areas gives a pronounced orange cast, and the eye is not able to adapt sufficiently to compensate for it. For this reason coloured couplers have no application to normal reversal processes intended for viewing, and the brilliance of some of these is due, at least in part, to *inter-layer* or *inter-image* effects which have beneficial results not unlike those produced by coloured couplers (Hanson and Horton, 1952).

There are several ways of demonstrating the presence of inter-image effects, and some of these are illustrated for a reversal material in Fig. 13. In Fig. 13.5(a), by plotting the appropriate analytical density, a measure of the amount of cyan image dye present is shown. The curve N shows the amount of cyan dye present in a neutral scale which was produced by giving additive red, green, and blue exposures; the curve R shows the amount of cyan produced when the red exposure only was given. Because these curves are different it is clear that the presence or absence of exposure in the other two layers affects the amount of cyan dye produced: in this case there is less cyan in reds (curve R) than in neutrals (curve N) and hence the effect to lighten the reds. The effects of the other two layers on the magenta layer, and on the yellow layer, can be shown similarly.

In Fig. 13.5(b) the analytical densities for all three image-dyes are shown for the case where the red and blue layers have been given exposure scales and the green layer uniform exposures at different intensities. Any tilt in the curves M_1, M_2, M_3, M_4, representing the amount of magenta dye present, is the result of an inter-image effect, because the green exposure was uniform. (The curves C and Y may be slightly shifted along the log exposure axis by variation in M, but for the sake of simplicity multiple C and Y curves have not been drawn.) Similar sets of curves can be drawn for the cases where the red and the blue layers have the uniform exposures.

In Fig. 13.5(c) results similar to those of Fig. 13.5(b) are shown but this time two layers have uniform exposures and one layer has an exposure scale. Any tilts in the C and M curves indicate inter-image effects. Again, the curve Y may be shifted along the log exposure axis, but this is not shown. Similar sets of curves can be drawn for the cases where the green and the red layers have the exposure scales.

In Fig. 13.5(d) all three layers have been given exposure scales at two different exposure levels to give two neutral scales (curves C, M, Y, and curves C', M', Y', both sets represented as being superimposed for simplicity). A scale of reds is then exposed having blue and green exposures at the CMY level, but the red exposure at the C'M'Y' level. The resulting curves would be the same as M, Y, and C' if there were no inter-image effects, and inter-image effects are therefore shown up by any differences. Thus the cyan curve in the reds might be like R instead of like C' in which case the difference between the curves R and C' shows the amount of inter-image effect in the cyan image in this scale of reds.

If the results shown in Fig. 13.5(b) and (c) were plotted using *integral* densities instead of analytical densities, any absence of tilt in the approximately horizontal curves indicates either that there is no unwanted dye-absorption operating, and that there is no inter-image effect, or that if there is an unwanted dye-absorption it is being exactly off-set by an inter-image effect.

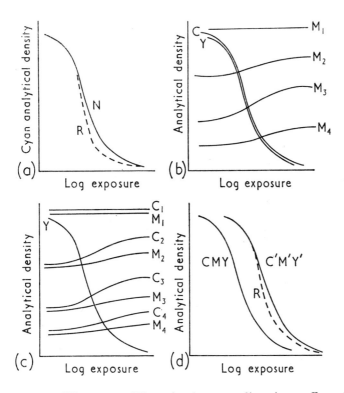

Fig. 13.5. Four different ways of illustrating the nature of inter-image effects which may be occurring.

13.5 Masking when making separations

In cases where coloured couplers cannot be used, some correction for the unwanted absorptions of cyan, magenta, and yellow dyes can be provided, as we have seen, by using contrast-masks exposed through suitable filters. But, in systems where the red, green, and blue records are available on separate negative or positive films, masking can in principle give full correction for unwanted absorptions, and also some correction for various other defects; this separate availability of the three records occurs most commonly when preparing half-tone printing surfaces in graphic-arts applications, but the principles involved are of wider interest and can have other applications.

For clarity, let us start with a simple example. Suppose we wish to correct for the unwanted absorptions of the magenta dye or ink used in a colour reproduction made from a transparency and that we are using a process in which three *separation negatives* are made from the transparency by printing or enlarging it through red, green, and blue filters, on to a suitable black-and-white film. If it were possible, in the final reproduction, to have an image provided by a perfect magenta dye, which had no unwanted absorptions, it would be invisible when viewed through blue and red filters. But images consisting of real magenta dyes, though nearly invisible when viewed through red filters, are visible as low contrast images when viewed through blue filters because of the unwanted blue absorption of magenta dyes. The real magenta dye image may therefore be thought of as consisting, approximately, of a full-contrast perfect magenta image, together with a low contrast unwanted 'yellow' image (giving the blue absorption). In most picture areas which are not white, all three dyes are present to some extent. It is therefore usually possible to reduce the *main* yellow dye image by an amount which is at every point in the picture equal to the low contrast unwanted 'yellow' image, and hence to overcome the effect of the unwanted blue absorption of the magenta dye. The practical procedure of such a scheme, when the original is a colour transparency, is as follows.

The colour transparency is printed on to a low contrast black-and-white film using green light for making the exposure. The mask so obtained is mainly a record of the magenta dye in the transparency, and is therefore also approximately a record of what the distribution of magenta dye will be in the final reproduction. The record, being a black-and-white negative, means that where the magenta dye is going to be heavy the mask is light, and *vice versa*. This mask is then bound up in register with the colour transparency. Its effect is to lighten areas which will be heavy in magenta, relative to those areas which will be light in magenta. Now, although the object of this mask is to overcome the unwanted absorption of the magenta dye, it is not used when the green separation negative is being made: it is only used when making the *blue* separation negative. (The reason for this is that since the unwanted absorption of the magenta dye is a blue absorption, it can only be corrected by reducing the *yellow* dye image appropriately, and hence the mask is used when making the blue separation negative, since it is from this negative that the yellow reproduction image is produced.) By having the mask over the transparency when the blue separation negative is being made, a low contrast positive image of what the magenta dye will be is added to its exposure. Hence when the positive yellow image is produced from this masked separation negative, there will be less yellow dye at points where the magenta dye will be heavy, but the normal amount of yellow where the magenta dye is absent. The same result can also be achieved by masking the separation negative rather than the transparency (although the mask must now be a positive image).

If the correct contrast is chosen for the mask, the effect of the unwanted absorption can be almost entirely cancelled out in this way. The correct contrast for this very simple case, in which only one unwanted absorption of one dye is being cancelled, is calculated as follows. If the density ratio of the unwanted blue to the wanted green absorption of the magenta dye or ink used in the reproduction is m_B/m, and the contrast of the final image is γ_m, then the contrast of the mask must be such that the main yellow image in the reproduction has superimposed upon it a negative image of contrast $(m_B/m)\gamma_m$. If the contrast of the main yellow image relative to the blue separation negative is γ_y, the contrast of the mask to be used with the blue separation negative must be $(m_B/m)(\gamma_m/\gamma_y)$; but if the mask is bound up with the transparency and used when making the blue separation negative, it must have a contrast of $(m_B/m)(\gamma_m/\gamma_y)/\gamma_B$, where γ_B is the contrast of the material on which the blue separation is made. The contrast of the film-process combination which should be used for making the mask depends, therefore, on how it is used; but it also depends upon how it is made: for if, instead of deriving it from the transparency using a green filter, it is made from the green separation negative, the contrast

Mask made from	Mask used with	Contrast of mask material	
		General case	Simple case
Transparency using green filter	Blue separation negative	$+\dfrac{(m_B/m)\,(\gamma_m/\gamma_y)}{\gamma_t}$	$+\dfrac{(m_B/m)}{\gamma_y}$
Transparency using green filter	Transparency when making blue separation negative	$-\dfrac{(m_B/m)\,(\gamma_m/\gamma_y)}{\gamma_t\gamma_B}$	$-(m_B/m)$
Green separation negative	Blue separation negative	$-\dfrac{(m_B/m)\,(\gamma_m/\gamma_y)}{\gamma_t\gamma_a}$	$\dfrac{(m_B/m)}{\gamma_y\gamma_a}$
Green separation negative	Transparency when making blue separation negative	$+\dfrac{(m_B/m)\,(\gamma_m/\gamma_y)}{\gamma_t\gamma_a\gamma_B}$	$+\dfrac{(m_B/m)}{\gamma_a}$

Fig. 13.6. Contrasts of mask materials required for correcting the unwanted blue absorption of a magenta dye, when the mask is used in various ways.

m_B/m = ratio of blue and green densities of magenta reproduction dye.

γ_m = contrast of magenta image in reproduction.

γ_y = contrast of yellow image in reproduction relative to that of the blue separation negative.

γ_t = contrast of green-filter image in the transparency.

γ_B = contrast of material on which the blue separation negative is made.

γ_a = contrast of material on which the green separation negative is made.

$+$ = reversal mask material (or successive negative-positive steps) required.

$-$ = negative mask material required.

245

required is altered. Fig. 13.6 shows the contrast which the mask *material* must have (in its process) in order to produce a mask having the correct contrast for various methods of working.

If the unwanted blue absorption of the magenta dye is the only unwanted absorption in the reproduction system, and the overall contrast of the reproduction is to be the same as that of the transparency, the above formula simplify because:

$$\gamma_B \gamma_y = 1$$
$$\gamma_G \gamma_m = 1$$
$$\gamma_t = \gamma_m$$

The corresponding values of the contrasts required by the mask material are listed in Fig. 13.6 under the column headed 'Simple Case'.

13.6 Masking for exact colour reproduction

Yule (Yule, 1938 and 1940) has investigated the possibilities of obtaining exact colour reproduction by means of masking. He concluded that exact duplication of a colour original composed of the *same dyes* as the reproduction was possible if six masks were used, provided that the dyes obeyed certain rules and that tone reproduction and colour balance were properly adjusted.

The rules which it is necessary, in Yule's theory, for the dyes to obey concern their properties when recorded on the separation negatives; or, if a densitometer is used which simulates the spectral sensitivities of the three filter-film combinations used for making the separation negatives, the rules can be formulated in terms of the *printing densities* measured on such an instrument. The rules have become known as the *Additivity and Proportionality Rules* and may be stated as follows:

Additivity Rule. The red printing-density of any mixture of the three dyes should be equal to the sum of the red printing-densities of the three dyes measured separately; and the same should be true of the green and blue printing-densities.

Proportionality Rule. When measured as printing-densities, the ratio of the wanted to the unwanted absorptions for each dye should be independent of the concentration of the dye.

In transparencies these rules are obeyed by most dyes if the red, green and blue filters used for exposing the separation negatives transmit light of one wavelength only; such filters are impracticable because of their very low transmissions, but the departures from the rules are not too serious if conventional narrow-cut red, green and blue filters are used. In reflection work the departures from the rules are greater, but non-linearities of tone reproduction can reduce the departures usefully.

Assuming, then, that all these conditions have been fulfilled, it is possible to achieve exact colour reproduction of an original consisting of a mixture of the same dyes as the reproduction. The reasons for this are as follows.

Because the original and the reproduction consist of mixtures of the same yes, exact reproduction must occur if the printing densities of the original, O_r, O_g, O_b, and those of the reproduction R_r, R_g, R_b, are the same. The conditions for exact colour reproduction are therefore

$$R_r = O_r$$
$$R_g = O_g$$
$$R_b = O_b$$

ut the additivity rule enables us to re-write these equations thus:

$$C_r + M_r + Y_r = O_r$$
$$C_g + M_g + Y_g = O_g$$
$$C_b + M_b + Y_b = O_b$$

he reproduction densities having been split up into the contributions from ach of the three dyes, C_r denoting the contribution of the cyan dye towards he total red printing-density, etc. If we re-write these equations thus

$$C_r + k_3 M_g + k_5 Y_b = O_r$$
$$k_1 C_r + M_g + k_6 Y_b = O_g$$
$$k_2 C_r + k_4 M_g + Y_b = O_b$$

where $k_1 = C_g/C_r$, $k_3 = M_r/M_g$ etc., the Proportionality Rule states that the values of k do not depend on the amounts of the dyes present, and they are herefore constants. We may therefore solve these equations for C_r, M_g, and Y_b, and obtain equations of the form:

$$C_r = a_1 O_r + a_2 O_g + a_3 O_b$$
$$M_g = a_4 O_r + a_5 O_g + a_6 O_b$$
$$Y_b = a_7 O_r + a_8 O_g + a_9 O_b$$

f, then, a red separation negative is exposed to have a contrast a_1, and is ombined with a green-light mask of contrast a_2 and a blue-light mask of ontrast a_3, and is then used to produce a cyan dye-image free of tone-distortion, the correct amount of cyan dye will be produced at each point in the picture. (If the masks are made from the transparency, they must be exposed n filter-film combinations having the same spectral sensitivities as used for he separation negatives.)

Similarly, a_5 and a_9 represent the contrasts of the other two separation negatives, and a_4, a_6, a_7, and a_8 the contrasts of the masks necessary to produce he correct amounts of magenta and yellow dye at each point in the picture. Hence, if the photographic steps are free of tone distortion, use of these eparation-negatives with their masks enables exact reproduction of the original o be achieved.

But what is the position if the original, instead of being composed entirely of mixtures of the dyes used in the reproduction, consists of *any* colours?

Yule has pointed out that, with six masks, exact colour reproduction is still possible (within the gamut of colours which the reproduction dyes can produce) if the filters used in exposing the separation negatives are such as to modify the spectral sensitivity of the emulsion in such a way as to match a set of *colour-matching functions* (see Section 6.4), provided that the reproduction dyes still obey the Additivity and Proportionality Rules (the dye densities now being measured using spectral sensitivities equivalent to a set of colour-matching functions).

Suppose the separation negatives are exposed with spectral sensitivities which match the C.I.E. colour-matching functions, $\bar{x}_\lambda$, $\bar{y}_\lambda$, $\bar{z}_\lambda$. Then any point in the original will be recorded on the separation negatives as three exposures E_x, E_y, and E_z which are proportional to the tristimulus values X, Y, and Z respectively, of the original. If $O_x = -\log E_x$, $O_y = -\log E_y$, and $O_z = -\log E_z$ we may regard these quantities as the densities of the original to the $\bar{x}_\lambda$, $\bar{y}_\lambda$, $\bar{z}_\lambda$ functions. Similarly if the densities of our reproduction to these functions are denoted by R_x, R_y, and R_z, then the conditions for exact reproduction are simply:

$$R_x = O_x$$
$$R_y = O_y$$
$$R_z = O_z$$

for this would imply that the tristimulus values of the reproduction were the same as those of the original, and hence to the C.I.E. standard observer the original and the reproduction would appear identical. The Additivity Rule enables us to re-write these equations thus:

$$C_x + M_x + Y_x = O_x$$
$$C_y + M_y + Y_y = O_y$$
$$C_z + M_z + Y_z = O_z$$

the reproduction densities to each of the three functions having been split up into the contributions from each of the three dyes, C_x denoting the contribution of the cyan dye towards the total density to the $\bar{x}$ function, etc. If we re-write these equations thus:

$$C_x + k'_3 M_y + k'_5 Y_z = O_x$$
$$k'_1 C_x + M_y + k'_6 Y_z = O_y$$
$$k'_2 C_x + k'_4 M_y + Y_z = O_z$$

where $k'_1 = C_y/C_x$, $k'_2 = C_z/C_x$ etc , the Proportionality Rule states that the values of k' do not depend on the amounts of the dyes present, and they are therefore constants. We may therefore solve these equations for C_x, M_y, and Y_z, and obtain equations of the form:

$$C_x = a_1 O_x + a_2 O_y + a_3 O_z$$
$$M_y = a_4 O_x + a_5 O_y + a_6 O_z$$
$$Y_z = a_7 O_x + a_8 O_y + a_9 O_z$$

C_x, M_y, and Y_z then denote the amounts of cyan, magenta, and yellow dye required at each point in the colour reproduction, in order to obtain an exact match with the original.

Plate 8. Arch comparison

These two photographs were taken from opposite sides of the same arch within a few moments of one another. The strongly directional light of the upper picture gives saturated colours. The extremely diffused light and heavy haze of the lower picture gives very desaturated colours.

From Kodachrome transparencies.

(See Section 5.5)

(a) Appearance of Tri-Mask image

(b) Uncorrected reproduction

(d) Cyan impression

(e) Magenta impression

Plate 9. Tri-Mask
The degree of improvement which can be produced by masking is illustrated by comparing (*b*) and (*c*); (*a*) shows the appearance of the Tri-Mask film image used to achieve this result; (*d*) (*e*) (*f*) and (*g*) show separately the cyan, magenta, yellow, and black images which when superimposed give the result shown in (*c*).

From an Ektachrome transparency.
(See Section 13.10)

(*c*) Reproduction using Tri-Mask film

(*f*) Yellow impression   (*g*) Black impression

Plate 10. Stream at Shere, Surrey
The saturation of blue skies and water is increased by the ultra-violet sensitivity of most colour films.
From an Ektachrome transparency.
(See Section 5.6)

The diagonal terms, a_1, a_5, and a_9, of the above equations denote, as before, the contrasts of the three separation negatives, while the remaining terms denote the contrasts of the six masks to be used in conjunction with the separation negatives when the coloured images are being printed. Although, for the sake of simplicity, we have assumed in this discussion that the spectral sensitivity curves used for making the separation negatives were the same as the $\bar{x}_\lambda$, $\bar{y}_\lambda$, $\bar{z}_\lambda$ curves, this is an unnecessary restriction: any set of colour-matching functions, that is to say, any linear combinations of the $\bar{x}_\lambda$, $\bar{y}_\lambda$, $\bar{z}_\lambda$ curves may be used; the only consequence is that the masking equations will call for different contrasts for the separation negatives and masks. Similarly, although we have regarded the densities of the dyes as being evaluated using spectral sensitivities equivalent to the $\bar{x}_\lambda$, $\bar{y}_\lambda$, $\bar{z}_\lambda$ functions, the use of any other set (even if different from the set used for making the separation negatives) does not invalidate the theory but only affects the values obtained for the contrasts of the separations and masks.

When dye-densities are measured using spectral sensitivities equivalent to colour-matching functions, the Additivity and Proportionality Rules are not usually obeyed. The functions are very much broader than the narrow-cut filters for which these rules hold reasonably well, and the rules break down quite considerably. But departures of characteristic curve shapes from linearity can be used to counteract the break-downs of the rules.

13.7 Masking for approximate colour reproduction

Various methods of obtaining approximately exact colour reproduction in the general case, where the original can consist of any colours, have been investigated theoretically (MacAdam, 1938; Marriage, 1940). Marriage pointed out that masking can either be used in an attempt to correct the spectral sensitivities of the original photographic material, or to correct for the unwanted absorptions of the dyes or inks, or both. Marriage considered that correcting for the unwanted absorptions was the more important function of masks and applied Yule's theory in this direction (Marriage, 1940). Miller also made this assumption (Miller, 1941) and applied matrix algebra, with great advantage, to the problem of evaluating the contrasts of the masks required for this purpose.

Marriage also pointed out that by means of masking it was possible to ensure that at least four colours were always reproduced exactly (Marriage, 1948). Marriage chose grass-green, flesh-pink, white and a grey. Including the latter two colours has the big advantage that all shades of grey from white to black are also reproduced very nearly correctly. This approach was extended by others (Brewer, Hanson and Horton, 1949) to the case where, instead of seeking exact colour reproduction of four colours, the masks are chosen so that the errors in a larger number of specially selected colours are kept to a minimum. Using the same criterion of minimum errors, Brewer and Hanson also investigated the relative importance of unwanted dye absorptions and the absence of negative portions in the spectral sensitivity curves (Brewer and Hanson, 1954). They concluded that the unwanted absorptions contributed the greater errors, but that absence of negative portions in the curves was by no means insignificant in comparison.

That it is possible, by suitable choice of masks, contrasts, and colour balance, to reproduce any four colours without error can be seen from the last set of equations if the terms a_{10}, a_{11}, and a_{12} are added thus:

$$C_x = a_1 O_x + a_2 O_y + a_3 O_z + a_{10}$$
$$M_y = a_4 O_x + a_5 O_y + a_6 O_z + a_{11}$$
$$Y_z = a_7 O_x + a_8 O_y + a_9 O_z + a_{12}$$

These extra three terms represent the variable of colour balance; they are all zero if exact colour reproduction of all colours is achieved, but if, as is always the case in practice, there are departures from exact reproduction, use can be made of this variable to reduce the average errors to the minimum. Thus, given four colours which must be reproduced correctly, the three equations for each colour provide 12 equations which may be solved for $a_1, a_2, a_3 \ldots a_{12}$; the values of these terms then give the contrasts, mask contrasts, and colour balance required for exact reproduction of the four chosen colours.

Using equations of this basic type, Brewer and Hanson determined the values of twelve coefficients representing image contrasts, mask contrasts, and colour balance, which resulted in minimal reproduction errors under various conditions (Brewer and Hanson, 1955). They did not, however, restrict their spectral sensitivity curves to linear combinations of the $\bar{x}_\lambda$, $\bar{y}_\lambda$, $\bar{z}_\lambda$ functions, but in addition tried sets with omitted negative portions, and also a set typical of those commonly used in practice. Sixty different picture test colours were considered in three groups of twenty, one group containing colours covering most of the gamut of the reproduction dyes considered, the other two groups being less saturated and as far as possible typical of average picture-taking experience. Their investigation produced a number of interesting results. First, it was found that, so long as no restriction was placed on the values of the coefficients, that is, so long as six masks of any contrast were allowed, there was very little to choose between one set of sensitivity curves and another. Secondly, the use of a set of sensitivity curves which overlapped one another considerably, such as the $\bar{x}_\lambda$, $\bar{y}_\lambda$, $\bar{z}_\lambda$ functions, led to much higher mask contrasts than the use of sensitivity curves which were more separated. Thirdly, omission of required negative portions of sensitivity curves resulted in some increase in mask contrasts but was less important than adequate separation of the curves. Fourthly, the particular choice of picture test colours affects the values obtained for the coefficients, a group containing more saturated colours leading to higher mask contrasts, but the effect is fairly small. Fifthly, the magnitude of the reproduction errors finally obtained was quite small. For typical picture colours, the average error was only about three just noticeable differences (for a two degree field); for more saturated colours it was about four times as great.

The practical application of these findings may seem a little remote in that the use of six masks is complicated, photographic processes are often non-linear, and dyes do not generally obey the additivity and proportionality rules. In negative-positive processes, however, coloured couplers provide practicable means of attaining a number of masks, and some products already thus incorporate three. One of the six masks is generally of so low a contrast as to be of little practical consequence, so that the addition of two more masks by means of coloured couplers or inter-image effects could provide all the masking needed. Moreover, in transparency processes, approximate linearity of the system, at least over the most important density range, is often attained. Using the minimum-errors criterion, the Additivity and Proportionality Rules need not be obeyed as far as the image dyes are concerned; but if masking is carried out by means of coloured couplers, the dyes colouring the couplers must obey the laws: over the most important density range they will probably do so approximately. It thus seems possible that a colour negative material might have sufficient masks built into it to enable a print to be made from it having remarkably small reproduction errors for average colours, at least, in the case where the print is a transparency.

It is inevitable, however, that departure of the sensitivity curves from linear combinations of the colour-matching functions renders the whole system vulnerable to failure in the face of any particular colour. And it is interesting to note that the very feature (separation of the sensitivity curves) which results in low-contrast masks, also, in general, results in large errors in colours having unusual spectral reflectance curves, such as was mentioned in Section 5.1 in connection with certain blue flowers. From the practical point of view, however, low-contrast masks are usually desirable in order that the system should not be either very critical to operate or very wasteful of light.

The conditions which call for low-contrast masks are preferable for systems in which no masking is possible, since the errors caused by omitting low-contrast masks are smaller than those caused by omitting high-contrast masks.

13.8 Calculation of mask contrasts

The calculation of mask contrasts is conveniently made by means of matrix algebra[1] (Miller, 1941). If the densities of the unwanted and the wanted absorptions of the reproduction dyes in a neutral density of 1.0 are as follows

	Cyan	*Magenta*	*Yellow*
Density to Red light	c	m_R	y_R
Density to Green light	c_G	m	y_G
Density to Blue light	c_B	m_B	y

[1] See Appendix 1.

255

then, if the overall contrast of the reproduction is to be the same as that of the original, the contrasts of the photographic materials for the required masks and separation negatives (when made from the original) are given by:

$$\begin{pmatrix} \gamma_R & \gamma_{GR} & \gamma_{BR} \\ \gamma_{RG} & \gamma_G & \gamma_{BG} \\ \gamma_{RB} & \gamma_{GB} & \gamma_B \end{pmatrix} = \begin{pmatrix} c & m_R & y_R \\ c_G & m & y_G \\ c_B & m_B & y \end{pmatrix}^{-1}$$

where γ_R, γ_G, and γ_B are the contrasts for the three separation negatives and γ_{GR} and γ_{BR} are the contrasts for masks to be made by green and blue light exposures respectively and used with the red separation negative when producing the cyan image. If the masks are used, not with the separation negative, but with the original, then the contrasts have to be divided by that of the red separation negative, γ_R, if this is different from unity and they have to be negatives instead of positives or *vice-versa*. Similarly γ_{RG} and γ_{BG} are the contrasts for the masks to be used with the green separation negative when the magenta image is printed, and γ_{RB} and γ_{GB} those for the masks to be used with the blue separation negatives when the yellow image is printed.

Very often several of the six masks called for are of such low contrast that they can be omitted without loss of quality. For instance, the following figures are fairly typical of dyes used in colour photography.

	Cyan	Magenta	Yellow
Density to Red light	0.868	0.017	0.023
Density to Green light	0.164	0.687	0.145
Density to Blue light	0.182	0.210	0.625

The contrasts for the required separation negatives and masks are then given by:

$$\begin{pmatrix} \gamma_R & \gamma_{GR} & \gamma_{BR} \\ \gamma_{RG} & \gamma_G & \gamma_{BG} \\ \gamma_{RB} & \gamma_{GB} & \gamma_G \end{pmatrix} = \begin{pmatrix} 0.868 & 0.017 & 0.023 \\ 0.164 & 0.687 & 0.145 \\ 0.182 & 0.210 & 0.625 \end{pmatrix}^{-1} = \begin{pmatrix} 1.165 & -0.017 & -0.039 \\ -0.222 & 1.572 & -0.357 \\ -0.265 & -0.523 & 1.733 \end{pmatrix}$$

Where the signs are positive the masks are negatives, where the signs are negative the masks are positives. The two masks to be used with the red separation negative are of such low contrast (0.017 and 0.039) that they can be neglected; this is because the unwanted red absorptions of the magenta and yellow dyes are small. See Plate 3 (page 60). The most contrasty mask is that made with green light and to be used with the blue separation negative (0.523); this is a consequence of the heavy blue unwanted absorption of the magenta dye.

When the original is a colour transparency, the masks may be used to correct for the unwanted absorption of the transparency dyes rather than for those of the reproduction dyes; in this case the densities used in the calculation must be those of the transparency dyes. Furthermore, in this type of calculation it is not difficult to correct for the unwanted absorptions of both sets of dyes and hence, at least in principle, to improve on the original transparency.

Mask exposed to	Mask used when making	Mask contrast	Provides correction for
Green light	Blue separation	0.5	Blue absorptions of Magenta and Cyan dyes
Red and blue light (Magenta filter)	Green separation	0.5	Average Green absorption of Cyan and Yellow dyes
	Red separation		Contrast of Cyan image

Fig. 13.7. Simplified masking procedure in which masks are made through green and magenta filters.

13.9 Simplified procedures

When masking is carried out manually the procedures are usually simplified as much as possible and the details established empirically. One procedure, illustrated in Fig. 13.7, is to make only two masks (in addition to a highlight mask if this is necessary), one through a green filter which is used when making the blue separation, and the other through a magenta filter which is used when making the green and red separations.

The mask made through the green filter and used when making the blue separation provides correction for the unwanted blue absorption of the magenta reproduction-dye; but if the reproduction-dyes are such that the ratio of the green density to the blue density is the same for the cyan dye as for the magenta, then this mask will also automatically correct for the unwanted blue density of the cyan. Dyes which have this common ratio are sometimes referred to as dyes of *balanced hue* (Hartsuch, 1958; Yule, 1967, page 53); all magenta dyes have higher green than blue densities and as this is also true of most cyan dyes, an approximate correction for their unwanted blue absorption usually takes place. The reason why a green-filter mask is able to correct for a cyan dye deficiency is as follows: the green-filter mask makes no allowance for the fact that the other mask will be reducing the amount of magenta required in areas where the cyan will be present; hence in these areas more masking will be provided than is required to correct for the magenta deficiencies and it is this excess masking in cyan-abundant areas which provides correction for the unwanted blue absorption of the cyan (Pollak, 1956).

The mask made through the magenta filter and used when making the green separation provides correction for the average green absorption of the cyan and yellow reproduction-dyes. The unwanted green absorption of the cyan dye is usually much greater than that of the yellow dye, so that what is really required is that the red light transmitted by the magenta filter should result in a higher contrast mask than that produced by the blue light; two

Mask exposed to	Mask used when making	Mask contrast	Provides correction for
Green light	Blue separation	0.5	Blue absorptions of Magenta and Cyan dyes
Red and blue light (Magenta filter)	Green separation	0.5	Average Green absorption of Cyan and Yellow dyes
Red and Green light (Orange filter)	Red separation	0.5	Contrast of Cyan image and Red absorption of Magenta dye
Narrow-band Yellow light	Black separation	0.5	Black printing surface

Fig. 13.8. Simplified masking procedure in which masks are made through green, magenta, and orange filters (and through a narrow-band yellow filter in connection with the black printer).

different contrasts cannot be properly achieved in only one mask, of course, but, if the magenta filter is chosen so that the blue light exposes the mask material less than the red light, some rough allowance for the difference in the green absorptions of the two dyes can result.

Although the unwanted red absorptions of the yellow and magenta dyes are usually small, it is convenient to use a mask when making the red separation, so that similar contrast can be provided for all three separations which then need only a single film-process combination. Strictly speaking, a mask whose function is only to control cyan contrast should be made through a red filter, but in practice it is found that the mask made through the magenta filter can be used with fairly good results. The contrasts of the film-process combinations used for making the masks in this procedure are usually both about 0.5.

The two-mask procedure outlined above has been elaborated for use in the preparation of half-tone printing surfaces by using four masks, as illustrated in Fig. 13.8, although one of the masks is used only to facilitate the preparation of the printing surface used for the black ink (which often has to be used because of the difficulty of reproducing good blacks with cyan, magenta, and yellow inks alone). Of the other three masks, one is made through a green filter and used as before when making the blue separation; another is made through a magenta filter but is now used only when making the green separation; the third is used mainly for reducing cyan contrast, but by making it through an orange filter instead of through a red filter, some correction for the unwanted red absorption of the magenta ink is also achieved. Once again, the single mask cannot properly achieve the two different functions required of it, but if the orange filter is chosen so that the exposure levels produced on the mask material by its red and green transmissions bear some relation to the relative importance of cyan contrast-control and correction for magenta unwanted red-absorption, then both functions will be served approximately. The contrasts of all the film-process combinations used for making the masks in this procedure are also usually about 0.5.

Layer	Layer sensitive to	Mask colour	Separation affected	Mask contrast	Provides correction for
1	Red and Blue light	Magenta	Green	0.5	Average Green absorption of Cyan and Yellow dyes
2	Red, Green and Blue light	Cyan	Red	0.5	Contrast of Cyan image, Red absorption of Magenta dye, and Red absorption of Yellow dye
Yellow filter layer					
3	Green light	Yellow	Blue	0.5	Blue absorptions of Magenta and Cyan dyes
Film base					

Fig. 13.9. Masking procedure provided by Gevaert Multimask film.

13.10 Special films for masking

When black-and-white masks are used in contact with colour transparencies for the production of separation negatives, it is necessary to change the masks appropriately for exposing each separation; as the masks have to be accurately registered with the transparency this is a tedious business. Multi-layer colour films have therefore been made available which produce mask-images consisting of cyan, magenta, and yellow dyes; these special films are designed so that when a transparency is printed on to them the cyan, magenta, and yellow images result in the red-light transmission constituting the required mask for making the red separation, and the green and blue transmissions the required masks for making the green and blue separations, respectively. A contact print of the transparency is therefore made on such a film and bound up in register with it: all three separation negatives can then be made by printing from the same transparency-mask combination, using red, green, and blue filters in the ordinary way. Two masking colour films of this type are available commercially, Gevaert *Multimask* film, and Kodak *Tri-Mask* film; their functions are shown diagrammatically in Figs. 13.9 and 13.10 respectively.

In Multimask film, Fig. 13.9, layers 1 and 3 perform exactly the same functions as the masks made through the magenta and green filters, respectively, in the procedure illustrated in Fig. 13.8; layer 2 performs a similar function to that of the mask made through the orange filter, but its blue sensitivity is greater than the small residual blue sensitivity usually provided by the orange filter, and hence a correction for unwanted red absorption of the yellow reproduction dye takes place. The contrasts of the cyan, magenta, and yellow mask-images are all about 0.5, so that a Multimask, when bound up with a transparency does not upset the grey-scale contrast-match.

Layer	Layer sensitive to	Mask colour	Separation affected	Mask contrast	Provides correction for
1	Blue light	Magenta	Green	0.1	Green absorption of Yellow dye
Yellow filter layer					
2	Green light	Cyan	Red	0.25	Red absorption of Magenta dye
3	Green light	Yellow	Blue	0.5	Blue absorptions of Magenta and Cyan dyes
4	Red light	Cyan	Red	0.25	Contrast of Cyan image
5	Red light	Magenta	Green	0.4	Green absorption of Cyan dye
Film Base					

Fig. 13.10. Masking procedure provided by Kodak Tri-Mask film.

In Tri-mask film, as shown in Fig. 13.10, the masking is slightly more elaborate. Layer 3 performs the same functions as those of the green-filter mask of Figs. 13.7 and 13.8. Layers 1 and 5 perform the same two functions as those of the magenta-filter mask; but the different contrasts of the unwanted green absorptions of the cyan and yellow reproduction dyes are corrected by mask-images of different contrasts, instead of by critical choice of the magenta filter to 'read' the green absorptions of the cyan and yellow transparency images at the correct ratio: the Tri-mask system is thus less sensitive to changes in the nature of the cyan and yellow transparency dyes. Layers 2 and 4 perform the same two functions as those of the orange-filter mask; but, once again, because the two mask-images are formed in different layers, their contrasts are adjusted independently, instead of depending on a critical choice of orange filter to 'read' the cyan and magenta transparency dye-images at the right contrast ratio; the Tri-Mask system is thus also less sensitive to changes in the nature of the cyan and magenta transparency dyes. The contrasts of the various mask-images in Tri-Mask film are shown in Fig. 13.10: the total image contrast in each dye-colour adds up to 0.5, so that a Tri-Mask, when bound up with a transparency, does not upset the grey-scale contrast-match. Plate 9 (page 250) illustrates the improvement obtainable with this type of film.

13.11 Non-linear masks

In most of the discussion in this chapter, it has been assumed that the colour reproduction systems with their masks can be represented by relationships which are always proportional to density; in other words that the equations relating densities are always linear. It was pointed out in Section 13.2, however, that the tone reproduction was sometimes sufficiently non-linear to require a special non-linear highlight mask (performing a tone-correcting function similar to that of the unswept shoulder of the inter-negative film described in Section 12.16); the possibility of the failure of densities to obey the additivity and proportionality rules was mentioned in Section 13.6; and the non-linear relationship between transmission and reflection densities in reflection print materials was discussed in Section 12.22. In half-tone colour printing, other sources of non-linear density distortion can be important, such as the tone-reproduction characteristics of the steps involved in preparing and using the printing surfaces, differences in gloss between one ink and another, and the fact that the way an ink-image prints often depends on the amount of ink, if any, already printed on each area (a form of inter-image effect).

There are, therefore, a number of reasons why non-linear steps may be desirable. For this reason, it is sometimes advantageous to use fairly broad red, green, and blue filters (instead of the usual narrow ones) when exposing the separation negatives, because the increased non-additivity and non-proportionality thus introduced is sometimes useful in correcting other non-linearities in the system. One difficulty of using non-linear *masks*, however, is that unless the non-linearity introduced is exactly the same in all three separations, unpleasant distortions will be produced in the grey scale. In the case of the highlight mask, the neutrality of the grey scale is ensured by using the same highlight mask when making all three separations; this is not a strictly correct procedure even for a tone-correcting highlight mask, but colour-correcting masks must of course be different for the three separations; and making sets of non-linear masks matched closely enough to avoid grey-scale distortion is difficult. This difficulty can, however, be largely overcome by using a technique known as *two-stage masking*.

In two-stage masking a set of separation negatives is first made without masking. These separations are then contact-printed on to a black-and-white film, which can be processed to give a contrast of 1.0, to yield three separation positives. If one of these separation positives is then bound up with the negative from which it was made the two images will cancel one another and only a uniform grey will result: but if a positive is bound up with one of the *other* negatives the two images will only cancel for colours which exposed equally the two separation negatives concerned; such equal exposure will occur for all grey colours (as well as for some others) and hence such negative-positive combinations will reproduce the grey scale as a uniform grey of single density. If, therefore, this type of negative-positive combination is used for making colour-correcting masks, even if they are non-linear they cannot affect the grey scale reproduction.

One way in which it has been found useful to apply the two-stage masking technique is as follows. The ink-images used in half-tone reflection printing often show marked non-additivity of their densities. For example, the density to blue light of a patch of yellow ink printed over a patch of magenta ink is frequently less than the sum of the blue densities of the two patches printed side by side. This means that if the contrast of the green-light mask (to be used in making the blue printer) is adjusted so as to give the right degree of correction for the unwanted blue absorption of the magenta ink on its own, it will give too much correction when the magenta ink has yellow printed over it (the unwanted absorption of an ink is sometimes called an *unwanted colour* unless it is printed with the ink which is meant to absorb in the area of unwanted absorption in which case the total absorption is called a *wanted colour*). Hence the green-filter colour-correcting mask is required to have a contrast which *decreases* as the amount of yellow ink present *increases*. This can be achieved by making this mask from a combination of the green separation negative and the blue separation positive and under-exposing when making the mask: this is so because in areas where there will be no yellow ink (unwanted colours in the blue separation) the separation positive will be light, and the mask will be well-exposed and therefore reproduced at normal contrast; but in areas where there *will* be yellow ink (wanted colours in the blue separation) the separation positive will be dense and the mask will be under-exposed and therefore reproduced at low contrast (on the toe of the characteristic curve of the masking film). The mask thus provides non-linear colour-correction, but has no effect on the grey scale. The mask can then be bound up with the uncorrected separation negative to give a corrected combination: however, the grey scale contrast will be higher than with the normal one-stage methods of masking, because in this case the colour-correcting mask does not reduce contrast; any contrast reduction required, therefore, has to be provided by other means.

It is possible for a single mask to correct for the unwanted blue absorptions of both the magenta and the cyan inks in two-stage masking, if, in addition to the reproduction dyes being of balanced hues (see Section 13.9), the effect of the presence of yellow ink on the non-additivity of the blue absorption of the cyan ink is similar to that with the magenta ink; this similarity does sometimes occur, enabling one mask to perform both functions.

The principles of two-stage masking can be incorporated into the operations performed by equipment used in half-tone printing for producing separations by scanning methods (see Chapter 21).

13.12 Patches for setting up masking procedures

When masking procedures are being determined empirically, it is often very helpful to position a few special colour patches so that they are reproduced on the edges of the separations and masks. If the dyes or inks used in the reproduction obey the proportionality and additivity rules, then single patches of cyan, magenta, and yellow suffice: the masking is then usually adjusted so that the cyan patch only reproduces on the corrected red separation, the magenta on the green, and the yellow on the blue; full correction will then have been made for the unwanted absorptions of the reproduction dyes or inks, and an exact copy could be made of an original consisting of mixtures of the same dyes or inks. If the proportionality and additivity rules are not obeyed, then patches of the dyes or inks both singly and in pairs can be used; the masking can then be adjusted so that single patches reproduce on their one appropriate separation only, and combination patches on their two appropriate separations only, a result which may require non-linear masks produced, for instance, by the two-stage masking technique. It must be remembered, however, that even when patches of both single and pairs of dyes or inks are reproduced correctly, the intermediate colours can still show errors, although these are often fairly small.

REFERENCES

Brewer, W. L., and Hanson, W. T., *J. Opt. Soc. Amer.*, **44**, 129 (1954).
Brewer, W. L., and Hanson, W. T., *J. Opt. Soc. Amer.*, **45**, 476 (1955).
Brewer, W. L., Hanson, W. T., and Horton, C. A., *J. Opt. Soc. Amer.*, **39**, 924 (1949).
Evans, R. M., *Penrose Annual*, **45**, 81 (1951) and *P.S.A. Journal*, p. 15 (February, 1954).
Evans, R. M., Hanson, W. T., and Brewer, W. L., *Principles of Colour Photography*, Wiley, New York (1953).
Hanson, W. T., *J. Opt. Soc. Amer.*, **40**, 166 (1950).
Hanson, W. T., and Horton, C. A., *J. Opt. Soc. Amer.*, **42**, 663 (1952).
Hartsuch, P. J., *Proc. Tech. Assoc. Graphic Arts*, **10**, 29 (1958).
MacAdam, D. L., *J. Opt. Soc. Amer.*, **28**, 466 (1938).
Marriage, A., *Photo. J.*, **80**, 364 (1940).
Marriage, A., *Phot. J.*, **88B**, 75 (1948).
Miller, C. W., *J. Opt. Soc. Amer.*, **31**, 477 (1941).
Neblette, C. B., *Photography, Its Materials and Processes*, Von Nostrand, New York, 6th Edition, p. 463 (1962).
Pollak, F., *J. Phot. Sci.*, **4**, 65 (1956).
Sant, A. J., *Phot. Sci. Eng.*, **5**, 181 (1961).
Watson, R. N., *J. Phot. Sci.*, **14**, 304 (1966).
Yule, J. A. C., *J. Opt. Soc. Amer.*, **78**, 419 and 481 (1938).
Yule, J. A. C., *Phot. J.*, **80**, 408 (1940).
Yule, J. A. C., *Phot. J.*, **84**, 321 (1944).
Yule, J. A. C., *Principles of Colour Reproduction*, Wiley, New York (1967).

CHAPTER 14

Printing Colour Negatives

1. Introduction – *2*. Printing studio negatives – *3*. Printing motion-picture negatives – *4*. Printing amateurs' negatives – *5*. The variables to be corrected – *6*. Early printers – *7*. Integrating to grey – *8*. The *1599* printer – *9*. Visual matching – *10*. Simultaneous additive printers – *11*. Variable time printers – *12*. Subtractive printers – *13*. Colour enlargers – *14*. Density classification – *15*. Factors affecting slope control – *16*. Methods of slope control

14.1 Introduction

Because of their various advantages (see Section 11.4, for instance), colour negatives are widely used as intermediates for the production of colour photographs. There are, however, many factors which can affect the colour balance and density of a print made from a colour negative; it is therefore usually necessary to adjust the exposure of the print-film or paper in both colour and intensity for each negative during the printing operation, in order to obtain correct positive images. But it is extremely difficult to determine, by inspecting it visually, the type and magnitude of the printing adjustments a colour negative requires. Various aids to correct printing are therefore used, their nature depending on the particular application.

14.2 Printing studio negatives

In certain studio work, the lighting can be carefully controlled in both colour and intensity; the transmission colour of the camera lenses can be matched (if necessary by using filters); a single batch of film can usually be used for a considerable period of time; only one film processing location is generally involved; and hence, once the correct printing conditions have been established for one typical negative, if subsequent negatives are all printed with light of the same intensity and colour, the prints will usually be somewhere near optimum in density and colour balance. From such prints, quite reliable visual estimates can usually be made of any changes necessary in the printing conditions to obtain prints of correct density and colour balance at the second attempt; and if fairly high prices can be charged for the final print, the loss

264

n discarding a fair proportion of the first prints (and even some of the second prints) is no great problem. For a variety of reasons, however, it is not always possible to control all the factors as closely as required, and some guidance may be necessary in making the *first* print if it is to be reasonably near optimum.

One method of producing first prints of reasonably good quality is to include a grey card in the scene, and to measure the red, green, and blue printing densities of its image in the processed negative; the correct printing conditions can then be calculated from these densities. If the negative is very large, a grey-card image of measurable size can usually be accommodated outside the area required for the final picture. But with small negatives the presence of the grey card would spoil the picture, and this method can then only be used when (as is often the case in professional work) several negatives are being exposed from similar scenes, as in a series of still pictures of similar subjects; the grey card can then appear only in an extra test-negative of the series. If a grey card has not, or cannot, be included in the scene, an area of known colour, such as a flesh colour, can be used for measurement instead, the printing conditions then being used to give the correct or desired result for the particular chosen colour.

The actual adjustment of the colour of the exposure is usually made by inserting pale cyan, magenta and yellow filters into the beam of an ordinary white-light enlarger, while density is controlled by altering either the exposure time or the lens aperture, or both.

14.3 Printing motion-picture negatives

The problems of printing professional motion-picture negatives are generally similar to those outlined above for studio work, and careful control of lighting, lenses, processing, and film-batches is usually exercised to good advantage. Densitometry of images of grey cards or other standard colours is also very useful. Additional difficulties, however, may be caused by varying lighting conditions on 'location' shots, by artistic requirements calling for prints of unusual density and colour balance in order to give a particular 'mood', and by the need for many different scenes on the negative film to be printed in quick succession, thus requiring a rapid succession of printing adjustments.

Some use is made of closed-circuit colour-television viewing-devices, in which a positive colour image is derived electrically from the negative and then judged visually to determine the printing adjustments; although such devices are costly, their value can often by justified in professional motion-picture printing where the total value of the finished prints of a feature film can be very considerable. (Professional still-photographers also make some use of this technique.)

The actual printing operation itself can be carried out either by contact, or by projection (usually referred to in the trade as *optical printing*). Projection must be used, of course, if any change in the size or the shape of the print has to be introduced; but contact printing is simpler, is less affected by dirt or scratches on the negative, and usually gives sharper results. Printers may advance the film continuously or a frame at a time (*step-printing*). The adjustment of density and colour balance, usually referred to as *timing*, may be carried out by inserting pale cyan, magenta, yellow, and neutral filters into the printing beam of a white-light printer; or *additive printers* may be used. In additive printers, separate beams of red, green, and blue light are combined uniformly in the printing gate, the adjustments of colour balance and density then being achieved by altering the relative and absolute intensities of the red, green, and blue beams: although this involves more complicated equipment it has the advantage that the exposures given to the three layers of the print film can be controlled independently, whereas the cyan, magenta, and yellow filters have unwanted absorptions so that each filter affects more than one layer.

Because changes in printing conditions may have to be made in rapid succession, it is usual in the professional motion-picture trade for the printing equipment to respond automatically to instructions punched into a paper tape (or other means of storing information) which is fed through the machine in synchronization with the negative film being printed.

14.4 Printing amateurs' negatives

When the colour negative is used for amateur snapshots a wider variety of lighting is encountered and other factors also vary more, so that printing adjustments are even more necessary: but in this market a reasonably low price for the prints is also an important requirement. It is therefore essential to adopt a method of printing which is quick, does not require very highly skilled operators, and does not call for prohibitively high capital investment in equipment, and yet gives a high yield of saleable results at the first printing. These requirements have been the subject of considerable technological efforts, and some remarkably successful solutions have been devised, as will now be described in the remaining sections of this chapter.

14.5 The variables to be corrected

The following factors can affect the colour balance and density of a print made from a colour negative:
  (1) intensity of scene illuminant
  (2) colour of scene illuminant
  (3) scene subject matter
  (4) camera lens transmission colour
  (5) lens aperture, exposure time, and film speed
  (6) film colour balance
  (7) film latent-image keeping properties
  (8) negative processing
  (9) printer settings

COLOUR PHOTOGRAPHY

(10) paper speed and colour balance
(11) paper latent-image keeping properties
(12) paper processing
(13) colour and intensity of print illuminant.

The cumulative effects of factors 1 to 8 on the colour balance and density of a typical sample of amateurs' negatives are shown in Fig. 14.1. It is clear that there is scope here for very wide fluctuations in the prints unless steps are taken to correct for the variations.

14.6 Early printers

In one type of printer (Eastman Kodak No. 1598), which was used in the early 1940's, correction was made for the exposure level, for the colour balance of the negative material, and for its processing (items, 1, 5, 6, and 8). Before each film was processed, a small patch of carefully controlled uniform light was printed on to a spare unexposed area at one end of the film. After processing, the red, green, and blue printing densities of this patch were measured, and each negative of the film was then punched with small holes along one edge, the size and positions of the holes indicating the colours and values of correcting filters necessary to adjust the colour of that negative material to a standard. When the negative was printed, the indicated filters were inserted into the printing beam, and then a photo-cell was used to adjust the position of a neutral density wedge in the beam so that at a fixed printing time the correct density was obtained on the print for negatives of average scene content. The photo-cell could not of course distinguish between an under-exposed light-scene (such as a snow field), and an over-exposed dark-scene (such as a coal heap), and would tend to print both as grey. The operator could therefore adjust the exposure above or below that called for by the photo-cell in order to obtain prints of the correct density, an operation known as *plus and minus* correction.

A useful measure of success was obtained with this method, but the colour balance of the prints was still rather variable, and it was clear that further control of the variables was desirable.

14.7 Integrating to grey

Modern printers designed for handling amateurs' negatives almost all depend on a principle first described by Evans in the following words: 'A more pleasing effect is often produced in colour prints if they are so made that instead of the colour balance being correct, in which grey is printed as grey, it is so adjusted that the whole picture integrates to grey' (Evans, 1946). At first sight this may sound an absurd approach to the problem, because if, for instance, it were applied to the case of a portrait of a girl wearing a red dress it would result in the whole picture having a blue-green cast. Evans, however, argued that the presence of the red dress would tend in any case to depress the sensitivity of the

267

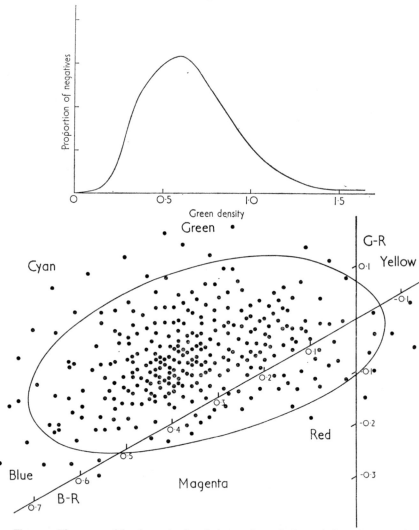

Fig. 14.1. The range of density and colour balance of a typical population of amateurs' colour negatives. The densities plotted are those of whole negatives measured through red, green, and blue filters against an unexposed area of film as zero.

Above: The distribution of green density.

Below: The distribution of colour balance (see Section 12.25).

The colour names indicate the direction in which the lighting or the subject matter would have to be altered in colour (from the average) for the negative to plot in that vicinity. If no corrections were made at the printing stage the prints would have a similar colour bias; the negatives themselves have biases of complementary colours.

The elliptical contour encloses approximately 90 per cent of the points.

eye to red and hence produce a physiological blue-green bias, so that to make the print slightly blue-green would not necessarily be a disadvantage. Whether these physiological effects are large enough in reflection prints to be very important is open to some doubt, although Bartleson has shown that an observer's adaptation certainly is affected to some extent by the colour balance of reflection prints (Bartleson, 1958) and their importance in projected transparencies has been demonstrated by Evans (Evans, 1943) and by Pinney and DeMarsh (Pinney and DeMarsh, 1963). What is beyond dispute, however, is that, as applied in practice, the 'integrating substantially to grey' principle has proved a major factor in the successful operation of amateur colour snapshot systems.

The easiest way of making prints which 'integrate substantially to grey' is to measure the average transmission of each negative through red, green, and blue filters and then expose the red-sensitive layer of the paper to an extent which is inversely proportional to the red transmission of the negative, and the green and blue layers of the paper for extents similarly related to the green and blue transmissions of the negative respectively. In fact, when this is done, it is not true that prints which exactly integrate to grey are obtained. This is because the measured transmissions of the negatives will depend mainly on the dark parts of the scene. Thus the prints will tend to integrate to grey in the shadows more than in the highlights (this effect is reduced, but not eliminated, by the fact that the negatives are of low contrast, the gamma usually being about 0.7).

By taking each negative as the arbiter of the exposure given to the paper, correction is made not only for the exposure level, for the colour balance of the negative material, and for its processing (items 1, 5, 6 and 8) but also for the colour of the scene illuminant, scene subject matter, camera lens transmission colour, and latent-image keeping properties (items, 2 3, 4, and 7). This results in a marked improvement in the consistency of the colour balance of the prints made from the majority of amateurs' negatives, but it does of course introduce errors when the subject matter contains large areas of saturated colours, particularly if they are dark (and hence light on the negative). The proportion of amateurs' negatives which suffer from *colour failure* in this way is, however, surprisingly small, and can be looked after by reprinting them with deliberate shifts from the 'integrating substantially to grey' condition; a series of plus and minus adjustments for colour (as well as those used for density) are generally provided for this purpose. The success of the 'integrating substantially to grey' method probably means that the shadow areas of most actual scenes photographed are in fact approximately grey themselves if integrated. Some measurements on outdoor scenes in England showed a marked tendency for whole scenes to integrate substantially to grey (Pitt and Selwyn, 1938).

14.8 The 1599 printer

The first printer to employ the 'integrating to grey' method of printing amateurs' colour negatives was the Eastman Kodak 1599 Printer, which is shown diagrammatically in Fig. 14.2. The negative is illuminated by a diffuser and an array of small lamps whose luminance can be varied; in early models this was done by means of a variac transformer (as shown in the figure) but later models use a saturable reactor. The diffuser has the dual function of making scratches and other negative defects far less noticeable than would be the case if the beam were specular, and it also spreads some of the light sideways, on to the monitoring photo-cells. The paper is exposed successively to red, green, and blue light by means of filters situated adjacent to the lens. A bank of barrier-layer photo-cells, each one covered by a red, a green, or a blue filter, receive light from the negative and produce three photo-currents which are compared one at a time with that from another barrier-layer photo-cell illuminated by a comparison lamp. The difference between the two photo-currents is amplified and used to adjust automatically the voltage of the array of small lamps until the two photo-currents are equal; an exposure for fixed time is then given for each colour in turn.

The sequence of operations is thus: insert the negative and activate the printer; the red filter moves into place but is covered with a dark shutter that remains in place for 0.3 seconds while the intensity is adjusted correctly for the red exposure; the dark shutter is removed from the beam, the red exposure of about $\frac{1}{2}$ second is given, and the exposure is terminated with the dark shutter; with the dark shutter in place the green filter replaces the red, the lamp voltage is readjusted, and an exposure of about $\frac{1}{2}$ second is given; in the same manner the blue filter replaces the green, the lamp voltage is again readjusted, and an exposure of about $\frac{1}{2}$ second is given. The lamp voltage adjustments are all made during the dark shutter time of 0.3 seconds. The plus and minus adjustments for colour and density are provided by potentiometers (labelled *colour classification* and *density classification* in the figure) which adjust the voltage of the comparison lamp; this voltage can also be made to depend partly on the voltage of the printing lamps by means of the 'shift transformer': in this way the final intensity of the printing light for each colour can be made to depend partly on the density of the negative, and when suitably adjusted this can increase the yield of good prints appreciably, a technique known as *slope control* (Pieronek, Syverud, and Voglesong, 1956; Hunt, 1960b), which will be more fully described later (Section 14.15).

The 1599 printer enabled a very high proportion of amateurs' negatives to be successfully printed at the first attempt and its introduction in 1946 was a major step forward in amateur colour photography. Although the total exposure cycle of the first 1599 printers was about $4\frac{1}{2}$ seconds, a very high rate of printing was achieved by virtue of the fact that each printer comprised three separate channels with three negative gates producing three rows of pictures side by side on a single web of paper. A good operator could in fact reach a rate of printing of around 1000 prints per hour. Later versions of the 1599 printer operate with total exposure cycles of about $2\frac{1}{4}$ seconds.

14.9 Visual matching

It will be appreciated that the 1599 printer is a rather complex piece of equipment and various attempts have been made to achieve similar results by simpler means. One of the earliest of these took place at the Eastman Kodak plant at Washington D.C. in 1947. An ordinary enlarger was modified so that the light from the negative could be integrated and compared visually with that from a standard lamp; cyan, magenta, and yellow colour-correcting filters were then inserted with the negative until the colour and luminance of the two fields matched, whereupon a single exposure for a fixed time was given to the paper. The method was certainly simple in terms of the equipment required, but the visual colour matching step was slow to perform to the required accuracy, and was very fatiguing for the operator. It is for these reasons that visual methods have never been successful in this field.

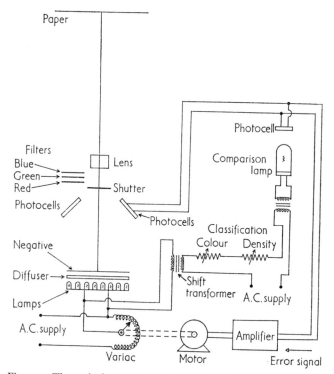

Fig. 14.2. The main features of the Eastman Kodak Printer type 1599.

14.10 Simultaneous additive printers

One of the reasons for the complexity of the 1599 printer is the fact that each is really three printers in one; and, as we have seen, this stemmed originally from the rather long exposure cycle of about 4 seconds for each print. This exposure cycle can be reduced in various ways. Thus time could be saved if the three exposures could be given simultaneously instead of successively, and a printer designed by Technicolor (Gundelfinger, Taylor, and Yancey, 1960) functioned in this way. In this printer the three printing beams were combined by means of dichroic mirrors so that all three layers of the paper were exposed at once. The printer was fully automatic, the negatives being previously punched with plus and minus data, and consequently its output was about twice that of the 1599 printer; but the pre-punching step meant that the overall output per operator was less than that of a 1599 printer.

14.11 Variable time printers

Another approach to shortening the exposure cycle has also been explored. The constant-time variable-intensity principle of exposure used in the 1599 printer means that all negatives are printed at the exposure time which is necessary for the densest negatives likely to be encountered. If, on the other hand, a constant intensity of negative illumination is used and the exposure *time* is varied, then although the densest negative will still require the same exposure time, all other negatives will require shorter exposure times, and hence the average printing time can be substantially reduced. One of the first printers to combine the two principles of 'integrating to grey' and 'variable-time' was the Eastman Kodak IVC printer, (Pieronek, Syverud, and Voglesong, 1956), and it was with this printer that the general colour photo-finishing programme (as distinct from the service given by manufacturers' own laboratories) commenced in the U.S.A. in 1956. The IVC printer contained only one printing beam, and was therefore correspondingly simpler, but the exposure cycle was sufficiently accelerated by the variable-time principle to enable rates of printing around half of that of the 1599 printer to be achieved.

The arrangements of the IVC printer are shown in Fig. 14.3. The red, green, and blue printing filters are situated between the lens and the paper, and immediately below the lens six vacuum photo-cells receive light from the negative, which is illuminated by a diffuser immediately beneath it. (In an earlier version of this printer no diffuser was used and the photo-cells received light from a beam splitter placed between the lens and the paper.) Two of these photo-cells are covered with red filters and at the commencement of the red exposure the photo-current from them is used to discharge a condenser through a predetermined voltage interval, whereupon a solenoid is actuated so that a shutter terminates the exposure. The denser the negative the longer this takes, and vice-versa, so that the exposure time of the red layer of the paper is made proportional to the opacity of the negative to red light, as required. Another two of the photo-cells are covered with green filters and the same condenser is used, but with (in general) a different predetermined voltage interval, to give a green exposure time proportional to the opacity of the negative to green light.

The last two photo-cells are covered with blue filters, and in a similar way control the length of the blue exposure. The normal plus and minus adjustments for both colour and density are provided by altering the predetermined voltage intervals through which the condenser must be discharged; slope control is provided by making this voltage interval gradually alter during the exposure time, the characteristics of the time-dependency being differently adjusted for the red, green, and blue channels, and being set so as to include any paper reciprocity-failure effects in the factors for which correction is made. Other printers similar to the IVC in principle of operation have been produced since.

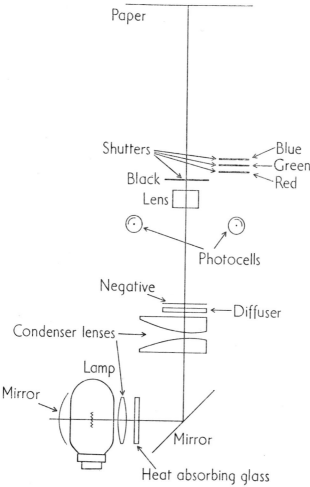

Fig. 14.3. The main features of the Eastman Kodak Printer type IVC.

A further method of accelerating the printing cycle is to combine the variable-time principle with simultaneous exposure of the paper to the red, green, and blue beams. This can be achieved if the printer contains three independent beams, mixed appropriately by beam splitters, or light integrators. A printer operating in this way was introduced by Agfa (Richardson, 1959; Blaxland, 1960).

14.12 Subtractive printers

For maximum efficiency in a printer it is clearly desirable to avoid wasting either time or light. Time can be saved by adopting the variable-time principle, and by exposing the three layers of the paper simultaneously instead of sequentially. Unfortunately, however, the use of red, green, and blue filters and of beam splitters or light integrators tends to waste light.

Greater efficiency is achieved by adopting the subtractive principle. In this case the negative is first printed with white light; then after the layer which required the least exposure is fully exposed, a filter is inserted to prevent any further exposure of that layer taking place; the exposure of the other two layers then proceeds until one of them is fully exposed, whereupon another filter is inserted to prevent any further exposure of that layer; when the third layer is fully exposed a third filter is inserted to prevent any further exposure of the third layer and the exposing cycle is complete. The three filters used are cyan to terminate the exposure of the red layer, magenta for the green layer, and yellow for the blue layer. The order in which they are inserted is dependent on the requirements of the particular negative, and light is lost only as a result of the unwanted absorptions of the cyan, magenta, and yellow filters during the part of the printing cycle for which they are in the beam. The actual insertion of the filters is carried out automatically, as in the case of the IVC printer, as the result of solenoids being actuated by the integration of photo-currents in condensers.

The Kodak S1 subtractive printer, installed at the Kodak processing station at Hemel Hempstead in 1957 and made available for sale in 1958 (Richardson, 1958; Hunt, 1960b) is shown diagrammatically in Fig. 14.4. It is seen that the cyan, magenta, and yellow shutter filters are placed below the negative instead of above the lens. The reason for this is that, because these filters have unwanted absorptions, their insertion not only terminates the exposure of one layer, but also somewhat reduces the level of exposure of the other two layers. By placing them below the negative, the level of illumination on the photo-cells is reduced in the same proportion, and as a result the exposure times are appropriately lengthened as required. It is, of course, necessary to place the shutter filters in such a position in the optical system that no shading across the negative occurs as the filters are inserted, for this would result in uneven colour balance across the prints. In the S1 printer a light-integrator (in the form of a box of mirrors with a 45° mirror at the bottom) is placed between the filters and the negative thus ensuring complete absence of colour shading.

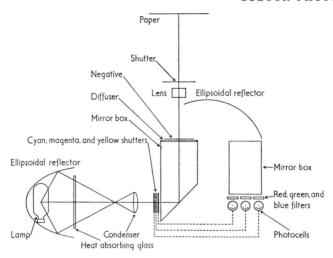

Fig. 14.4. The main features of the Kodak Colour Printer type S1.

In the interests of high efficiency the lamp is placed at one focus of a semi-ellipsoidal reflector, a lens collects the light from the other focus and passes it through the filters and into the light-integrator. A diffuser at the top of this integrator ensures that the effects of negative defects are reduced, and also provides light off the optical axis for the photo-cells. The transfer of the light from the negative to the photo-cells employs another ellipsoidal reflector, the negative being at one focus and the top of another light-integrating mirror-box at the other. Three photo-cells are used, one is covered with a red, one with a green, and one with a blue filter (later versions of this printer have two blue photo-cells in order to increase blue-sensitivity), and they are placed immediately beneath the light-integrator; they thus receive substantially scrambled light from the negative. The usual plus and minus adjustments are provided in the same way as on the IVC printer by altering the predetermined voltage intervals and hence the exposure times. It is, however, now necessary to have three independent integrating condensers (and associated circuits) since the three exposure determinations occur simultaneously. The rate of printing on the S1 printer with its single channel is about three-quarters of that of the three channels of the 1599 printer. The Kodak S4 printer, introduced subsequently, is similar to the S1, but has the photo-cells in pairs just below the lens (as in the IVC printer) and incorporates more convenient methods of dealing with negatives of various sizes.

Another printer using the subtractive principle was introduced in the U.S.A. by the Pako Company in 1958 (Blaxland, 1960). In this printer, the cyan, magenta, and yellow filters are placed between the lens and the paper and are controlled by a single photo-multiplier tube in front of which rotates a red, green, and blue filter wheel so as to sample the colour of the light reflected from a beam splitter placed between the filters and the paper.

The Eastman Kodak 5S printer, introduced in 1959, utilizes the same basic principles as the S1 printer, but has the cyan, magenta, and yellow filters above the lens (in the same position as the additive filters in the IVC printer) and the photo-cells just beneath the lens (as in the IVC printer). The photo-cells are therefore not affected by the insertion of the cyan, magenta, and yellow filters, and this feature is used to make the printer operate at a lower level of colour correction (Bartleson and Huboi, 1956). In this way the amount of colour failure is reduced, and although this is an advantage, it is obtained at the expense of some reduction in correction for the other factors, such as lighting, and the colour balance of the negative material and its processing. Because of the lower level of colour correction on this printer (and on certain others), it is necessary to print negatives exposed to clear flash and to daylight at slightly different settings (Goddard and Huboi, 1958).

A variable-time printer which is partly additive and partly subtractive has been developed by Ilford Limited (Coote, 1961). It has two tungsten lamps, one fitted with a magenta filter and the other with a cyan filter. The light from the two lamps is mixed to give a uniform illumination at the negative plane. The exposure of the red, green, and blue layers of the paper takes place simultaneously, but the blue layer receives light from both lamps. The exposure of the red layer is terminated by the substitution of a blue filter in place of the magenta filter, and the termination of the green exposure by the substitution of a blue filter instead of the cyan filter. The blue exposure is terminated by the insertion of a yellow filter. The yellow filter need not be inserted last because, if extra green or red exposure is needed, this can still be obtained through the cyan or magenta filter respectively. The filters are actuated by means of three photo-multiplier tubes which receive light from a beam splitter placed between the lens and the paper.

14.13 Colour enlargers

The printers referred to above for use with amateurs' negatives mostly produce 'en-prints' of sizes between $3\frac{1}{2}$ inches square and $3\frac{1}{2} \times 5$ inches; the 5S printer, however, can print sizes up to 5×7 inches, and a similar printer, the Eastman Kodak 8S printer, can print sizes up to 8×10 inches. The term 'enlarger', as distinct from 'printer', therefore normally denotes nowadays a piece of equipment which differs not so much in the size of the final print produced as in being very much less complicated in construction and having greater flexibility in use.

For printing amateurs' negatives it is just as desirable for an enlarger, as for a printer, to incorporate the 'integrating to grey' principle. Although in one sense the simplest arrangement would be to give successive variable-time exposures through red, green, and blue filters, this has a number of disadvantages: first, the method, as we have seen, is inefficient, and this can lead to very long exposure times when dense negatives are printed at high magnifications; secondly, there is the danger of unsharpness caused by movement between the exposures, or by vibration produced by changing the filters; and thirdly, the variable-time principle may involve reciprocity failure of the paper, and while, as in the case of printers, this could be compensated for by slope control circuits, it is generally desirable to avoid this complication in enlargers if possible.

One solution to these problems was incorporated in the Kodak Colour Enlarger (Richardson, 1959; Hunt, 1960a). In this enlarger colour correcting filters are used to adjust the colour of the light illuminating the negative until, after passing through the latter, it integrates to a standard colour. The method is thus basically similar to that used in the Washington trials

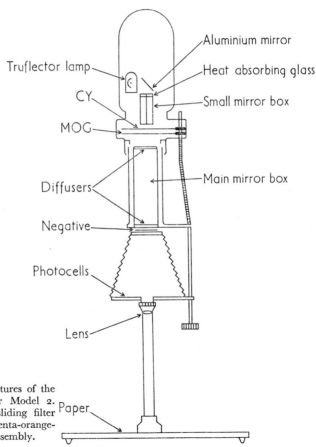

Fig. 14.5. The main features of the Kodak Colour Enlarger Model 2. CY: cyan-clear-yellow sliding filter assembly. MOG: magenta-orange-green sliding filter assembly.

in 1947, but barrier-layer photo-cells covered with red, green, and blue filters are used to detect the position of correct filtration. Other differences are that continuously variable filtration is provided by gradually covering the top of a light-integrating mirror-box with filters of a single value for each colour (cyan, magenta, and yellow); density control is achieved by adjusting the aperture of the enlarging lens until a barrier-layer photo-cell at the paper plane indicates a standard signal. The general arrangements in one version of this enlarger are shown in Fig. 14.5, while Fig. 14.6 shows the associated filter arrangements (Calkin, Hunt, and Letzer, 1961; Hunt, 1963). It is seen that the cyan and yellow filters are in one slide and are separated by a clear gap, while the magenta and a green filter are in another slide, and are separated

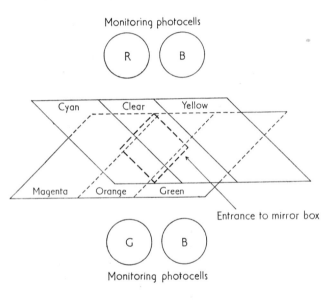

Fig. 14.6. The filter arrangements used in the Kodak Colour Enlarger Model 2. First, the cyan-clear-yellow filter assembly is adjusted in position until the attenuated currents from the red and blue photo-cells are equal. Secondly, the magenta-orange-green filter assembly is adjusted in position until the attenuated currents from the green and blue photo-cells are equal. The attenuations are chosen so that these equalities occur when the colour of the light produces prints of correct colour balance from average negatives on the batch of paper being used. The magenta, orange, and green filters are chosen so that their red to blue transmission ratios are all the same, and this ensures that movement of this filter assembly does not upset the red to blue equality previously achieved by adjusting the other filter assembly. Because magenta filters have lower blue than red transmission, the green filter has to be a yellowish-green in hue.

by a pale orange filter. Movement of the cyan-clear-yellow assembly is used to obtain the required ratio of red to blue light, while movement of the magenta-orange-green assembly then achieves the required ratio of green to blue (or red) light. For this second adjustment to leave unchanged the red to blue ratio obtained by the first adjustment three conditions have to be met: first, the ratio of red to blue transmission of the orange filter must be the same as that of the magenta filter, so that the ratio of the red to blue light is independent of the relative amounts of magenta and orange filter in the beam; secondly, the ratio of red to blue transmission of the green filter must be the same as that of the orange filter, for the same reason; and thirdly, the two filter assemblies must act independently of one another. This last condition can be met either by having the two assemblies completely out of focus with respect to each other or by having them effectively operating at right angles to one another in uniform illumination. The way in which this has been achieved in this enlarger is shown in Figs. 14.5 and 14.6, the small-mirror box above the filters giving the required uniformity of illumination at the filter plane (McRae and Halliday, 1966; Blaxland, 1961).

Another feature of this enlarger is as follows: by making the gap between the cyan and yellow filters, and the width of the orange filter between the magenta and green filters, rather narrower than the width of the illuminated area, a more uniform relationship is obtained between the position of the assembly and the amount of filtration produced, and also the luminance level varies less. Plus and minus adjustments are made by attenuating the photo-currents appropriately before adjusting the filtration until equality of response from the three channels is obtained, this being the criterion for correct balance.

The principles of this enlarger have been incorporated in a colour enlarger introduced by Durst (Blaxland, 1965).

It is possible to make filtering arrangements similar to those used in the enlarger described above, but with *both* filter assemblies independent of one another in adjustment. One solution to this problem is shown in Fig. 14.8.

14.14 Density classification

The adoption of the 'integrating to grey' principle was a major development in the amateur colour snapshot business, and has been incorporated in various types of equipment, including the fairly simple, high output, subtractive printer. This has resulted in colour snapshots becoming widely produced both in manufacturers' processing laboratories and also in independent photo-finishing establishments. High levels of good quality prints are obtained at the first printing, but it is still necessary to use individual plus and minus adjustments to allow for variations in density distribution on the negatives. This is a skilled operation and it would be a considerable advantage to be able to make this step automatic. The need for this is accentuated by the fact that in many parts of the world, the colour snapshot business has large seasonal fluctuations. It seems unlikely that automatic density classification could ever be correct for all negatives, but even skilled operators make some errors and it would be a useful advantage if a machine could be made which performed no worse than they do.

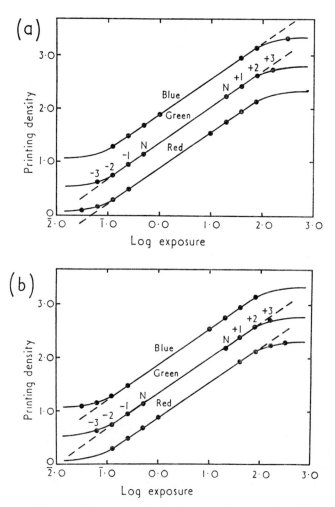

Fig. 14.7. Characteristic curves of a colour negative material with incorporated masks. The dots show the way in which the toe and shoulder of each curve is approached as the exposure is varied above and below normal by 3 stops.

(a) Bluish exposures.

(b) Yellowish exposures.

14.15 Factors affecting slope control

Slope control enables adjustments to be made to the colour balance and density of prints made from dense (over-exposed) negatives relative to that of prints made from light (under-exposed) negatives. There are several reasons why such adjustments are necessary.

First, the shapes of the characteristic curves of the negative material play a part. The reason for this is as follows. The photo-cells will be mainly affected by the darker parts of the scenes, because these parts are the lighter parts of the negatives. In most scenes, however, it is the colour rendering of the medium and light tones which is of the main importance in determining the apparent colour balance of the prints. Hence, unless there is a constant relationship between the colour balance and density of the light and dark parts of the negatives, consistent print quality cannot be obtained. Therefore any departure of the characteristic curves of the negative material from the straight-line condition will affect the results in a way which is dependent on negative density. Some examples will help to demonstrate these effects.

In Fig. 14.7 are shown sets of curves typical of a colour negative material with incorporated masks. The parts of the curves used for a typical scene for various levels of exposure are shown in Fig. 14.7(a) for bluish illuminants and in Fig. 14.7(b) for yellowish illuminants. The separation along the log exposure axis of the points marked 'N' on the green curve is considered to be that used by a normally-exposed scene, and is equal to 1.6 log units, a figure arrived at by taking as an average log luminance range for outdoor scenes a value of 2.2, from which has been subtracted a camera flare factor of 0.6 (James and Higgins, 1960). As the exposure is increased this range of 1.6 log units will move up the green curve, and the points marked +1, +2, and +3 show the positions of the lightest parts of the scene for exposures of one, two, and three stops more than normal. Similarly, the points marked −1, −2, and −3 show the positions of the darkest parts of the scene for exposures of one, two, and three stops less than normal. The sets of points on the red and blue curves show similar data for the red- and blue-sensitive layers of the film; it will be seen that in Fig. 14.7(a) the points have moved one stop up the blue curve and down the red curve as a consequence of the greater blue and lower red content of the bluish illuminant, whereas in Fig. 14.7(b) the points have moved one stop down the blue curve and up the red curve because of the lower blue and greater red content of the yellowish illuminant.

It is clear from Fig. 14.7(a) that with the bluish illuminant the shadows in under-exposed negatives have higher red-densities and slightly higher green densities than if the straight line parts of the curves extended indefinitely (broken lines); this causes the printer to give more red, and slightly more green exposure, with the result that the lighter areas in the prints are too cyan-blue. On the other hand, with the yellowish illuminant, Fig. 14.7(b), the shadows in under-exposed negatives have higher blue, and slightly higher green, densities than if the curves were all straight; this causes the printer to give more blue and

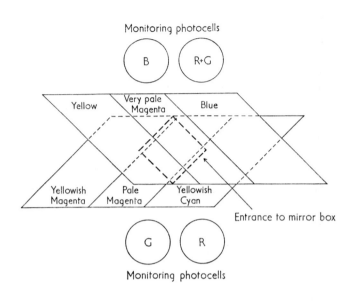

Monitoring photocells

Direction of movement of filter assemblies

Fig. 14.8. The filter arrangements used in the Kodak Colour Printer Type S3.
The yellow-(very pale magenta)-blue filter assembly is adjusted in position until
the attenuated currents from the blue and red-plus-green photo-cells are equal. The
position of the (yellowish magenta)-(pale magenta)-(yellowish cyan) filter assembly
is adjusted simultaneously until the attenuated currents from the red and green photo-
cells are equal. The yellow, very pale magenta, and blue filters are chosen so that
their red to green transmission ratios are all the same, and this ensures that movement
of this filter assembly does not affect the red to green ratio being monitored by the
other photo-cells. The yellowish magenta filter absorbs most of the green light and
half of the blue light; the yellowish cyan filter absorbs most of the red light and
half of the blue light; therefore operation of this filter assembly does not affect the
blue to red-plus-green equality being obtained with the other filter assembly. To
achieve this result with real filters, the pale magenta filter is chosen to have: (a)
twice the blue transmission of the yellowish magenta and yellowish cyan; (b) the
same red transmission as the yellowish magenta filter ensuring that the latter does
not affect the amount of red light present; (c) the same green transmission as the
yellowish cyan filter ensuring that the latter does not affect the amount of green light
present.

slightly more green exposure so that the lighter areas in the prints are too yellow-red. At the over-exposure end, with the bluish illuminant, Fig. 14.7(a), the light parts of the scene have too little blue, and slightly too little green, density so that they will appear too yellow-red in the prints; whereas with the yellowish illuminant, Fig. 14.7(b), the light parts of the scene have too little red, and slightly too little green, density, so that they will appear too cyan-blue on the prints.

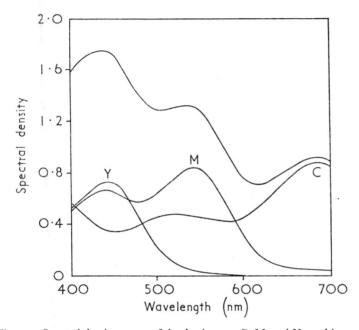

Fig. 14.9. Spectral density curves of the dye images, C, M, and Y, used in a negative material with incorporated masks. The curves shown represent the combined densities of the dyes and the appropriate proportions of unused coloured couplers characteristic of a middle density area. The top curve is equal to the sum of the other three and represents the result when the material is exposed to an approximately neutral subject.

For negatives which are not under- or over-exposed any kinks or bends in a curve (which are not exactly paralleled at the corresponding exposure level in the other two curves), may similarly have important effects on the prints. Since the quality of prints made from severely over- and under-exposed negatives can never be good in any case, slope control is generally aimed mainly at improving those negatives whose important densities lie away from the extreme toe and shoulder portions of the film characteristic: the range covered is usually about three stops (eight times) above and below the normal exposure.

If the negative curves are straight but not parallel, then, as negative density varies, consistency of density and colour balance on the prints will be obtained if the printing system is such as to correct fully for variations in the red, green, and blue transmissions of the negatives; if this full correction is not made then non-parallelism of the negative curves will produce variations in the prints which will be functions of negative density level.

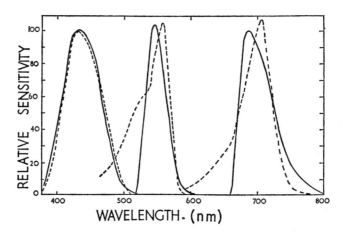

WAVELENGTH. (nm)

Fig. 14.10. Spectral sensitivity curves of colour printing paper (broken lines) and of photocells filtered with red, green, and blue filters (full lines), typical of those often used in practice.

The second factor affecting slope characteristics is the relationship between the spectral sensitivities of the filtered photo-cells and those of the paper. The spectral density curves of the dyes used in colour negative materials are not 'flat-topped', a typical set being shown in Fig. 14.9. If these dyes each absorbed uniformly throughout three separate parts of the spectrum, in each of which only one layer of the paper had any sensitivity, then, provided each filtered photo-cell had sensitivity only in one of the three parts, it would not matter how its sensitivity varied within that part. But the dyes have quite marked peaks and hence, if the sensitivity curve of one of the layers of the paper had a peak at a wavelength which coincided with one of the negative dye peaks, but the corresponding filtered photo-cell had its maximum sensitivity at a wavelength off the negative dye peak, then as that dye varied in concentration in the negative its effect on the paper could be greater than on the filtered photo-cell; if this were the case, as the density of negatives increased the monitoring system would increase the exposures by too little and the prints would be deficient in the corresponding dye. The best way of avoiding this situation

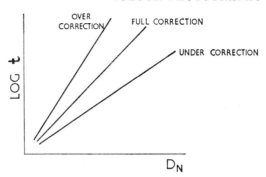

Fig. 14.11. Variation of the logarithm of the exposure time (log *t*) with the density (D_N) of the whole area of negatives for different states of correction.

is so to filter the photo-cells that the resulting sensitivity is identical with that of the paper. In practice this is very difficult to achieve because photographic sensitivity generally falls very steeply on the long wavelength side of the sensitivity band, whereas filter absorption curves with steep slopes can only be achieved on the short wavelength side of a transmission band. The best that can be achieved is often similar to that shown in Fig. 14.10 and the effect of the differences shown is often that the printer, by monitoring somewhat off the negative dye peak, under-estimates the densities and therefore under-corrects for them, a state termed *under-correction;* the converse case of over-estimation of the density, when the paper sensitivities are more off-peak than the monitoring, is termed *over-correction.* In Fig. 14.11 these two states, together with that of *full-correction,* are illustrated for one of the three channels of a colour printer by plotting log exposure time log *t* (assuming that the illumination of the negative remains at a constant level) against the density D_N of the whole area of negatives.

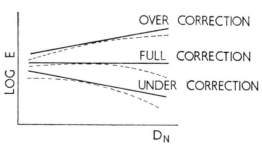

Fig. 14.12. Variation of the logarithm of the effective exposure (log E) with the density of the negative (D_N) for different states of correction: full lines, without paper reciprocity effects; broken lines, with paper reciprocity effects.

The third factor affecting slope control (in variable-time printers only) is the *reciprocity characteristic* of the paper. In black-and-white materials it is well known that if an exposure time is increased by a factor of ten to compensate for a reduction in intensity to one-tenth, then the result is not exactly the same. In colour materials slight differences in the reciprocity characteristics of three layers of a paper can result in important variations of colour balance. If, therefore, the effects of paper reciprocity are now combined with printer monitor mismatch, the type of result depicted in Figs. 14.12 and 14.13 can be obtained. In Fig. 14.12 the full lines represent the same data as shown in Fig. 14.11 but this time the log of the exposure (log E) of the paper has been plotted as ordinate; this log exposure would vary linearly with print density if the paper exhibited no reciprocity effects. The dotted lines show how the result might be modified by reciprocity effects of the paper. Fig. 14.13 shows how these effects, operating at different magnitudes in the three channels of a colour printer, might be combined in a practical case; in this figure, print density (D_P) is plotted against negative density. In this example thin negatives produce dark magenta-blue prints, while dense negatives produce light yellow-green prints.

The fourth factor affecting slope control is the reciprocity characteristic of the electronics of the printer; by suitable choice of circuits and conditions the effect of this can usually be made small compared with the other factors.

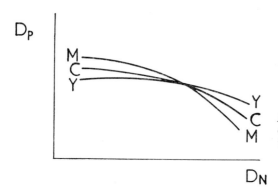

Fig. 14.13. Possible variation of print density (D_P) with the density (D_N) of the whole area of negatives in each layer (C, M, and Y) of the paper.

14.16 Methods of slope control

It is the function of the slope control circuits of a colour printer to modify situations such as those depicted in Fig. 14.13 to more favourable states. In Section 14.8 it was pointed out that the shift transformers of the 1599 printers could make the red, green, and blue exposures partially dependent on negative density; thus, by separate adjustment of the shift transformer in each of the three colour channels, the curves of the type shown in Fig. 14.13 can be approximately superimposed and tilted to be as flat as possible, so as to yield prints of roughly constant density and colour balance from negatives of widely different densities.

Another method of slope control, which is widely used on variable time printers, is to make the sensitivity of the electronic integrating circuits vary with time during the exposure cycle (Pieronek, Syverud, and Voglesong, 1956). One way of accomplishing this will now be described as an example. The exposure, E, given by each channel of a variable time printer is not only dependent on the current from the photo-cell but is also proportional to the voltage, V, through which its integrating condenser has to be charged before the exposure terminating mechanism is set in motion. If this voltage is made to vary with time, then, since dense negatives require longer exposures than thin negatives, it is possible to alter the exposures in a way that is dependent on negative density, and hence the possibility is provided of altering the characteristics of Fig. 14.13.

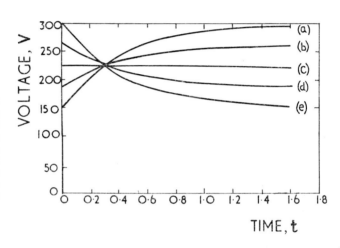

Fig. 14.14. The voltage (V), through which the integrating condenser has to be charged, can be made to vary with time (t) by switching it from one voltage to another through a suitable resistor-capacitor circuit.

The voltage, V, can be made time-dependent by switching from one value to another through a resistor-capacitor circuit having an appropriate time-constant. In such a circuit the difference, V_t, between the voltage at any instant and the final voltage varies exponentially with time; that is to say, in each unit of time the logarithm of this voltage difference, V_t, alters by the same amount. This type of characteristic is of little use for slope control. what is required is linearity of log voltage with *log time* not linearity with *time*. An approximation to the required characteristic is obtained, however, when the varying voltage difference, V_t, is added to, or subtracted from, a constant voltage V_c.

In order to examine the nature of this approximation in some detail, let us first consider the case where the varying voltage difference, V_t, covers a range of 150 volts and is added to a constant voltage, V_c, of 150. Thus, as depicted in Fig. 14.14, curve (a), the voltage, V, starts at 150 and gradually rises to 300, the rate of growth being exponential with time. In Fig. 14.15, log V, instead of V, has been plotted against log time instead of time, and it is seen that curve (a) has now become approximately a straight line over a range of times of about one log unit (ten to one). The other curves, (b), (c), (d), and (e) in Figs. 14.14 and 14.15 represent the cases where the constant voltage and the range of the varying voltage have the following values:

$$\begin{array}{lll}
\text{(b)} & V_c = 187.5 & V_t = 75 \\
\text{(c)} & V_c = 225 & V_t = 0 \\
\text{(d)} & V_c = 262.5 & V_t = -75 \\
\text{(e)} & V_c = 300 & V_t = -150
\end{array}$$

It is seen that in each case the exponential curve shape in Fig. 14.14 has become approximately linear over a range of one log unit in time in Fig. 14.15. It will be noted also that the curves all pass through a common point $(V = 225)$ at approximately the centre of the range of log times for which the curves are linear and it is to achieve this result that the rather odd values of V_c and V_t listed above were chosen. It is thus clear that by adjusting V_c and V_t in this way, it is possible to adjust the slope of the log V, log t curve.

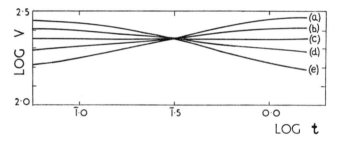

Fig. 14.15. The data of Fig. 14.14 replotted as the logarithm of the voltage against the logarithm of the time.

When this is done in a printer, since the density on the print is approximately proportional to the log exposure received by the paper, and this log exposure is proportional to the log voltage through which the integrating condenser has to be charged, the effect is to tilt the print-density versus negative-density curves of the type in Fig. 14.13. By having separate facilities for adjusting the slope of the log V, log t relationship in each of the three channels of the printer it becomes possible to make the curves of Fig. 14.13 more nearly coincident, and hence to reduce the variation of colour balance with exposure time, and also to make them more nearly horizontal and hence to reduce the variation of print density with exposure time. This procedure is known as adjusting *slope value*.

The range of densities of the whole area of negatives usually encountered in practice amounts to about 1.2 (this corresponds, for negatives of gamma 0.67, to a log exposure range of 1.8, or 6 stops, generally from three stops under-exposed to three stops over-exposed). This range of 1.2 in density is very similar to the range of log times for which the slope-control characteristic is approximately linear, and hence the slope control can be made to cover most of the important part of the curves of Fig. 14.7. This is ensured in practice by having the resistor in the resistor-condenser circuit adjustable; the effect of altering the resistance is to multiply all the times operating in the slope circuit by a constant factor, and thus to shift the log V, log t curves along the log t axis, as shown in Fig. 14.16. This adjustment is known as altering *slope centre*. Since the mid-voltage point is approximately in the centre of the part of the log-time range for which the characteristic is linear, it is customary to adjust the slope centre so that normally-exposed negatives print at the mid-voltage point, as is the case for the middle curve in Fig. 14.16 (log 225 = 2.35).

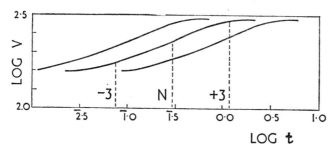

Fig. 14.16. Movement of the log V, log t characteristic along the log t axis in order to accommodate, mainly on the straight line region, the range of negative densities from three stops under-exposed (-3) to three stops over-exposed ($+3$).

It can be seen from Fig. 14.16 that a positive slope, that is, log V increasing with log t, results in a lengthening of exposure times for dense negatives and a shortening of exposure times for thin negatives; hence the print densities will be increased when dense negatives are printed, and it is this type of correction which is required to make the results of Fig. 14.13 more nearly horizontal. Negative slope, that is log V, decreasing with log t, results in the opposite effects. By careful adjustment of the sign and magnitude of the slope value the appropriate correction can therefore be obtained, and when the time range over which this correction operates is at the appropriate slope centre, the majority of the negatives are affected. Proper adjustment of slope value and slope centre controls in each integrating circuit enables a high yield of good prints to be obtained from negatives covering a wide range of exposure levels.

REFERENCES

Bartleson, C. J., *Phot. Sci. Eng.*, **2,** 32 (1958).
Bartleson, C. J., and Huboi, R. W., *J. Soc. Mot. Pic. Tel. Eng.*, **65,** 205 (1956).
Blaxland, J., *Brit. J. Phot.*, **107,** 638 (1960).
Blaxland, J., *Brit. J. Phot.*, **108,** 706 (1961).
Blaxland, J., *Brit. J. Phot.*, **113,** 1029 (1965).
Calkin, R. B., Hunt, R. W. G., and Letzer, E. K., *Phot. Sci. Eng.*, **5,** 366 (1961).
Coote, J. H., *Perspective*, **3,** 265 (1961).
Evans, R. M., *J. Opt. Soc. Amer.*, **33,** 579 (1943).
Evans, R. M., British Patent 660,099; U.S. Patent 2,571, 697 (1946).
Goddard, M. C., and Huboi, R. W., U.S. Patent 3,029,691 (1958).
Gundelfinger, A. M., Taylor, E. A., and Yancey, R. W., *Phot Sci. Eng.*, **4,** 141 (1960).
Hunt, R. W. G., *J. Phot. Sci.*, **8,** 186 (1960a).
Hunt, R. W. G., *J. Phot. Sci.*, **8,** 212 (1960b).
Hunt, R. W. G., *J. Phot. Sci.*, **11,** 109 (1963).
James, T. H., and Higgins, G. C., *Fundamentals of Photographic Theory* (2nd Edition), Morgan and Morgan, New York, pp. 237 and 241 (1960).
McRae, D. H., and Halliday, R. E. J., *J. Soc. Mot. Pic. Tel. Eng.*, **75,** 846 (1966).
Pieronek, V. R., Syverud, W. L., and Voglesong, W. F., *Photogr. Sci. Techn.* (*P.S.A. Technical Quarterly Series II*), **3,** 145 (1956).
Pinney, J. E., and DeMarsh, E. E., *J. Phot. Sci.*, **11,** 249 (1963).
Pitt, F. H. G., and Selwyn, E. W. H., *Phot. J.*, **78,** 115 (1938).
Richardson, A. W., *Brit. J. Phot.*, **105,** 639 (1958).
Richardson, A. W., *Brit. J. Phot.*, **106,** 497 (1959).

CHAPTER 15

The Chemistry of
Colour Photography

1. Colour development – *2.* Developing agents – *3.* Couplers – *4.* Coloured couplers – *5.* The dye-coupling reaction – *6.* The physical form of dye images – *7.* Colour developing solutions – *8.* Silver bleaching – *9.* Processing sequences – *10.* Dye-bleach and dye-removal systems

15.1 Colour development

IT has been known for many years that when certain developing agents are used to develop ordinary black-and-white photographic materials, a coloured deposit occurs as well as the silver image. Thus pyrogallol produces a brown stain and, since this is laid down in proportion to the silver image, it can be considered as a dye image. In this case the dye consists of polymerized oxidized developer. This method of forming dye images is sometimes called *primary colour development.*

Another method can be described as *self-coupling development;* in this case molecules of the developing agent, after becoming oxidized by developing the silver image, then react with the unoxidized form to produce the dye image. In this case the developing agent could be a leuco dye. Thus Homolka in 1907 found that indoxyl and thioindoxyl when used as developing agents produced blue and red dye images of indigo and thioindigo, respectively, in addition to the silver image. But none of the above systems of producing dye images has ever been useful in colour photography, because of the poor properties of both the developing agents that can be used and the dyes which they form.

Almost all modern processes depend on what is sometimes called *secondary colour development* in which the oxidized developer reacts with another substance, normally called a coupler, to form the required dye image. The differences between these three types of dye image formation can be illustrated thus:

291

(a) *Primary colour development*

$$\text{Developing agent} + Ag^+Br^- \rightarrow \begin{array}{c}\text{Oxidized developing}\\\text{agent which is an}\\\text{insoluble dye.}\end{array} + Ag + H^+ + Br^-$$

(b) *Self-coupling development*

$$\text{Developing agent} + Ag^+Br^- \rightarrow \begin{array}{c}\text{Oxidized}\\\text{developing agent}\end{array} + Ag + H^+ + Br^-$$

$+$ developing agent

insoluble dye

(c) *Secondary colour development*

$$\text{Developing agent} + Ag^+Br^- \rightarrow \begin{array}{c}\text{Oxidized}\\\text{developing agent}\end{array} + Ag + H^+ + Br^-$$

$+$ coupler

insoluble dye

It will be seen that in all three cases both silver and dye images are formed and hydrogen and bromide ions are added to the solution.

It was Rudolf Fischer who, in 1912, first demonstrated the use of couplers to form image dyes by secondary colour development, and it is interesting that the work he did at this time still forms the basis of almost every modern colour photographic process. For not only did he demonstrate the general principle of dye-coupling development, but the art is still confined to one of the two types of developing agent, and to two of the five types of dye, described by him.

The two types of developing agent described by Fischer are, *p*-aminophenol and *p*-phenylenediamine (or their derivatives).

$$NH_2 \text{—} \langle \text{—} \rangle \text{—} OH \qquad NH_2 \text{—} \langle \text{—} \rangle \text{—} NH_2$$

p-aminophenol   *p*-phenylenediamine
                          (or *p*-aminoaniline)

The five types of dye, which Fischer discovered could be formed when silver images are developed by these two developing agents in the presence of suitable couplers, are as follows (where R represents alkyl radicals, CH_3, C_2H_5, etc.):

indophenols $\quad O = \langle\!\!\!\rangle = N' - \langle\!\!\!\rangle - OH$

indoanilines $\quad O = \langle\!\!\!\rangle = N - \langle\!\!\!\rangle - NR_2$

indamines $\quad NH = \langle\!\!\!\rangle = N - \langle\!\!\!\rangle - NR_2$

indothiophenols $\quad O = \langle\!\!\!\rangle = N - \langle\!\!\!\rangle - SH$

azomethines $\quad {}^{X}_{Y}\!\!> C = N - \langle\!\!\!\rangle - NR_2$

These classes of dye were already known when Fischer did his work, but it was he who discovered that the photographic latent image could be used to promote their formation from 'coupler' and 'developing agent'. Of these dyes only the indoaniline and azomethine types have been found to possess the necessary properties, the others all suffering from some serious defects: thus the indamines cannot be formed quickly enough, and the colour of the indophenols is sensitive to slight changes in acidity. Since it is only p-phenylene-diamine and its derivatives that can form the indoaniline and azomethine dyes, it has become virtually the only colour developing agent to be used, p-aminophenol being of only theoretical interest.

15.2 Developing agents

A good photographic developing agent must react with the latent image at a reasonable rate, it must show good discrimination between the exposed and unexposed silver halide grains so as to develop the image with little or no 'fog', it must not decompose too rapidly as a result of aerial oxidation or other causes, and for colour work it must of course result in the formation of dyes having good colour and stability. Because of failure in a number of these respects, little application has been found for p-phenylenediamine itself, and its derivatives have been used instead. Combination with the couplers occurs at a free amino (NH_2) group, so that in devising derivatives, whatever other changes are made, a free amino group must be retained.

The only p-phenylenediamine derivatives which have found practical use as colour developing agents are those in which both the hydrogen atoms of one of the amino groups are replaced by alkyl groups thus:

$$NH_2 - \langle\!\!\!\rangle - N {<}^{R}_{R}$$

293

Of these N:N-dialkyl-p-phenylenediamines the two simplest are:

N:N-dimethyl-p-phenylenediamine
(p-aminodimethylaniline)

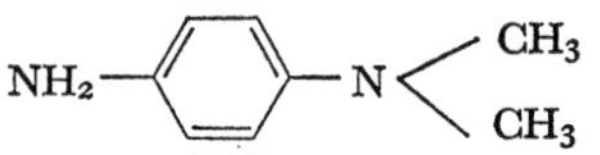

N:N-diethyl-p-phenylenediamine
(or p-aminodiethylaniline)

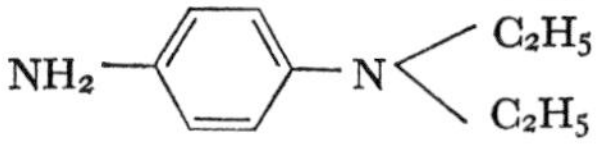

The second of these has proved of considerable practical value.

To effect development, the developing agent molecule must donate an electron to a silver ion, and it has been found that the addition of an alkyl group to the benzene ring, at the *ortho* position relative to the coupling amino group, facilitates this donation and thus increases the activity of the developing agent and reduces development times. This leads to structures of the general type:

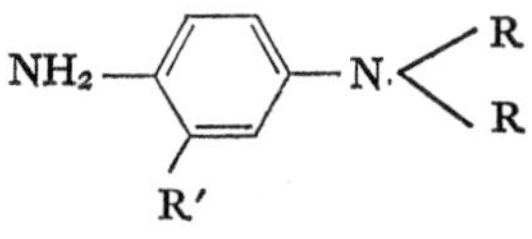

of which a specific example is:

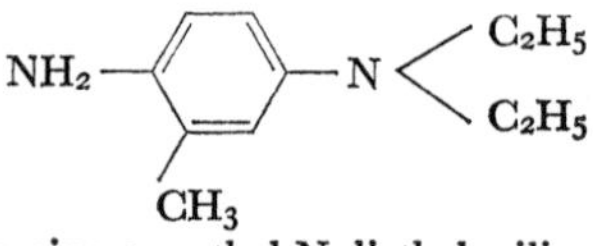

4-amino-3-methyl-N-diethylaniline.

A serious hazard with all these developing agents is that on contact with human skin dermatitis is frequently caused; moreover, subjects who are affected in this way do not acquire a resistance to the effect but actually become increasingly sensitive to it. Efforts have therefore been made to produce derivatives which are less prone to cause dermatitis and this often results in one of the groups attached to the substituted amino group being modified, giving the general structure:

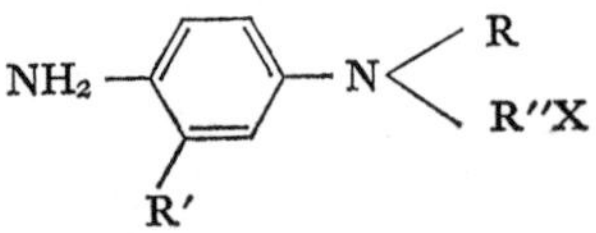

where R, and R' are alkyl groups and R'' is an alkylene group bearing the substituent X. Examples of this type of structure are:

$$NH_2 - \hspace{-1em}\bigcirc\hspace{-1em} - N \hspace{-0.5em}<\hspace{-0.5em} \begin{array}{l} C_2H_5 \\ C_2H_4OH \end{array}$$

$$NH_2 - \hspace{-1em}\bigcirc\hspace{-1em} - N \hspace{-0.5em}<\hspace{-0.5em} \begin{array}{l} C_2H_5 \\ C_2H_4NSO_2CH_3 \\ \hspace{2.5em}| \\ \hspace{2.5em}H \end{array}$$
$$CH_3$$

$$NH_2 - \hspace{-1em}\bigcirc\hspace{-1em} - N \hspace{-0.5em}<\hspace{-0.5em} \begin{array}{l} C_2H_5 \\ C_2H_4OH \end{array}$$
$$CH_3$$

These p-phenylenediamine derivatives are easily oxidized by air and they are therefore usually made available as salts or complexes. In this way their stability as dry solids can be made quite satisfactory, and a further advantage is that their solubility in water is much improved, thus facilitating the mixing of developer solutions. The following are examples of developing agent salts:

$$NH_2 - \hspace{-1em}\bigcirc\hspace{-1em} - N \hspace{-0.5em}<\hspace{-0.5em} \begin{array}{l} C_2H_5 \\ C_2H_5 \end{array} \cdot HCl$$

Kodak developing agent CD1.

$$NH_2 - \hspace{-1em}\bigcirc\hspace{-1em} - N \hspace{-0.5em}<\hspace{-0.5em} \begin{array}{l} C_2H_5 \\ C_2H_5 \end{array} \cdot HCl$$
$$CH_3$$

Kodak developing agent CD2.

$$NH_2 - \hspace{-1em}\bigcirc\hspace{-1em} - N \hspace{-0.5em}<\hspace{-0.5em} \begin{array}{l} C_2H_5 \\ C_2H_4NSO_2CH_3 \\ \hspace{2.5em}| \\ \hspace{2.5em}H \end{array} \cdot \tfrac{3}{2}H_2SO_4 \cdot H_2O$$
$$CH_3$$

Kodak developing agent CD3.

15.3 Couplers

While useful colour developing agents are all derivations of a single basic structure, p-phenylenediamine, useful couplers cover a much wider range of compounds. They can, however, be divided into three main groups:

(a) Compounds with an active open-chain methylene ($-CH_2-$) group.

(b) Compounds with an active cyclic methylene ($\ldots-CH_2-\ldots$) group.

(c) Phenolic compounds with an active methine ($-CH =$) group.

Yellow couplers are usually in group (a), magenta in groups (a) and (b), and cyan in group (c).

Thus yellow couplers are usually of the form

$$X - CH_2 - Y$$

where $X = RCO$, and $Y = R'CO$ or $R'NHCO$. The coupling takes place by replacement of the two hydrogen atoms, so that the formation of a yellow dye image can be represented thus:

$$\begin{array}{c} X \\ | \\ CH_2 \\ | \\ Y \end{array} + NH_2 -\!\!\!\langle\bigcirc\rangle\!\!\!- N\!\!\begin{array}{c} {}^{/}C_2H_5 \\ {}_{\backslash}C_2H_5 \end{array} \quad + 4Ag^+Br^-$$

Coupler   Developing agent

$$\longrightarrow \begin{array}{c} X \\ | \\ C = N -\!\!\!\langle\bigcirc\rangle\!\!\!- N\!\!\begin{array}{c} {}^{/}C_2H_5 \\ {}_{\backslash}C_2H_5 \end{array} + 4Ag + 4H^+ + 4Br^- \\ | \\ Y \end{array}$$

Azomethine dye

A most useful class of cyclic methylene magenta couplers are pyrazolones having the form:

$$\begin{array}{c} X-C\!-\!CH_2 \\ \|\quad\;\; | \\ N\quad C = O \\ \diagdown\!\diagup \\ N \\ | \\ Ar \end{array}$$

where Ar is an aromatic (containing a benzene ring) group and X is another group. As with the yellow couplers, the coupling occurs by the replacement of the two hydrogen atoms thus:

$$\begin{array}{c} X-C\!-\!CH_2 \\ \|\quad\;\; | \\ N\quad C = O \\ \diagdown\!\diagup \\ N \\ | \\ Ar \end{array} + NH_2 -\!\!\!\langle\bigcirc\rangle\!\!\!- N\!\!\begin{array}{c} {}^{/}C_2H_5 \\ {}_{\backslash}C_2H_5 \end{array} + 4Ag^+Br^-$$

Coupler   Developing agent

$$\longrightarrow \begin{array}{c} X-C\!-\!C = N -\!\!\!\langle\bigcirc\rangle\!\!\!- N\!\!\begin{array}{c} {}^{/}C_2H_5 \\ {}_{\backslash}C_2H_5 \end{array} + 4Ag + 4H^+ + 4Br^- \\ \|\quad\;\; | \\ N\quad C = O \\ \diagdown\!\diagup \\ N \\ | \\ Ar \end{array}$$

Ar   Azomethine dye

In the phenolic cyan couplers coupling takes place by replacement of the hydrogen atom at the position in the ring opposite (*para*) to a hydroxyl (—OH) group. The simplest compound of this class is phenol:

but couplers can also be based on α-naphthol

and have the general structure

where **X** and **Y** are various groups.
The coupling reaction can therefore be represented thus:

Coupler   Developing agent

Indoaniline dye

Sometimes the hydrogen atom at the coupling position of the coupler is replaced by a chlorine atom, and in this case the coupling reaction occurs thus:

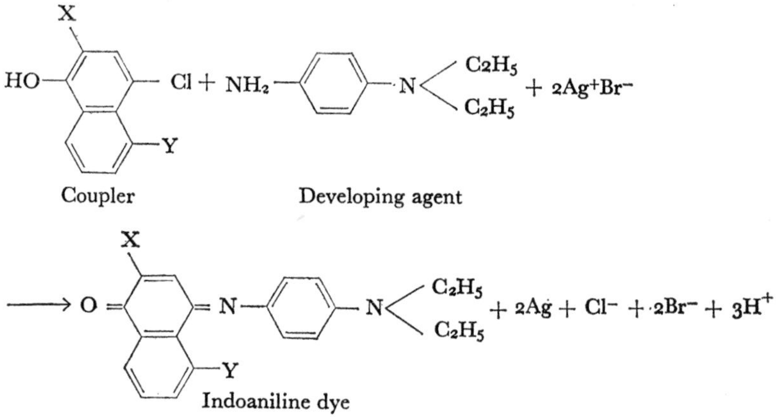

Coupler   Developing agent

Indoaniline dye

It is seen that the same dye is formed as before but each molecule of developing agent now only results in two molecules of silver bromide being reduced instead of four; thus the same amount of dye is produced from only half the amount of latent-image silver.

A very large number, probably thousands, of couplers of various structures have been made and tried for colour processes. Amongst the properties of the coupler which are important in deciding upon its usefulness are:

> its rate of reaction
> its solubility
> its proneness to wandering
> its colour
> the solubility of the dye formed
> the stability of the dye formed
> the colour of the dye formed.

The rate of reaction of couplers is an important property since very lengthy colour development is generally inconvenient, and it is obviously desirable in most colour processes for the three dye images to be formed at similar rates. The rate of reaction will be affected by the amount of silver halide required to be reduced to form a molecule of dye, but other features of the coupler structure besides the presence or absence of a halogen atom at the point of coupling are important in this respect. If a coupler forms too much dye, there can be mixed with it a 'competing' coupler producing with oxidized developer a soluble compound which washes out, thus reducing the final amount of dye in the image.

If the coupler is to be used in the developing solutions, as in the Kodachrome type of process, it must clearly be soluble in them; it must also be able to penetrate the gelatin layers and hence the molecule must be fairly small. If, on the other hand, the coupler is to be dispersed in oily droplets in the emulsion layers, as in the Kodacolor system, it must have the necessary solubility in the oil used, sych as tricresyl phosphate, triphenyl phosphate, *n*-butyl phthalate, or *n*-hexyl benzoate, etc. If the coupler is dispersed directly in the emulsion layers as in the Agfacolor system, it must not wander from one layer to another; this feature is generally achieved by making the coupler molecule so large, by the addition of a 'ballast' group, that it cannot pass through the sponge-like network of the gelatin layer. Even when the couplers are dispersed in oily droplets, it is necessary to add a ballast to prevent wandering.

In most instances it is required that a coupler be colourless itself, so that non-image areas are clear; in some colour negatives, however, it can be advantageous for the coupler to be coloured (see Section 13.3) and this again is achieved by modifications to its structure.

As regards the dye formed by the coupler, it must be insoluble (unless the process is one in which the dye is required to transfer from the layer con-

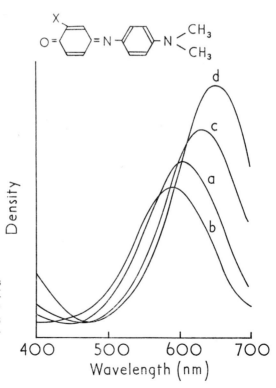

Fig. 15.1. Spectral absorption curves of dyes related to phenol blue. X indicates (a) H (phenol blue); (b) CH_3; (c) Cl; (d) CH $=$ $CHCOC_6H_5$ (Evans, Hanson, and Brewer, 1953).

taining the silver image to a mordanted receiving sheet; in this latter case insolubility after mordanting is what is required). The dye must be stable to light, heat and humidity, and, while complete stability of any organic dye seems almost impossible to achieve, the couplers now used in many processes give dyes of stability adequate for most purposes.

Finally, of course, the colour of the dye should be as near as possible to the ideal required for the particular process. Some examples of the way in which the colour can be varied in a simple system by structural changes are shown in Fig. 15.1. The colour in the image is also affected by its physical form in the photographic layer, but this will be dealt with in Section 15.6.

In view of all the above considerations, it is not surprising that much effort has gone into modifying coupler structures in order to gain better characteristics. In the case of yellows, the most useful are generally acylacetamides:

$$RCOCH_2CON{\Large<}^a_b$$

An example of this type of coupler is:

$$OC_{15}H_{31}$$

ω-Benzoylacet-(2-n-pentadecyloxy)-4- sulphoanilide.

In this example the pentadecyl group $(C_{15}H_{31})$ is the ballast, while the sulphonic acid group (SO_3H) confers solubility in aqueous media.

As has already been pointed out, the most useful magenta couplers found so far are pyrazolones.

An example of a magenta pyrazolone is:

1-phenyl-3-benzamidopyrazol-5-one.

As already indicated, the most useful cyan couplers are based on naphthol and an example of a cyan ballasted coupler is:

1-stearoylamido-4(1′-hydroxy-2′-naphthoylamido)-benzene-3-sulphonic acid.

In this example, the SO_3H group provides the solubility, and the $C_{17}H_{35}$ group provides the ballast to prevent wandering; the magenta coupler cited has no large ballast group and is thus suitable for use in developing solutions.

15.4 Coloured couplers

By using couplers which are themselves coloured, then, as described in Section 13.3, a very convenient method of colour correction by masking can be achieved. A coupler can be made coloured by adding to it a suitable chromophoric substituent, and masking is achieved if this colour is present in proportion to the amount of *unused* coupler in the image.

One way of achieving this is to add the chromophore group after development has taken place. For example, if a coupler which forms magenta dye can, in its uncoupled state, be converted to a yellow dye without harming the magenta image, then a yellow positive image can be formed from the unused coupler so as to mask the magenta negative image; an example of this principle was used in the Icicolor process in the following way. The magenta-forming coupler, a styryl pyrazolone, was heated with an aromatic aldehyde before coating to form a mixture of a yellow styryl dye and an aldehyde-bis-pyrazolone; in the colour developer this yellow dye was completely discharged, irrespective of the presence of developable silver halide, and oxidized developer converted the coupler to magenta dye in exposed areas as usual; but subsequent treatment with formaldehyde reformed the yellow dye in the areas where the coupler had not been used and hence masking was achieved. A reddish mask was also formed in the Icicolor cyan layer by incorporating the formaldehyde in a stop bath following the colour development step: the simultaneous presence of formaldehyde and colour developing agent (carried over by the film into the stop bath) resulted in the unused cyan coupler being converted to an intermediate compound which was converted to the required reddish colour subsequently in an acid bleach bath. (Gehret, 1964; Ganguin and MacDonald, 1966.)

Another way of achieving masking by the use of coloured couplers is to add the chromophoric substituent to the coupler before processing and to arrange that the coupling step destroys the colour of the coupler, so that its coloration remains only where it is unused. This can be done by adding the chromophore group to the coupler at the coupling position so that the colour development step consists of replacing it by the oxidized developer fragment. The following is an example of this type of reaction:

$$C_6H_5CONH-\underset{\underset{\overset{|}{N}}{\|}}{C}-\underset{\underset{\overset{\|}{C=O}}{|}}{CH}-N = N-C_6H_5 + NH_2\text{—}\underset{}{\bigcirc}\text{—}N\begin{smallmatrix}C_2H_5\\C_2H_5\end{smallmatrix} + 2Ag^+Br^-$$

N
|
C$_6$H$_5$

Coloured Coupler   Developing agent

$$\longrightarrow \quad C_6H_5CONH-\underset{\underset{\overset{|}{N}}{\|}}{C}-\underset{\underset{\overset{\|}{C=O}}{|}}{C} = N\text{—}\bigcirc\text{—}N\begin{smallmatrix}C_2H_5\\C_2H_5\end{smallmatrix} + C_6H_6 + 2Ag + 2H^+ + 2Br^- + N_2$$

N
|
C$_6$H$_5$

Azomethine dye

It is seen that, as in the case where a chlorine atom was substituted at the coupling position in a cyan coupler, so the substitution of the chromophore at the coupling position of this magenta coupler results in only two silver bromide molecules being required for the formation of each molecule of dye. it is often convenient in practice to work with a mixture of coloured and uncoloured couplers, because by adjusting their relative quantities the amount of coloration in the non-image areas can then be controlled quite accurately.

15.5 The dye-coupling reaction

The equations given earlier for the dye-coupling reactions are only simplifications: in the actual process a number of intermediate compounds are formed, some of which are highly unstable and therefore of very short life. The developing agent, on reacting with the silver ions, is oxidized to a quinone diimine, thus:

$$H_2\ddot{N}\text{—}\bigcirc\text{—}\ddot{N}R_2 + 2Ag^+ \longrightarrow H-\overset{+}{\underset{\cdot\cdot}{N}}\text{—}\bigcirc\text{—}NR_2 + 2Ag + H^+$$

Two contributing structures to the resonance-stabilized quinone diimine are:

$$H-N=\bigcirc=\overset{+}{N}R_2 \longleftrightarrow H-\overset{+}{\underset{\cdot\cdot}{N}}\text{—}\bigcirc\text{—}NR_2$$

There is good evidence that at the alkalinity used in development (pH 10 to 12) the quinone diimine is the coupling species. A leuco dye is first formed, thus:

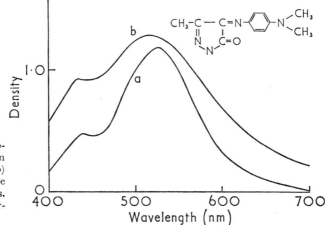

The leuco dye is then oxidized to the dye:

The quinone diimine and its semiquinone precursor are also involved in competing side reactions.

Fig. 15.2. Spectral absorption curves of a dye (a) in solution (Methanol); (b) in a photographic image when laid down in clumps. (Vittum, and Weissburger, 1954.)

15.6 The physical form of dye images

If a dye is laid down in large clumps (for example, around large silver grains) with clear interstices, the same degradation of colour will occur as is the case with an ink printed as a half-tone dot pattern (Pollak, 1955; Pollak and Hepher,

1956); the use of the dye at high concentrations over part of the area exaggerates the effects of the unwanted absorptions as compared to the use of the dye at a lower concentration over all of the area (Gledhill and Julian, 1962). An example of this is given in Fig. 15.2. If, however, the dye is formed more uniformly and without clear interstices, as would be facilitated if the dye image consisted of several layers of dye 'grains', then the absorption is more like that in solution. Occasionally, the dye in the image shows a sharper absorption band than in solution, with the absorption peak shifted to shorter wavelengths as shown in Fig. 15.3; this may indicate that the dye in the image is microcrystalline instead of being in the usual amorphous state.

Another physical factor affecting the colour of the dye is the number of times the light passes through it and, as explained in Section 11.8, this has the effect of exaggerating the unwanted absorptions of a dye when it is used in reflection prints.

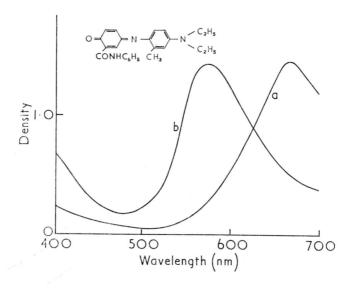

Fig. 15.3. Spectral absorption curves of a dye (a) in solution (n-butyl acetate); (b) in a photographic image when laid down in microcrystalline form. (Vittum and Weissburger, 1954.)

15.7 Colour developing solutions

In addition to the developing agent, a colour developing solution has to have a number of other constituents. First, because most developing agents act as such on photographic latent images only when in alkaline solution, it is necessary to have suitable alkalis, usually sodium carbonate and caustic soda (sodium hydroxide). Then a buffer is required to maintain the alkalinity at as nearly as possible a constant level, and this may be provided by a sodium carbonate and bicarbonate mixture (the bicarbonate usually being derived from the reaction between the carbonate and the developing agent salt), or a sodium metaborate and borax mixture, or a dibasic and tribasic sodium phosphate mixture, according to the alkalinity (pH) required. A small amount of sulphite acts as a preservative by combining with any developing agent which has become partially oxidized by contact with air (the inert colourless compound formed is far less injurious to the developer than the partially oxidized developing agent which accelerates further oxidation and leads eventually to the formation of brown stains). Then additions are made to reduce the tendency for *un*exposed silver-halide grains to develop; these are termed *antifoggants*, and often take the form of bromide ions, added as potassium bromide, or organic antifoggants may be used instead or in addition. Further additions may be made to obtain various effects: competing developing agents to reduce dye formation; anti-stain agents to lower the density in undeveloped areas; and accelerators such as thiocyanate (to act as a silver halide solvent) and benzyl alcohol (which accelerates the dye-forming reaction). Constituents may also be added to promote the occurrence of favourable inter-image effects (see Section 13.4).

15.8 Silver bleaching

Although the required dye image is complete as soon as the colour development step has been terminated, unless the dye is at this point transferred to another support the photographic material must then be given a series of treatments in order that all harmful residues are removed. It is thus necessary to remove the silver image, which if left behind would greatly darken the dye image; and also the unused silver halide must be removed, because it darkens on exposure to light and would therefore produce a dark and stained appearance. Removal of unused silver halide is accomplished in the usual way by 'fixing' in 'hypo' (sodium thiosulphate), and the unwanted silver is also removed at the same stage, by reconverting it at an earlier stage to silver halide by means of a suitable bleach such as potassium ferricyanide. The bleaching reaction can then be represented by:

$$Ag + K_3Fe(CN)_6 + KBr \longrightarrow AgBr + K_4Fe(CN)_6$$

and the fixing step by:

$$AgBr + Na_2S_2O_3 \longrightarrow NaAgS_2O_3 + NaBr$$
$$NaAgS_2O_3 + Na_2S_2O_3 \longrightarrow Na_3[Ag(S_2O_3)_2]$$

the constituent on the right-hand side of the last equation being soluble and therefore washing out. Another common bleaching agent is potassium bi-chromate; and sometimes ammonium thiosulphate, $(NH_4)_2S_2O_3$, is used for fixing, having the advantage of being more rapid in the case of emulsions containing iodide.

It is sometimes convenient to bleach and fix in the same solution, and such solutions are known as *blixes*. If the blix can be used quickly and then discarded, it can be made by simply combining ferricyanide and hypo. However, this mixture quickly decomposes and therefore for conventional types of processing an iron-sequestrene type of blix is often used. In this type of blix, the bleaching action occurs by a ferrous-ferric reduction, just as is the case for a ferricyanide bleach, but the ferric iron is combined as a complex with ethylenediaminetetra-acetic acid (E.D.T.A.), and this prevents it from reacting with hypo when it is added to form the blix.

15.9 Processing sequences

It can be seen from the above that the minimum number of solutions required to form a dye image in a photographic emulsion layer is two: a developer and a blix; in addition, the material requires washing after the blix in order to remove all traces of silver and silver salts, and a wash between the developer and blix is desirable in order to avoid contamination of the latter by the former. In practice, however, it is rarely possible to keep colour processing sequences down to this simple two solution, four step procedure, and they are often elaborated in one or more of the following ways.

Instead of the wash between the developer and the blix an acid *stop* bath is usually preferable since this more effectively isolates the developer from the blix and also provides an abrupt (and therefore well-controlled) end-point to the development process. But because the fixing capacity of blix baths is usually somewhat limited, a stop-fix between the developer and blix is better still. This bath can be based on a mixture of sodium bisulphite to give the acidity, and sodium thiosulphate (hypo) to give the fixing action. The *undeveloped* silver halide is thus removed at this stage, and hence the blix bath has only to bleach and fix the silver which was developed in forming the image. We thus have a three solution, four step process consisting of develop, stop-fix, blix and wash.

These procedures satisfactorily remove the unwanted silver image and the unused silver halide, but in incorporated-coupler materials unused coupler is left behind. Ideally this should also be removed but no simple means have been found for extracting it. The material can, however, be treated with a *stabilizer* designed to reduce the tendency of the unused coupler to react to the detriment of the image. Thus immersion in an alkaline formalin bath sometimes prevents the coupler from reacting with the dye image and recon-verting it to the leuco form. The formalin also has a useful hardening action on the gelatin which makes the final result tougher and less liable to scratching.

It is also often found that the stability of the image dyes to fading by exposure to light can be improved by adjusting the final acidity of the image layer to a particular buffered value, and this type of treatment or *conditioning* may also reduce the tendency for the unused coupler to *print out*, that is, become yellow on exposure to light.

Better final image stability can therefore often be obtained by adding a stabilizing step or a conditioning step to the three solution process outlined above, giving a four solution process, or a five solution process if both are used. If two extra washes are added, the number of steps may then reach eight: develop, stop-fix, wash, blix, wash, stabilize, wash, condition.

It is possible to combine a fixing stage with the stabilizing step, by adding sodium thiosulphate (hypo) to the alkaline formalin, thus obtaining an alkaline formalin hardening fixing bath. This makes it possible to use a bleach instead of a blix, and sometimes this has certain advantages. Thus some image dyes do not oxidize very readily in the developer from the leuco to the final form, and the bleach, being an oxidizing agent, can be used to complete this reaction. It might be thought that with fixing at the stabilizing stage, no fixing would be necessary before the bleach so that the stop-fix could be replaced by a simple stop bath. There is sometimes, however, a tendency for developing agent to be adsorbed on to undeveloped silver halide grains in such a way that the stop bath or a wash does not remove them, and the developing agent then oxidizes in the bleach to form undesirable stains. A five solution process using a bleach instead of a blix might therefore be: develop, stop-fix, wash, bleach, wash, alkaline formalin hardening fix, wash, condition.

Finally, by splitting the stop-fix and the stabilize-fix each into their separate components a seven solution process is obtained, which with four washes comprises the following eleven steps: develop, stop, fix, wash, bleach, wash, fix, wash, stabilize, wash, condition.

Which particular process is used in any instance will depend on many factors, including the type of emulsion, the couplers, whether optimum image stability is required, the type of processing machine used, and the relative importance of cost, speed, and convenience in getting the final image. Of course, in materials in which the couplers are not incorporated, the colour development stage has to be triplicated so as to produce the cyan, magenta, and yellow images separately, and in reversal processes the colour section has to be preceded by negative (black-and-white) development and re-exposure steps, usually with a stop-bath and a wash in between them. The negative development step may be specially designed to promote the occurrence of favourable inter-image effects (see Section 13.4). Sometimes the re-exposure step is carried out chemically by adding a suitable fogging agent to the colour developer.

Processing times can be shortened by using the solutions at high temperatures, and because colour processes tend to be longer than those for black-and-white materials the black-and-white standard of 68°F is often replaced by

75°F, 85°F, or even temperatures of 100°F or more for special applications. The photographic materials have to be specially hardened to stand up to the higher temperatures and this may be done in manufacture, or the first step in the process may be a special prehardening step (sometimes followed immediately by a neutralizer to prepare the film for the developer). A coupler-incorporated reversal colour film might then have a processing sequence as follows: preharden, neutralize, first development, first stop-bath, wash, colour development, second stop-bath, wash, bleach, fix, wash, stabilize (Beilfuss, Thomas, and Zuidema, 1966); in this case the fixing and stabilizing steps are not combined, and a conditioning bath is not included.

In order to obtain images which are as sharp as possible, films usually incorporate an *anti-halation layer* to absorb light reflected from the bottom surface of the film base. Thus the back of the film base may be coated with a thin gelatin *backing-layer* containing dyes which dissolve or bleach during processing. Or a layer of silver between the bottom emulsion layer and the base may be used, in which case it is removed by the usual bleaching and fixing steps. But another form of anti-halation layer which is widely used consists of colloidal carbon in a resin, coated on the bottom surface of the base; this backing-layer is made so that it hydrolyses in alkali, and it therefore softens in the developer and can be removed. However, it is usually necessary to rub the surface in order to ensure that the backing is completely removed, and this is more conveniently done in a pre-bath than in the developer: processes intended for films having this type of backing may therefore incorporate an alkaline pre-bath and buffing stage. The buffing step is really only convenient when the film to be processed consists of long lengths, and the resin type of backing is therefore usually confined to motion picture films or still-picture films which can be joined together in long lengths for processing.

15.10 Dye-bleach and dye-removal systems

In the colour development systems based on Rudolf Fischer's work the image dyes are formed in the layers of the material during photographic development of the silver image. Some commercial success, however, has been attained with systems in which the dyes are formed by ordinary chemical means first and then incorporated in the layers; variation in concentration of the dye from point to point in the layer is then achieved by bleaching or removing it as a function of the silver photographic image.

In one such method the silver of the developed photographic image is used to bleach azo dyes in the presence of halogen acids. The reaction can be represented thus:

$$RN = NR' + 4H^+Cl^- + 4Ag \xrightarrow[\text{Catalyst}]{\text{Organic}} RNH_2 + R'NH_2 + 4Ag^+Cl^-$$

Azo dye \hspace{4cm} Bleached dye

In this case the dye is bleached most where the material has been exposed most, and hence a positive image is obtained directly. The material requires fixing after dye-bleaching, in order to remove the silver halide formed at this step. This type of process is sometimes known as *Gasparcolour* because Gaspar patented a number of its features. It was used commercially by Ilford for the material on which they made positive reflection prints from positive transparencies from 1953 to 1962. The processing steps comprised: develop, fix, dye-bleach, fix (Collins, 1960; *British Journal of Photography*, 1962). The dye-bleach bath usually contains a silver-halide complexing agent, such as thiourea, $(NH_2)CS(NH_2)$, which, by forming a complex with the silver chloride, keeps the silver-ion concentration low and hence maintains the reaction in the right direction. The function of the organic catalyst is to become reduced by the silver and then to become re-oxidized by reducing (and thus bleaching) the dye; this is important because both the dye and the silver are insoluble. A typical catalyst is 2,3 diaminophenazine. In the *Cilchrome* version of the process, colour saturation is increased by inter-image effects caused by adding the catalyst to the developer instead of to the bleach (Meyer, 1965).

An alternative to bleaching the incorporated dyes is to alter their solubility as a function of the silver photographic image. In the Polacolor system (Crawley, 1963) use is made of the fact that the solubility of catechol or hydroquinone varies as it is used to develop silver halide. Thus hydroquinone, for example, when made alkaline with sodium salts, ionizes and becomes soluble and very active as a developing agent. As a result of developing the silver halide, however, it is oxidized to quinone which is unreactive and of low solubility. These reactions can be represented thus:

$$OH - \langle \bigcirc \rangle - OH + 2NaOH \longrightarrow \left[O - \langle \bigcirc \rangle - O \right]^{--} + 2Na^+ + 2H_2O$$

Insoluble in acid conditions   Active and soluble

$$\left[O - \langle \bigcirc \rangle - O \right]^{--} + 2Ag^+Br^- \longrightarrow O = \langle \bigcirc \rangle = O + 2Ag^+2Br^-$$

Inactive and insoluble

If now a dye molecule is suitably attached to a hydroquinone molecule, the solubility of the combination can be made to alter in the above way, so that the dye is insolubilized around the developed silver. This process can be represented thus:

309

$$\text{RN} = \text{N}-\text{X} \underset{\text{O}_-}{\overset{\text{O}^-}{\underset{}{\bigcirc}}} + 2\text{Ag}^+\text{Br}^- \longrightarrow \text{RN} = \text{N}-\text{X} \underset{\text{O}}{\overset{\text{O}}{\underset{}{\bigcirc}}} + 2\text{Ag} + 2\text{Br}^-$$

| Azo-dye ionized hydroquinone compound (soluble) | Azo-dye quinone compound (insoluble) |

$$\text{RN} = \text{N}-\text{X} \underset{\text{OH}}{\overset{\text{OH}}{\underset{}{\bigcirc}}} + 2\text{NaOH} \longrightarrow \text{RN} = \text{N}-\text{X} \underset{\text{O}_-}{\overset{\text{O}^-}{\underset{}{\bigcirc}}} + 2\text{Na}^+ + \text{H}_2\text{O}$$

| Azo-dye hydroquinone compound (insoluble in acid conditions) | Azo-dye ionized-hydroquinone compound (active and soluble) |

After the formation in this way of an insoluble dye image, the rest of the dye can be washed out in an alkaline solution, and the silver bleached and fixed in the usual way. Most insoluble dye will be formed where most silver has been developed and therefore the dye image is distributed in the same sense as the silver image, thus normally giving a negative.

It is possible, however, to use this system to give direct positive images by using not the insoluble dye, but the soluble dye. In this case, after soaking in alkali to activate and solubilize the hydroquinone, the material is held in intimate contact with a suitable receiving sheet containing a mordant. Any dye that is still soluble then transfers to the receiving sheet where it is insolubilized by combining with the mordant. In this case most dye is obtained on the receiving sheet where least silver has been developed and hence a direct positive image is obtained. This arrangement has the advantage that the unwanted silver image and the unused silver halide are left behind in the original material which is discarded, and the processing therefore reduced to the very simple sequence: develop, and transfer; this enables the entire process to be completed in less than one minute.

The way in which the Polacolor system operates is depicted in Fig. 15.4. The negative material consists of three silver halide layers sensitized in the conventional manner and coated in the usual order, red next to the base, green in the middle and blue at the outside. On the base side of each layer, however, is coated a layer of dye-developer, cyan next to the red layer, magenta next to the green layer, and yellow next to the blue layer, as shown in Fig. 15.4. The yellow dye-developer layer acts as the usual yellow filter layer preventing blue light from reaching the red and green sensitive layers. The negative is processed in the camera, one picture at a time, by drawing it, together with the receiving sheet, through a pair of pressure rollers; the receiving sheet has attached to it small pods containing a viscous solution of alkali, and passage through the rollers ruptures the pods and enables the alkali to activate the dye-developers. The dye-developers then diffuse in all directions but preferentially towards the receiving sheet because of the falling concentration gradient in that direction. Wherever they encounter developable silver halide grains the dye-developer molecules will be insolubilized and will not transfer, as required to give a positive image. In order to obtain a correctly coloured

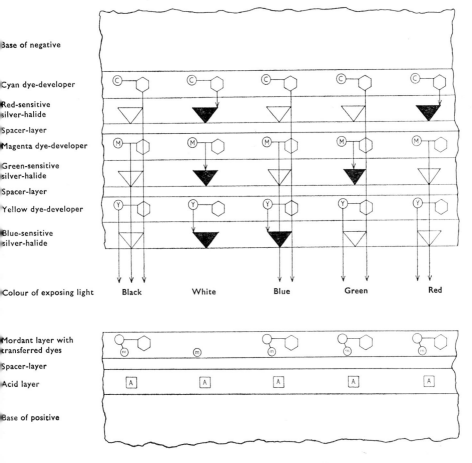

Fig. 15.4. Diagrammatic representation of the Polacolor process.

image, however, it is also necessary that the process of insolubilization of each of the three types of dye-developers be specific to its own layer; thus the cyan dye-developer must be insolubilized only by exposed silver halide grains in the red sensitive layer. To achieve this, the Polacolor system depends on the fact that before the cyan dye-developer can reach the green layer it must pass through the red layer, a spacer layer, and the magenta dye-developer layer; it will therefore take much longer to reach the green layer than the magenta dye-developer which is immediately next to it. Hence, by the time the cyan dye-developer has reached the green layer, the latter has been more or less fully developed by the magenta dye-developer and can therefore have little or no effect on the migrating cyan dye-developer molecules. Similar diffusion time factors are used to prevent the development of the blue sensitive layer by either the cyan or the magenta dye-developers; equally, any development of the green or red layers by back diffusion of the yellow or magenta dye-developers is also avoided by diffusion-time considerations. The structure of the receiving sheet is as shown at the bottom of Fig. 15.4. Its top layer contains the mordant to insolubilize the dye-developer molecules emerging from the negative material. If the receiving sheet contained nothing else, the prints would be strongly alkaline on removal from the negative, because of the transfer of alkali, as well as solubilized dye. Strongly alkaline prints would be very unpleasant to handle, and the alkaline condition would adversely affect the permanence of the dye images. It is therefore necessary to neutralize the alkali and this is the function of the bottom layer of the receiving sheet This contains acid molecules, made non-wandering by having long-chain ballast groups attached to them. The spacer layer between the mordant layer and the acid layer slows down the rate at which the alkali reaches the acid layer, thus enabling the negative and mordant layer to remain strongly alkaline as required during development, but towards the end of the development time sufficient alkali reaches the acid layer to react with it and form enough water to swell the spacer layer and assist in the neutralization reaction.

A feature of all systems in which the dyes are present in the photographic maerilal at the time of exposure is that some light is lost by absorption. These light losses are minimized if the structure is as shown in Fig. 15.4: the dyes are beneath, rather than mixed with, their associated light-sensitive layers; and the light passes through the dyes in the order yellow, magenta, cyan, so that the only unwanted absorptions involved are the green and red absorptions of the yellow dye and the red absorption of the magenta dye, which are usually quite small.

A similar transfer process can also be devised for systems using conventional colour development. Of course, the dyes can only transfer if they are highly mobile, but the couplers from which they are formed must be non-wandering, or highly immobile, since they must be incorporated in the original emulsion layers. One solution to the problem is to attach a large ballast group to the couplers at the coupling position; the oxidized developer can then replace the ballast group on coupling, thus forming a mobile dye from an immobile coupler. A reaction of this type in the case of a yellow coupler can be represented by the following:

$$X-SO_3H$$

$$H-\overset{|}{\underset{|}{C}}-Z-C_nH_{2n+1} + NH_2 - \underset{}{\bigcirc} - N \underset{C_2H_5}{\overset{C_2H_5}{<}}$$

$$Y$$

Immobile Coupler   Developing agent

$$X-SO_3H$$

$$\longrightarrow \quad \overset{|}{\underset{|}{C}} = N - \underset{}{\bigcirc} - N \underset{C_2H_5}{\overset{C_2H_5}{<}} + ZC_nH_{2n+2} + H_2$$

$$Y$$

Soluble dye

If the value of n in the C_nH_{2n+1} group is fairly large (n = 15 or more), then the coupler molecule will be large enough to be fairly immobile; the dye molecule, however, has no ballast, and is therefore quite small, and is soluble on account of the sulphonic acid (SO_3H) group. After development it can therefore transfer to a receiving sheet, if the latter is held in moist contact with it; a suitable mordant in the receiving sheet can then immobilize the dye once again to give an insoluble final image. Thus, as in the hydroquinone system, the processing sequence is simply: develop, and transfer.

REFERENCES

Beilfuss, H. R., Thomas, D. S., and Zuidema, J. W., *J. Soc. Mot. Pic. Tel. Eng.*, **75**, 344 (1966).
British Journal of Photography, **109**, 904 (1962).
Collins, R. B., *Phot. J.*, **100**, 173 (1960).
Crawley, G., *Brit. J. Phot.*, **110**, 76 (1963).
Ganguin, K. O., and MacDonald, E., *J. Phot. Sci.*, **14**, 260 (1966).
Gledhill, R. J., and Julian, D. B., *J. Opt. Soc. Amer.*, **53**, 239 (1963).
Gehret, E. C., *Brit. J. Phot.*, **111**, 818 (1964).
Meyer, A., *J. Phot. Sci.*, **13**, 90 1965).
Pollak, F., *J. Phot. Sci.*, **3**, 112 (1955).
Pollak, F., and Hepher, M., *Penrose Annual*, **50**, 106 (1956).

GENERAL REFERENCES

Bent, R. L., Brown, G. H., Glesmann, M. C., Harnish, D. P., Tremmel, C. G., and Weissburger, A., *Phot. Sci. Eng.*, **8**, 125 (1964).

Evans, R. M., Hanson, W. T., and Brewer, W. L., *Principles of Colour Photography*, pp. 257–266, Wiley, New York (1953).

Glafkides, P., *Photographic Chemistry* (translated by K. M. Hornsby), **2**, 593–615, Fountain Press, London (1960).

Hornsby, K. M., *Basic Photographic Chemistry*, Fountain Press, London (1956).

James, T. H., and Higgins, G. C., *Fundamentals of Photographic Theory* (2nd Edition), pp. 119–122, Morgan and Morgan, New York (1960).

Mees, C. E. K., and James, T. H., *The Theory of Photographic Process* (3rd Edition), pp. 382–396, Macmillan, New York (1966).

Neblette, C. B., *Photography: Its Materials and Processes* (Sixth Edition), pp. 240–248, Van Nostrand, New York (1962).

Thirtle, J. R., and Zwick, D. M., in *Encyclopedia of Chemical Technology*, **5**, 812–845, Wiley (1964).

Vittum, P. W., *J. Soc. Mot. Pic. Tel. Eng.*, **71**, 937 (1962).

Vittum, P. W., and Weissburger, A., *J. Phot. Sci.*, **2**, 81 (1954) and *J. Phot. Sci.*, **6**, 157 (1958).

PART THREE
COLOUR TELEVISION

CHAPTER 16

The Transmission of Colour Television Signals

1. Introduction – *2.* Band-width – *3.* Interlacing – *4.* Single side-band transmission – *5.* The field-sequential system – *6.* Dot-interlacing – *7.* Blue-saving – *8.* Band-saving – *9.* Colour difference signals – *10.* Band-sharing – *11.* The effect of band-sharing on monochrome receivers – *12.* Carrier-sharing – *13.* Choice of spectral sensitivity curves for cameras *14.* Gamma correction – *15.* Two-signal colour television

16.1 Introduction

THE transmission of colour television signals presents some formidable problems: the principles upon which some solutions have been found will be discussed in this chapter. A more detailed discussion of particular systems of transmission is given in Chapter 19; Chapters 17 and 18 deal with cameras and receivers for colour television, and the use of colour film in colour television is considered in Chapter 20.

16.2 Band-width

It will be appreciated that, just as two powerful sound radio stations cannot be received without interference unless their frequencies (or wavelengths) are adequately separated, in a similar way each television station must have its own adequate frequency space, or *band-width* as it is usually termed. However, the radio spectrum is a limited one, and television has to be fitted in to the existing demands made upon it by sound radio, radio-telephony and telegraphy, police and military radio communications, shipping and aircraft signals, radar, etc. Now television, by its very nature, requires far more band-width than is required for transmitting sound, and the problem of finding adequate room for each station is much more acute. In *colour* television it is necessary to transmit, not one picture, but three: if this were done in such a way as to take three times as much band-width as is used for monochrome television the problems of fitting all the stations in without interference would be tremendous. It is therefore important to save as much band-width as possible when transmitting colour television pictures and much effort has been applied to this end.

The reason why television requires so much more band-width can be seen in the following way. In sound radio it is a common experience that when a receiving set is slightly detuned from a station the low notes fade out first, and the higher notes last, so that in its detuned position the reception becomes squeaky and high-pitched. The reason for this is that the high notes are of higher frequency than the low notes, and hence modify the carrier wave frequency more. Thus, consider a medium wavelength station operating at a carrier frequency of, say, 1000 kilocycles (1,000,000 cycles) per second[1] (which corresponds to a wavelength of about 300 metres[2]), and transmitting sound frequencies of about 50 cycles per second (low notes) and about 5000 cycles per second (high notes). Modulation of a 1,000,000 c.p.s. (cycles per second) carrier wave at 50 c.p.s. will produce some energy at frequencies of 1,000,050 and 999,950 c.p.s. (corresponding to wavelengths of 299.985 and 300.015 metres) which are very little different from the basic 1,000,000 c.p.s. But modulation at 5000 c.p.s. results in some energy at frequencies of 1,005,000 and 995,000 c.p.s. (corresponding to wavelengths of 298.5 and 301.5 metres) a much more significant change.

In television, the number of modulations required per second is very much greater than the maximum required in sound radio. Let us take, for example, a system employing 525 lines and 30 complete pictures per second. The number of lines limits the fineness of the detail which can be resolved in the vertical direction to a grid of 525 black-and-white horizontal stripes, that is $\frac{1}{2} \times 525$ pairs of black and white stripes. If the system is to have the same resolving power in the horizontal direction as in the vertical, it must be possible to resolve $\frac{1}{2} \times 525 \times 4/3$ pairs of stripes, the factor of $4/3$ being introduced to allow for the fact that television pictures are not square, but have an aspect ratio of $4/3$. Thus each line of the system may receive $\frac{1}{2} \times 525 \times 4/3$ complete modulations (from black through white to black again) per scan. But there are 525 lines, and 30 pictures per second, so that the number of modulations possible per second is given by:

$$\tfrac{1}{2} \times 525 \times (4/3) \times 525 \times 30 = 5,512,500$$

or approximately 5.5 megacycles per second. (In practice, however, owing to the necessity of transmitting synchronizing information in addition to the picture information, not all 525 lines are used in the picture and the maximum

---

[1] The more descriptive term *cycles per second* has been used instead of *hertz* for the benefit of the general reader. Thus kilocycles per second (Kc/s) are used instead of kilohertz (KHz) and megacycles per second (Mc/s) instead of megahertz (MHz).

[2] The frequency multiplied by the wavelength is always equal to the speed of propagation of the wave, in this case the speed of light which is 3×10^8 metres per second.

frequency actually used in this system is generally only about 4 megacycles per second to obtain symmetrical resolution (Jesty, 1957).

It is clear, from the above, that television systems are required to transmit very much higher frequencies than ordinary sound radio systems; and since the modulating frequency can be as high as about 5 megacycles per second, the carrier frequencies have to be not less than about 50 megacycles per second, corresponding to a wavelength of about 6 metres. (Incidentally, it is for this reason that, whereas sound-radio signals can be transmitted round the earth's surface, television signals are limited to rather less than a 100-mile radius at ground level, because signals of frequencies in the 50 megacycle range are not appreciably diffracted or reflected by the ionosphere in the upper atmosphere, and therefore can only be received satisfactorily within the transmitting station's horizon, or via a satellite relay station.)

A carrier wave of 50 megacycles per second modulated at frequencies up to 5 megacycles per second will produce some energy over the frequency range 45 to 55 megacycles per second (corresponding to a wavelength range of 6.7 to 5.5 metres). Thus the more detail required in a television picture, the greater will be the band-width of the signal, and the greater will be the amount of frequency or wavelength space required to accommodate it. In fact the calculation shows that the maximum modulating frequency increases in proportion to the square of the number of lines in the picture; it is also proportional to the number of pictures per second.

The 525 line, 30 pictures per second, system is that which has been adopted in the U.S.A. In Great Britain a 405 line, 25 pictures per second, system using about 3 megacycles per second maximum modulating frequency was employed exclusively until 1964, when a 625 line, 25 pictures per second, system using about $5\frac{1}{2}$ megacycles per second maximum modulating frequency was introduced in addition; this 625 line system has been adopted as standard for Europe, and this is the system used in Europe for colour.

16.3 Interlacing

The range of modulating frequencies required in these systems would in fact be higher still, but for the use of a technique known as *inter-lacing*. If the number of individual pictures per second composing the display is too low, an unpleasant flickering is apparent. Although about 25 pictures per second are used in photographic motion pictures, it is usually arranged for the light to be interrupted by a shutter once during the projection of each picture as well as between successive pictures, so that the light flickers at about 50 times per second, and this is not very noticeable. In television, however, interruption of the electron beam during the scanning of a picture would result only in the disappearance of the part of the picture being scanned at the time; and interruption of the light emitted by the fluorescent powder on the tube would produce variations in luminance over the area of the picture because the interruption would occur at different points in the time-cycle of the after-glow of the phosphor at different parts of the picture.

But 25 to 30 pictures per second is too low a frequency for flicker to be avoided and hence some means of increasing the frequency is required. To transmit twice the number of pictures per second would require twice as much band-width, but by using *inter-lacing*, the apparent flicker frequency is doubled without any increase in band-width being necessary. In an inter-laced picture the electron beam first produces all the odd lines of the picture, the first, the third, the fifth etc., and then adds the even lines in between them. The parts of the picture composed by all the even or all the odd lines are called *fields*. Thus, by means of inter-lacing, a 25 pictures per second system involves 50 fields per second; and, although each field contains only half the total number of picture lines, 50 fields per second are almost as good as 50 pictures per second, as far as absence of flicker is concerned. Flicker becomes more noticeable as the luminance of the picture is increased, and one advantage of the 30-pictures-per-second (60-fields-per-second) systems over the 25-pictures-per-second (50-fields-per-second) systems is that higher picture luminances can be used without flicker being unpleasantly noticeable. Inter-lacing is already used in monochrome television so that its use in colour television does not give a further band-width advantage.

16.4 Single side-band transmission

Another method of reducing the amount of band-width required is to transmit only those frequencies which are equal to or *higher* than that of the carrier wave; the frequencies below the carrier frequency are exactly similar to those above, and to transmit both these *side-bands* of frequency is therefore unnecessary, since either side-band carries all the information. Consequently most television. stations filter out most of the frequencies below (or above) the carrier frequency, and transmit only one of the side bands, a technique known as *single* (or *asymmetric* or *vestigial*) *side-band transmission*. Hence the band-widths required are approximately equal to the maximum modulating frequency, and not to twice that value as indicated in Section 16.2.

Single side-band transmission is already used in monochrome television so that its use in colour television does not give a further band-width advantage.

16.5 The field sequential system

The simplest colour television system is the field sequential system, in which red, green, and blue filters rotate in front of a single colour television camera, and similar filters rotate in synchronism over the viewing tube of the receiving set. Unfortunately, however, there are three reasons why such a system cannot easily be adopted for wide scale broadcasting. In the first place, the picture frequency necessary to avoid flicker and colour break-up in such a system is about three times that necessary in black-and-white systems, so that existing black-and-white television receiving sets would not be able to receive the colour broadcasts in monochrome without modifications being necessary; such systems are called *incompatible*. In the second place the rotating filter wheel is an undesirable feature in the receiver. (It has been suggested that a stationary filter be used, consisting of narrow red, green, and blue strips. In front of this a lenticular screen oscillates so that the viewer sees the picture through the strips of only one colour at a time, the colours being changed in rapid succession (Grunwald, 1950; Morrison and Faulkner, 1951; Rehorn, 1951); but rapidly moving parts are still required.) In the third place, the transmission of three times as many pictures per second requires the use of three times as much band-width; for a red, a green, and a blue picture would have to be transmitted for every black-and-white picture, entailing, on a 25 pictures per second system, for instance, 75 colour-pictures per second (these colour-pictures are generally referred to as *frames*). With inter-lacing this becomes 25 pictures, 75 frames, and 150 fields per second. This field frequency is sufficient to overcome all flicker from the colour filter wheel, except for very rapidly moving objects which can show some fringing or 'break-up', particularly if they are highly coloured.

Interlacing does not alter the maximum modulating frequency of a system if the speed at which the electron beam moves along each line is unchanged. The modulating frequencies in a field sequential system of 150 interlaced fields per second are therefore the same as those of a 75 (non-interlaced) colour-pictures per second system and are therefore three times those of a black and white system of 25 pictures (or 50 interlaced fields) per second. Maximum modulating frequencies of up to about 15 megacycles per second thus become necessary, and this means that the number of colour television stations which could operate within a given band of wavelengths would be reduced to one third of the number of black-and-white stations. For this reason, and because of the incompatibility of high picture-frequency systems with black-and-white receivers, the simple field sequential system of colour television is not well suited to public broadcasting. However, it can give good quality with fairly simple equipment and techniques, and for this reason it finds applications in closed circuit colour television; this has been used, for instance, to televise surgical operations in order to train medical students. Its application to public broadcasting has been confined to the short period from 1950 to 1951 when the version proposed by C.B.S. (the Columbia Broadcasting System) was adopted by the Federal Communications Commission (F.C.C.) in America: 144 fields per second were used with 405 lines and only 2 megacycles for each of the three pictures (which were therefore of rather poor definition), making a total of 6 megacycles band-width; defence requirements in 1951 prevented further use of this system and subsequently an entirely different system was adopted in the U.S.A.

16.6 Dot-interlacing

In an attempt to reduce total band-width and yet still be able to transmit three-colour pictures of high definition an interesting technique known as *dot-interlacing* (Gouriet, 1952) was suggested. In this method the modulations are broken up into very short pulses so that the final picture is made up of lines of dots, rather than of continuous lines. These dots are then interlaced. That is, the second time any given line is scanned the dots are all shifted to positions mid-way between those that they occupied during the first scan. For stationary, or slowly moving objects, in the the scene, persistence of vision then enables detail to be recognized which is twice as fine as that of the dot pattern in any one scan and this reduces the required band-width from three times to only one and a half times that required for a black-and-white picture of the same definition. For moving objects, however, some loss of horizontal definition does occur. Dot-interlacing, in the simple form outlined above, was not adopted because all three signals are transmitted at the same definition but this does not make the best use of the available band-width, because for a given band-width, pictures of greater apparent sharpness can be obtained if three signals are transmitted with unequal individual band-widths.

16.7 Blue-saving

Various other methods of reducing the band-width required by colour television have been suggested, one of which we may call 'Blue-saving'. The human eye is able to distinguish fine detail illuminated by red or green light much better than when blue light is used. But in a colour television system, it is only the fine detail which results in the higher modulating frequencies being used. Thus a picture of one thick black tree trunk seen against a white sky, will result in modulations every time the scanning beam crosses the tree trunk, which, for each colour, will be once per line per picture, or, in a 525-line 30-picture per second system, a mere 15,750 times per second.[1] But a picture of a forest of 200 tree trunks will naturally result in 200 times the number of modulations of the scanning beam, and hence a frequency of 3,150,000 times per second. Since, however, at normal viewing distances the eye is incapable of seeing the 200 tree trunks in the blue picture there is no point in transmitting it. Thus an electronic filter could be fitted somewhere in the blue channel which effectively eliminated all signals of frequencies higher than those which result in detail which is just perceptible in the blue picture at normal viewing distances. In this way the band-width required for the blue picture can be reduced from 5 megacycles per second to about 1 megacycle per second.

The reduction in definition permissible in the blue record has long been recognized in colour photography. Thus registration of the yellow image in subtractive transfer systems is known to be less critical than that of the cyan

[1] Higher harmonics of this frequency will generally also be produced, but less strongly. This does not vitiate the main point of the argument, however.

and magenta images, and the blue layers of integral tripacks can be of coarser grain than the green and red layers. It is also advantageous to coat the blue sensitive layer first in an integral tripack, because the bottom layer has to be exposed through the other two layers and always has lower definition. With the bromide emulsions used in camera materials the natural blue sensitivity of the red and green sensitive layers renders such an arrangement impossible but in chloride, or chlorobromide, emulsions the natural sensitivity

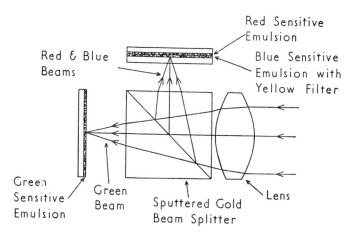

Red Sensitive Emulsion

Red & Blue Beams

Blue Sensitive Emulsion with Yellow Filter

Green Sensitive Emulsion

Green Beam

Sputtered Gold Beam Splitter

Lens

Fig. 16.1. Diagrammatic representation of the Technicolor camera as used in colour cinematography before the introduction of integral tripack negative films.

band is displaced far enough into the ultra-violet to enable a sensitizing dye to provide a region of blue sensitivity to which the red and green emulsions are not sensitive. Chloride and chlorobromide emulsions are too slow for camera use but as print films are quite fast enough, and are used in Eastman Colour Print Film, for instance, which has the green layer on top, the red layer in the middle, and the blue layer at the bottom of the tripack (see Section 10.11).

One interesting application of the 'Blue-saving' technique is to be found in the Marconi two-tube colour television camera. This camera is closely analogous to the Technicolor camera which, until the advent of integral tripack films suitable for motion-picture work, was widely used in colour cinematography. In the Technicolor camera a prism block situated immediately behind the lens is divided diagonally by a gold reflecting surface. This transmits green light freely, but reflects red and blue light strongly. Thus two images are formed, one in green light, which exposes a green sensitized film, and the other in red and blue light which expose a sandwich of an unsensitized film and a red-sensitized film as shown in Fig. 16.1. The arrangement in the Marconi two-tube colour television camera is basically very similar, as shown in Fig. 16.2. A dichroic mirror situated behind the lens transmits green light freely, but reflects red and blue light. The green light falls on one camera tube, while the red and blue light is imaged on another, by means of a relay lens. In order to distinguish between the red and the blue images a grid of alternate yellow and transparent lines is situated in the plane of the first image of this beam. The yellow lines absorb the blue light but not the red, so that as the picture is scanned the blue image has a high frequency oscillation

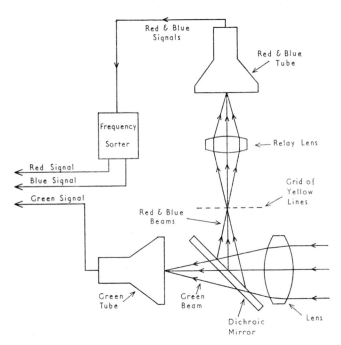

Fig. 16.2. Diagrammatic representation of the Marconi two-tube camera proposed for use in colour television.

imposed upon it. In order to obtain the red picture on its own, therefore, it is only necessary to filter out this and all higher frequencies; this is not a difficult electronic task. The blue picture is then readily obtained by subtracting the red response from the combined response of the blue and red together. The necessity for filtering out the high frequencies in order to separate the two pictures does result in loss of definition, not only in the blue picture but also in the red. However, this eases the problem of registering the two images exactly, and in any case a certain amount of 'red-saving' is permissible since the eye is also somewhat less sensitive to fine red detail, as compared with green detail, though the reduction is much less than in the case of the blue detail.

Blue-saving cannot be used in the field-sequential system because, even if the blue picture were transmitted with reduced band-width, the green picture would still have to be scanned in a third of the time and would therefore still produce frequencies three times as high and hence require three times the band-width.

16.8 Band-saving

The ability of the eye to see fine detail depends for the most part on differences in *luminance* in the pattern and only to a much smaller extent on *colour* contrast. Thus the visibility of white letters on a dark grey background, when viewed from a distance, is not improved very much by adding colour contrast to the existing luminance contrast: yellow letters on a dark blue background, or orange letters on a dark green background, for instance, having the same luminance differences, are scarcely any clearer.

This suggests that if the information in a colour television picture could be divided into its luminance content and its colour content, then only the luminance information need be transmitted at high definition, and band-width could be saved by transmitting the colour information at reduced definition. This is in fact what is done, with remarkably good effect.

From the television camera, three electrical signals, E_R, E_G, E_B (usually expressed as voltages), are obtained which are proportional at each point of the picture to its red, green, and blue contents, R, G, B, as analysed by the spectral sensitivities of the three channels of the camera. (Proportionality between the electrical and corresponding optical signals at both the camera and the receiver is assumed for the moment for the sake of simplicity; the effects of the non-linearities which occur in real systems will be considered later.) The luminance, L, at any point in the picture will be given by:

$$L = L_R R + L_G G + L_B B$$

where L_R, L_G, L_B are the luminances of the units in which the red, green, and blue contents are measured. It is therefore possible to produce an electrical signal E_L, which is proportional to the luminance, L, by adding together the same proportions of the signals E_R, E_G, E_B, thus (assuming that the constants of proportionality between the electrical and optical signals are the same for all three channels):

$$E_L = L_R E_R + L_G E_G + L_B E_B$$

If now the three signals transmitted were not E_R, E_G, E_B, but E_L, and two of the other signals, say E_R and E_B, then the signal E_L could be transmitted with broad band-width, and the signals E_R and E_B with narrow band-width. The receiver would then have to recover the E_G signal necessary to produce the final display by performing the operation

$$E_G = \frac{1}{L_G}E_L - \frac{L_R}{L_G}E_R - \frac{L_B}{L_G}E_B$$

12 A

When this is done, if two colours form a pattern of such fineness of detail that the chromaticity difference is not transmitted by the E_R and E_B signals, but the luminance difference is successfully transmitted by the E_L signal, then the receiver will display a chromaticity equal to the average of that of the two colours, upon which will be superimposed the luminance difference produced by the E_L signal. That this procedure results in the display of the correct luminance can be seen as follows. Suppose that the true E_R and E_B signals for some areas are altered to E_R+A and E_B+B as a result of the chromaticity averaging. The resulting signals used for the display will then be modified to:

$$E_{RM} = E_R+A$$

$$E_{GM} = \frac{1}{L_G}E_L-\frac{L_R}{L_G}(E_R+A)-\frac{L_B}{L_G}(E_B+B)$$

$$E_{BM} = E_B+B$$

The luminance displayed will then be proportional to:

$$L_RE_{RM}+L_GE_{GM}+L_BE_{BM}$$
$$= L_R(E_R+A)+E_L-L_R(E_R+A)-L_B(E_B+B)+L_B(E_B+B)$$
$$= E_L$$

It is thus clear that the luminance displayed is the same as that corresponding to the unmodified signals E_R and E_B, and hence the luminance is correctly reproduced in spite of errors in chromaticity. This is an important result and is known as the *constant luminance principle*.

It is found that by transmitting a separate high-definition luminance signal very considerable savings in band-width can be achieved. If the system is such that the luminance signal has a band-width b, then the two other signals only require about $\frac{1}{4}b$ each, making a total of $1\frac{1}{2}b$ (Hunt, 1967), instead of $3b$ required by the field sequential system. Although a band-width of $1\frac{1}{2}b$ is no better than that of the dot-interlacing system (Section 16.6) further reductions in band-width can be made when two of the signals require much less band-width than the third, as will be discussed in Sections 16.10 and 16.12; this gives systems employing a luminance signal and two colour signals a decisive advantage over those employing three colour signals.

There are two further advantages arising from the use of a separate luminance signal. First, the modifying signals, A and B, introduced above, can arise from any source, and hence if the E_R and E_B signals suffer from interference, for instance, they will not affect the luminance displayed. This has a beneficial effect, because the eye is more sensitive to luminance changes than to chromaticity changes (it is on this principle that the flicker photometer depends); it is found that about $2\frac{1}{2}$ times as much noise can be tolerated in colour difference signals as in luminance signals. In general, the E_L signal will suffer from interference as well, but the effects of this will not be made worse by the presence of interference in the E_R and E_B signals.

The second additional advantage of one of the three transmitted signals being a luminance signal is that it can be used very effectively for the production of monochrome pictures on black-and-white receivers: it is then only necessary for these receivers to ignore the colour signals in order to produce monochrome versions of colour transmissions. The use of a luminance signal therefore greatly facilitates *compatibility*.

Although the algebra showed that the correct value of E_L was always obtained, even when E_R and E_B were in error, this will not be true if negative values of E_{GM} are obtained: the receiver cannot produce negative amounts of green light. The modified green signal, E_{GM}, is given by:

$$E_{GM} = \frac{1}{L_G}E_L - \frac{L_R}{L_G}(E_R + A) - \frac{L_B}{L_G}(E_B + B)$$

If A and B are sufficiently large and positive the value of E_{GM} can become negative. This will happen for saturated purple colours, for instance. Saturated purples are matched by mixtures of red and blue only, so that E_G will be zero. Hence, for these colours

$$E_G = 0 = \frac{1}{L_G}E_L - \frac{L_R}{L_G}E_R - \frac{L_B}{L_G}E_B$$

and hence
$$E_{GM} = -\frac{L_R}{L_G}A - \frac{L_B}{L_G}B$$

Suppose we have a fine pattern of light and dark saturated purple of the same chromaticity. The E_R and E_B signals will be modified to average values, so that for the light areas E_{RM} and E_{BM} will be smaller than E_R and E_B. A and B are therefore both negative and hence E_{GM} is positive and will result in the area being lightened to the correct luminance. But for the dark areas, E_{RM} and E_{BM} will be larger than E_R and E_B, so that A and B will be positive, making E_{GM} negative. But the receiver cannot produce the 'negative' amount of green light necessary to reduce the luminance, and so the luminance of the dark part of the pattern is too high. This type of error, however, is only likely to occur in patterns such that the green signal is small (that is, fairly saturated purples) and the luminance difference large.

16.9 Colour difference signals

There are several advantages if, instead of transmitting the signals E_L, E_R, E_B, the luminance signal is accompanied by two *colour difference* or *chrominance* signals, such as $E_R - E_L$, and $E_B - E_L$. The receiver then recovers a signal $E_G - E_L$ by performing the operation:

$$E_G - E_L = \frac{1 - L_R - L_G - L_B}{L_G}E_L - \frac{L_R}{L_G}(E_R - E_L) - \frac{L_B}{L_G}(E_B - E_L)$$

The advantages of using difference signals are only fully realized, however, if the luminance signal is compounded from the E_R, E_G, E_B signals so that it is equal to

$$lE_R + m E_G + n E_B$$

where
$$l = L_R/(L_R + L_G + L_B)$$
$$m = L_G/(L_R + L_G + L_B)$$
$$n = L_B/(L_R + L_G + L_B)$$

so that
$$l + m + n = 1.0$$

We shall call this new luminance signal E_Y (the suffix Y indicating, not yellow, but the Y of the C.I.E. $(X)(Y)(Z)$ system) to distinguish it from E_L; E_Y is still a true measure of luminance but is now expressed in units $L_R + L_G + L_B$ times as large as those used for E_L.

The colour difference signals now become $E_R - E_Y$ and $E_B - E_Y$, and the receiver can recover a signal $E_G - E_Y$ by performing the operation

$$E_G - E_Y = -\frac{l}{m}(E_R - E_Y) - \frac{n}{m}(E_B - E_Y)$$

(to which the expression for $E_G - E_L$ reduces when E_Y, l, m, and n are substituted for E_L, L_R, L_G, and L_B). This is a simpler operation than that necessary to recover the signal $E_G - E_L$, and has the important advantage that since only the two low-definition signals $E_R - E_Y$ and $E_B - E_Y$ are involved, a mixing circuit of low frequency response can be used for this operation with consequent savings in the cost and complexity of the receiver.

The high definition signal E_Y can now be added to all three signals $E_R - E_Y$, $E_G - E_Y$, $E_B - E_Y$, to obtain the signals E_R, E_G, E_B necessary for the display. One convenient way of doing this is to apply the three low definition colour difference signals $E_R - E_Y$, $E_G - E_Y$, $E_B - E_Y$, to the grids of three electron guns, and the same high-definition luminance signal E_Y to their three cathodes (see Section 18.1).

The use of colour difference signals of this type has further advantages, which, however, are only fully realized if another arbitrary condition is applied. It is further arranged that the relative sensitivities of the three channels of the camera are such that for whites, greys, and blacks $E_R = E_G = E_B$. Because $l + m + n = 1$, and $E_Y = lE_R + mE_G + nE_B$, it follows that for whites, greys, and blacks $E_R = E_G = E_B = E_Y$; hence for these colours, the colour difference signals $E_R - E_Y$ and $E_B - E_Y$ are both zero. This has two further advantages.

First, variations in the relative strengths of the three signals E_Y, $E_R - E_Y$, $E_B - E_Y$, does not affect the colour balance of the grey scale in the reproduction.

Secondly, because most scenes consist mainly of colours of fairly low colour saturation, the need for transmitting information additional to that contained by the E_Y signal is reduced, and hence *cross-talk* (that is, interference between the luminance and colour-difference signals) in band-sharing systems (to be considered later) is minimized.

The constant luminance principle still applies when colour difference signals are used: this can be shown, as above, by calculating the displayed luminance when spurious signals A and B are added to the colour difference signals.

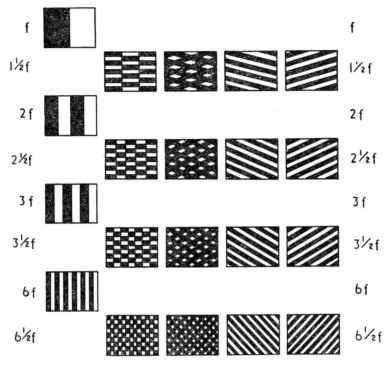

Fig. 16.3. Patterns which for a hypothetical 9-line television field produce fundamental frequencies f, $1\frac{1}{2}f$, $2f$, $2\frac{1}{2}f$, $3f$, $3\frac{1}{2}f$, $6f$, and $6\frac{1}{2}f$, where f is the line frequency.

16.10 Band-sharing

The reduction of the band-width required from $3b$ for a full definition system to only $1\frac{1}{2}b$ for a luminance signal system is obviously a most important saving. It would be ideal, however, if colour television signals could be sent out with the use of no more band-width than for monochrome signals. This may at first sight seem impossible, for clearly there is more information in a colour picture than in a black-and-white one. But if the monochrome signal was not using its band-width to the greatest efficiency, then the colour information might be added to it, without the band-width having to be increased at all. This is the principle of *band-sharing*.

It was pointed out earlier in this chapter that the higher modulating frequencies were only produced by fine detail. Since a television picture is scanned by a series of horizontal lines, some modulating frequencies will be more commonly produced than others (Mertz and Gray, 1934). Thus in a 525-line 30-pictures-per-second system, a single vertical bar would be traversed by the scanning spot 15,750 times per second, and thus would give a 15,750 c.p.s. modulation. If we call this *line-frequency* f, it is clear that h vertical bars, equally spaced in the picture, will give fundamental frequencies

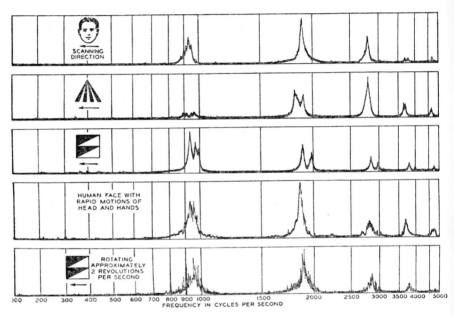

Fig. 16.4. 'Spectra' of four black-and-white television transmissions. The energy is concentrated at frequencies which are multiples of the line frequency (in this case 940 cycles per second). (Mertz and Gray, 1934.)

of hf cycles per second. The only way in which fundamental frequencies of $(h+\frac{1}{2})f$, where h is a whole number, can be produced are for the bars to be displaced by the width of half a bar on each successive line of a field.

In Fig. 16.3 the situation is depicted diagrammatically for the simple case of a 9-line field with an aspect ratio of 4 to 3. Patterns of bars resulting in fundamental frequencies of f, $2f$, $3f$, and $6f$ are shown in the first column, while the second column shows patterns giving fundamental frequencies of $1\frac{1}{2}f$, $2\frac{1}{2}f$, $3\frac{1}{2}f$, and $6\frac{1}{2}f$. The third, fourth, and fifth columns show patterns of sloping bars which approximate to the pattern of the second column, and would therefore produce substantially the same fundamental frequencies $1\frac{1}{2}f$, $2\frac{1}{2}f$, $3\frac{1}{2}f$, and $6\frac{1}{2}f$. It is seen that the angle of the pattern giving a fundamental requency of $6\frac{1}{2}f$ is approximately $45°$. With a field of $\frac{1}{2} \times 525$ lines, instead of $\mathfrak{z}$ lines, the fundamental frequency corresponding to a pattern of lines at $45°$ s given by: $(\frac{1}{2} \times 525 \times 4/3 + \frac{1}{2})f$ which is almost identical with the maximum frequency of the system: $(\frac{1}{2} \times 525 \times 4/3)f$. The $45°$ pattern therefore represents the end of the series of patterns giving the intermediate fundamental frequencies $(h + \frac{1}{2})f$.

Now in the vast majority of television scenes, fragments of vertical bar patterns of the first column of Fig. 16.3 are far more common than fragments of the chequered or sloping bar patterns of the other columns of Fig. 16.3; hence in the average television transmission there are peaks of energy at frequencies which are multiples of f, and there are troughs in between; an example of this is shown in Fig. 16.4.

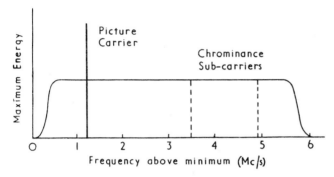

Fig. 16.5. Hypothetical band sharing method of transmitting colour television signals. The two chrominance (or colour-difference) subcarriers have frequencies which are odd multiples of half the line frequency, and are high in the luminance band.

Furthermore, in most television scenes there is less fine detail than coarse detail, so that the higher frequencies carry less energy than the lower. It has therefore become customary to transmit the colour difference signals on sub-carriers having frequencies high in the luminance band, and carefully chosen to be suitable odd multiples of half the line-frequency, f, in order to coincide with the energy troughs of the luminance signal. In Fig. 16.5, a hypothetical system in which the two colour difference signals are transmitted on two separate sub-carriers high in the luminance band, is shown diagrammatically.

In these diagrams, which are frequently used in discussions on television transmission, the energy transmitted at each frequency is plotted against the frequency. The diagram is not a true plot, however, but only a diagrammatic representation in which the maximum energy permissible is shown at all frequencies. It will be noted that the carrier frequency is not in the centre of the band, as one would expect on the grounds that its modulation by the signal would produce a symmetrical frequency pattern, because vestigial sideband transmission is being used; but it is not usually possible to cut out *all* of the unwanted side-band and it is usually present with a much restricted band-width as shown in Fig. 16.5. In band-sharing systems, double-side-band transmission is generally used for the colour difference signals, however, in order to reduce the intensity of *cross-talk*, that is, interference between them, or between them and the luminance signal.

The colour-difference signals will result in the sub-carrier having energy not only at its own frequency, but also at various frequencies above and below it; but, again, because of the relative rarity of chequered or sloping bar patterns the energy will be concentrated at frequencies which differ from the sub-carrier frequency by multiples of the line frequency f. Hence, if the sub-carrier frequency is $(h+\frac{1}{2})f$, the energy of the sub-carrier signal will be concentrated at frequencies $(h+\frac{1}{2})f+jf$, where j is another whole number. (This corresponds to odd multiples of half the line frequency.) The frequencies at which the sub-carrier usually has energy therefore correspond to those at which the main carrier usually does not have energy. The two energy-frequency distributions are therefore mainly inter-leaved.

The receiving set, of course, has to distinguish between the luminance and colour-difference signals and this is accomplished by means of electronic devices which divide the incoming signals into those of frequencies which approximate either to multiples of the line frequency f, or to odd multiples of half the line frequency. The former are treated as luminance signals, and the latter as colour-difference signals, and for the reasons already stated this is substantially a correct interpretation. Sometimes, however, as for instance with some of the patterns shown in Fig. 16.3, a luminance signal will be interpreted and displayed by the receiver as a colour-difference signal, and vice-versa. This can only happen in fine detail, however, and then only with certain types of picture pattern.

16.11 The effect of band-sharing on monochrome receivers

When a band-sharing signal is picked up by an unmodified monochrome receiver, the energy is not divided into two parts, corresponding to multiples of the line frequency and to odd multiples of half the line frequency, as in a colour receiver. The result is that the colour-difference signals are displayed as luminance signals, but are broken up into a chequer-board pattern by the oscillation imposed by the sub-carrier, successive lines of each *field* displaying the pattern shifted horizontally by one pattern unit. This does have a disturbing effect on monochrome reception of colour transmissions, but since the colour difference signals are zero for whites, greys, and blacks, the effect is absent for these colours and is small for the prevalent pale colours: in saturated colours, however, it can be noticeable, although the sub-carrier oscillation causes luminance to be added in the light parts of the pattern and subtracted in the dark parts, so that the average luminance when viewed from a distance sufficient for the pattern not to be resolved will be unaltered; (actually, because of the non-linearity of the light output of the receiver relative to its electrical input, a net gain in luminance occurs from the pattern, but this partially offsets another error which causes the luminance of saturated colours displayed on monochrome receivers to be too low, as will be discussed in Section 16.14 on Gamma Correction.)

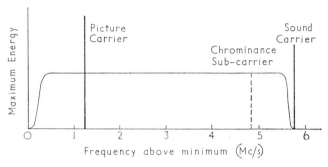

Fig. 16.6. Carrier-sharing system. The two chrominance (or colour-difference) signals both have the same carrier-frequency, which is an odd multiple of half the line frequency and is high in the luminance band, but the two signals have a 90°-phase difference, or are transmitted on alternate lines of each field.

16.12 Carrier-sharing

Although the choice of odd multiples of half the line frequency high in the frequency range is helpful in avoiding interference between the colour-difference and luminance signals there is really insufficient space for two sub-carriers (each with side-bands of about $\pm\frac{1}{4}b$) in the luminance band. The concept of carrier sharing has therefore been introduced (Fig. 16.6). In this scheme the two colour-difference signals are transmitted at the same sub-carrier frequency, but using either signals a quarter of a cycle out of phase with one another, or transmitting each colour-difference signal only on alternate lines of each field of the picture; the receiving sets then have to be fitted with phase-sensitive detectors or line-delay arrangements so that the two signals can be distinguished. This is discussed further in Chapter 19.

16.13 Choice of spectral sensitivity curves for cameras

As explained in Chapter 6, if three reproduction stimuli R, G, B have been chosen for a colour television display device, then the camera should have spectral sensitivity curves corresponding to the three colour-matching functions $\bar{r}_\lambda$, $\bar{g}_\lambda$, $\bar{b}_\lambda$, which define the amounts of these three stimuli needed to match each wavelength of the spectrum. A typical set of functions of this type was shown in Fig. 6.4 for monochromatic stimuli, and in Fig. 16.7 a set for stimuli typical of those used in colour television is shown; these curves have both positive and negative regions, and although this presents certain difficulties in adopting them in television cameras, their use would ensure exact colour reproduction of all colours within the triangle formed in the chromaticity chart by the three points representing the stimuli R, G, B. This arrangement is shown as the first alternative in Fig. 16.8.

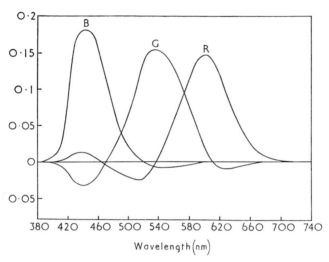

Fig. 16.7. Colour-matching functions corresponding to the red, green, and blue colours produced by phosphors typical of those used in colour television receivers.

The incorporation of the negative regions of the spectral sensitivity curves of the camera is very awkward, but the same result can be achieved by using an all positive set of colour-matching functions such as the C.I.E. $\bar{x}_\lambda$, $\bar{y}_\lambda$, $\bar{z}_\lambda$ functions and then obtaining the required tristimulus values R, G, B, from X, Y, Z, preferably *before* transmission, so as to avoid having to carry out this rather complicated step at the receiver. The manipulations required are the same as those described in Section 7.4 for *colour transformations*, and are usually referred to in colour television as *matrixing*. The operations required are of the form

$$E_R = a_1 E_X + a_2 E_Y + a_3 E_Z$$
$$E_G = a_4 E_X + a_5 E_Y + a_6 E_Z$$
$$E_B = a_7 E_X + a_8 E_Y + a_9 E_Z$$

where a_1 to a_9 are constants. This arrangement is shown as the second alternative of Fig. 16.8.

It is not necessary with this arrangement for the all-positive camera sensitivity curves to be the $\bar{x}_\lambda$, $\bar{y}_\lambda$, $\bar{z}_\lambda$ curves: any set of matching functions could in principle be used. But if one of the three curves is the $\bar{y}_\lambda$ curve, then the corresponding tristimulus value is equal to Y, which enables the E_Y signal to be obtained directly. However, this apparently advantageous arrangement involves complications because of the effects of non-linearities in practical systems (see Section 17.7).

	Camera sensitivity curves	Extra manipulation of signals	Receiver reproduction colours	Final result displayed
I	Matching functions with negative portions	None	Colours Corresponding to camera matching functions	Exact reproduction of all colours within receiver gamut
2	All positive matching functions	Matrixing at camera or at receiver	Colours corresponding to matrixed camera matching functions	
3		None	Colours of the same hue as those corresponding to camera matching functions	All colours slightly desaturated
4	Positive parts of matching functions which have some negative portions	None	Colours corresponding to complete camera matching functions.	Some errors in most colours
5		Matrixing at camera or at receiver		Small errors in most colours

Fig. 16.8. The effects of alternative camera sensitivity curves on colour fidelity.

The third alternative arrangement shown in Fig. 16.8 is to adopt the Ives-Abney-Yule compromise described in Section 6.9. The all positive sensitivity curves are now chosen so as to be equal to a set of colour-matching functions corresponding to stimuli P_1, P_2, P_3, having the same dominant wavelength as the reproduction stimuli R, G, B. This arrangement has the advantages that it confines errors to slight losses in colour saturation which are not very noticeable; it avoids the abrupt change in colour fidelity experienced in the first two arrangements as the edges of the R, G, B triangle are

335

crossed; and it does not require a matrixing operation for the signals, a step which inevitably tends to reduce signal-to-noise ratio (because although signal voltages can be added or subtracted at will, uncorrelated 'noise' voltages always add).

The fourth alternative arrangement shown in Fig. 16.8, is widely used and consists of using the positive parts only of the colour-matching functions corresponding to the reproduction stimuli. Since one or more of such colour-matching functions are usually negative at any wavelength, this alternative tends to produce some errors in most colours. It is found, in practice, however, that the errors involved are not prohibitively large. Although the arrangement is almost certainly not the best from the point of view of colour fidelity, it does have the advantage of being simple, and experience with colour photography has shown that the shape of the three spectral sensitivity curves is not very critical for most colours (see Fig. 4.3 for instance).

Another advantage of using the positive parts only of the colour-matching functions is that the resulting red and green curves are usually more widely separated along the wavelength axis than is the case for typical all-positive curves (this can be seen by comparing the sets of curves of Figs. 16.7, 6.4, 6.17, and 7.3 on the one hand with those of Figs. 6.3, 6.13, and 7.6 on the other hand). This greater wavelength separation of the positive parts means that they are more easily produced efficiently in cameras using dichroic beam-splitting mirrors (see Chapter 17). This advantage is gained at the price of departing irrevocably from exact colorimetric analysis of the scene, but Sproson has shown that if positive part sensitivity curves are used with matrixing the colorimetric errors likely to occur in practice can be reduced to quite small values, if the constants in the matrix are worked out empirically to minimize the errors for typical scene colours (Sproson, 1966). This is shown as the fifth alternative in Fig. 16.8.

The neglect of the negative portions of the matching functions results, in the fourth alternative of Fig. 16.8, in the luminance signal being based, in effect, on a three-humped spectral sensitivity curve instead of on the single-humped $\bar{y}_\lambda$ curve which is required to give true luminance; the result is that the luminances displayed on both monochrome and colour receivers suffer from errors, and these can be quite large, notably in the case of blues which are lightened appreciably. The matrixing used in the fifth alternative of Fig. 16.8 can also result in these luminance errors being greatly reduced.

16.14 Gamma correction

So far, a linear relation has been assumed between the electrical and corresponding optical signals at both the camera and the receiver. But the light output from receiver tubes is not linear: it is approximately proportional to the square of the applied voltage. Thus if the logarithm of the applied voltage is plotted against the logarithm of the resulting tube luminance the slope of the line obtained (that is, the gamma) is about 2.0 (2.2 is the accepted index for colour receivers).

From the point of view of signal-to-noise ratio, a high contrast is desirable because the darker portions of the picture, where noise is most obvious, tend to be reproduced nearly black. But while a monochrome picture which has a contrast of about 2 is at least tolerable, a colour picture will exhibit colour distortion.

Suppose E_R, E_G, E_B are intended to produce a colour $R(R)+G(G)+B(B)$ on a linear display. If, instead, they are applied to a square law display, the resulting colour is $R^2(R)+G^2(G)+B^2(B)$. For example, if $R = 1$, $G = \frac{1}{2}$, $B = \frac{1}{2}$ and unit quantities of (R), (G), and (B) result in a white (W), then the intended colour is equivalent to $\frac{1}{2}(W)+\frac{1}{2}(R)$. But the displayed colour will be $R = 1$, $G = \frac{1}{4}$, $B = \frac{1}{4}$, or $\frac{1}{4}(W)+\frac{3}{4}(R)$. Hence the luminance has decreased, and the saturation has increased. A simple means of correcting for this is to pre-distort the signals E_R, E_G, E_B, at the transmitter to $E_R{}^{1/\gamma}$, $E_G{}^{1/\gamma}$, $E_B{}^{1/\gamma}$; the luminance signal is then transmitted as $E_Y' = lE_R{}^{1/\gamma}+mE_G{}^{1/\gamma}+nE_B{}^{1/\gamma}$, and the colour difference signals as $E_R{}^{1/\gamma}-E_Y'$ and $E_B{}^{1/\gamma}-E_Y'$.

At the receiver the voltages $E_R{}^{1/\gamma}$, $E_G{}^{1/\gamma}$, $E_B{}^{1/\gamma}$, are recovered as usual, and then applied to the appropriate tubes (with power law γ) to give the correct R, G, B.

This method gives distortionless large area reproduction. But the luminance carried by E_Y' (which would be displayed by a monochrome receiver all over the picture, and by a colour receiver in fine detail) is $(E_Y')^\gamma$. The ratio of luminance carried by E_Y' to the true luminance is:

$$\frac{(E_Y')^\gamma}{E_Y} = \frac{(lE_R{}^{1/\gamma}+mE_G{}^{1/\gamma}+nE_B{}^{1/\gamma})^\gamma}{lE_R+mE_G+nE_B}$$

For the worst case (saturated blue) this ratio is:

$$\frac{n^\gamma E_B}{nE_B} = n^{\gamma-1}=0.11^{1.2} = 0.07$$

assuming a value of 0.11 for n which is fairly typical.

So in this case the luminance signal E_Y carries only 7% of the true luminance; hence small-area saturated colours are reproduced too dark. Also compatibility suffers, as a monochrome receiver will display too little luminance; however, in practice, the effect of the non-linearity of the cathode-ray tube characteristic on the dots produced by the chrominance sub-carrier increases the 7% quoted to about 50% (see Section 16.11). Thus monochrome errors are not too bad, and large area colour is correct. But as E_Y' does not carry all the luminance, the remainder must be carried by the sub-carrier modulation, and hence the constant luminance principle is not obeyed, with the result that the subjective effect of noise and interference is increased.

A further point is that, as the sub-carrier modulation is severely limited in band-width, definition will suffer because the luminance content of the sub-carrier will also be limited in band-width. But for white, $E_R = E_G = E_B$, and $\dfrac{(E_Y')^\gamma}{E_Y} = 1$, and for the more prevalent neutral shades the ratio will not be very much less than unity. Hence the above short-comings are evident only for the higher saturations.

There are several alternative methods for gamma correction, but in general these involve additional complications at the receiver. For instance, if the luminance signal was composed *before* E_R, E_G, and E_B were predistorted, and the signals transmitted were $E_R{}^{1/\gamma} - E_Y{}^{1/\gamma}$, $E_B{}^{1/\gamma} - E_Y{}^{1/\gamma}$, and $E_Y{}^{1/\gamma}$ then the above difficulties would not arise. But the recovery of the green signal is then much more complicated, requiring the signals first to be raised to the power γ, then mixed to obtain E_G, and then re-distorted to the power $1/\gamma$, before finally applying them to the tube.

16.15 Two-signal colour television

It has been suggested that the number of different colours actually required to build up a satisfactory colour television picture is considerably less than that which a full three colour system can offer. Thus in a black-and-white television picture, although in theory an infinite number of intermediate tones between black and white can be transmitted and received, in practice the average system is such that only about 30 different tones, including black and white, can be successfully discriminated by the viewer. Therefore, instead of designing a colour television system so that *any* point on the chromaticity diagram (within the R, G, B triangle) could be produced, the area of the triangle could be divided into, say, 33 areas, as shown in Fig. 16.9, and arrangements made so that only the chromaticities represented by the 33 points in the centres of these 33 areas can be reproduced; 33 different chromaticities may sound a small number, until it is realized that each of these 33 chromaticities can be reproduced at any one of 30 luminances, thus providing a total of 990 different colours. There is in fact little doubt that this range of colours would be quite adequate for all but a few exceptional scenes, where subtle differences in chromaticity over some small area of the colour triangle were of particular interest.

It is clear that with such a system only two separate signals need be transmitted, the usual luminance signal, and just one chrominance signal. The television camera would have to code the red, green, and blue colour information into a signal representing the area number, and the receiving set would have to decode this number into the corresponding amounts of red, green, and blue light. This involves extra circuits in both the camera and the receiver, but the additional expense is not embarrassing in the former because only a few cameras are required. The additional expense in the receiver has to be set against the simplification of avoiding the need for phase-sensitive detection or line-delay arrangements.

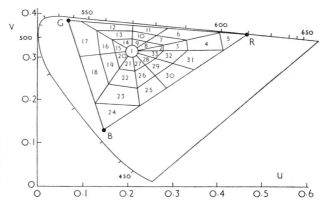

Fig. 16.9. Division of an R, G, B triangle into 33 discrete areas for two-signal colour television transmission.

The main difficulty with such a system, however, is that slight variations in the strength of the chrominance signal produce abrupt changes in colour. In a conventional three signal system such changes are confined to variations in colour saturation, but the hue is not changed since the chrominance signals are both 'difference from white' signals.

REFERENCES

Gouriet, G. G., *Electronic Engineering*, **24**, 166 (1952).
Grunwald, F. S., U.S. Patent 2,670,400 (1950).
Hunt, R. W. G., *J. Roy. Television Soc.*, Fleming Memorial Lecture (1967).
Jesty, L. C., *Wireless World*, **63**, 304 (1957).
Mertz, P., and Gray, F., *Bell. Syst. Tech. J.*, **13**, 464 (1934).
Morrison, J. L. D., and Faulkner, W. J., U.S. Patent 2,687,450 (1951).
Rehorn, M. P., U.S. Patent 2,689,879 (1951).
Sproson, W. N., private communication (1966).

GENERAL REFERENCES

Carnt, P. S., and Townsend, G. B., *Colour Television: N.T.S.C. Principles and Practice*, Iliffe, London (1961).
Fink, D. G., *Colour Television Standards*, McGraw Hill, New York (1955).
Gouriet, G. G., *An Introduction to Colour Television*, The Television Society, London (1955).
Jesty, L. C., *J. Television Society*, **7**, 488 (1954).
Kaufman, M., and Thomas, H., *Introduction to Colour T.V.*, John F. Rider, New York (1954).
Loughren, A. V., *J. Soc. Mot. Pic. Tel. Eng.*, **60**, 321 and 596 (1953).
Proc. Inst. Radio Engnrs., **39**, 1124–1331 (1951).
Proc. Inst. Radio Engnrs., **41**, 838–858 (1953).
Proc. Inst. Radio Engnrs., **42**, 5–344 (1954).
Proc. Inst. Radio Engnrs., **43**, 742–748 (1955).
The Television Society, London, *A Bibliography of Colour Television* (1954).
The Television Society, London, *A Bibliography of Colour Television, Supplement* (1955).
Zworykin, V. K., and Morton, G. A., *The Electronics of image Transmission in Colour and Monochrome,* Chapman & Hall, London (1954).

CHAPTER 17

Cameras for Colour Television

17.1 Introduction

TELEVISION systems operate by converting the information from a two-dimensional image of a scene into a one-dimensional signal; after transmission this signal is re-formed once more into a two-dimensional reproduction. This transformation of information from two dimensions to one is accomplished at the camera by the process of *scanning* the original image line by line in time-sequence. The two-dimensional reproduction is reformed at the receiver by the inverse process of building up the picture line by line from the transmitted signal which is varying with time. Cameras are required in small numbers at few locations for operation by technically skilled personnel; receivers, on the other hand, are wanted in enormous numbers at many locations, for operation, for the most part, by completely unskilled users. The engineering requirements for cameras and receivers are therefore rather different: in cameras, quality and flexibility are of major importance; in receivers, low cost, infrequent maintenance, and simplicity of operation are the prime requirements.

17.2 Early camera tubes

The cameras used in the earliest experimental forms of television broke the picture into a series of lines by optical or mechanical means. Thus if a disc of the type shown in Fig. 17.1 were rotated in front of an image, an analysis into a series of slightly curved lines would result. These optical and mechanical scanning devices, however, were only capable of producing pictures of rather low definition, having generally fewer than 100 lines per picture. The advent of high definition television, involving several hundred lines per picture, was made possible by electronic scanning devices, of which the earliest was the *iconoscope* invented by Zworykin in 1928 and depicted in Fig. 17.2(a). An image

Picture area

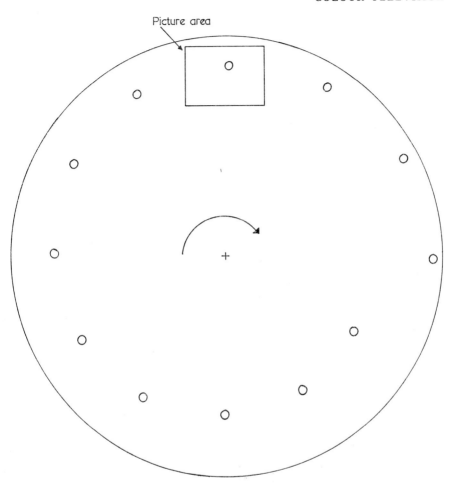

Fig. 17.1. Rotating disc used for mechanical scanning in early television systems.

of the outside scene is made to fall on a mosaic of activated silver specks on a layer of mica; each speck is separated from the others and acts as a small photo-cell. When light falls on a cell electrons are emitted as a function of the amount of incident light and hence an image of electric charge is formed. This photo-cathode surface is then scanned by a beam of high velocity electrons (accelerated through 1000 volts) which causes secondary emission of electrons, and this results in a net loss of electrons from the mosaic to a collecting plate so that current flows from the collector; but areas which have been exposed to light have already lost some electrons by photoemission, and they therefore lose fewer electrons by secondary emission and hence result in less current flowing when they are scanned by the electron beam. The relation between the current and the intensity of the light in the image is roughly that the change in current is proportional to the square root of the change in intensity of the light, and although this may at first sight seem an undesirable relationship,

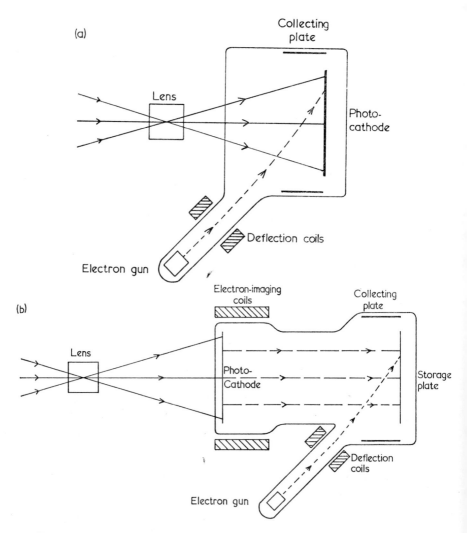

Fig. 17.2. Early television camera tubes: (a) iconoscope; (b) image iconoscope. Full lines: light; broken lines: electrons.

it is in fact very useful, because television-receiver *picture-tubes* usually have characteristics such that the light output is approximately proportional to the square of the applied signal, so that the two devices together give an approximately linear overall result. As is the case for all television camera tubes (or *pick-up* tubes, as they are sometimes called), the various components of the iconoscope are all housed in an evacuated glass envelope.

Fig. 17.2(b) illustrates the features of the *image-iconoscope* in which greater sensitivity is achieved by forming the optical image on a semi-transparent photo-cathode, and then accelerating the photo-electrons produced so as to make them strike a storage plate with an image-wise distribution; this results in secondary emission of electrons from the storage plate, so that when this is scanned by a beam of high velocity electrons, the current from a collecting plate is a function of the light intensity of the scene, as in the iconoscope.

The iconoscope and image-iconoscope tubes are not suitable for colour television because the uncontrolled secondary electrons distort the tone reproduction as a function of the luminance of neighbouring areas; since the distribution of light in the three colour images is different, the distortions would also be different, and hence spurious colours would be produced.

Fig. 17.3(a) illustrates the main features of the *C.P.S. Emitron* or *Orthicon* tube. The image is formed on a thin mica sheet which carries a transparent conducting layer on the front and a photosensitive layer on the back. The photo-electrons emitted from the back surface are collected at an anode leaving an image of electric charge. This electrical image is then scanned by a beam of low-velocity electrons, whose energy is just insufficient to reach the photosensitive layer in black areas of the scene; but in light areas the existence of a positive charge, caused by the loss of photoelectrons, enables the scanning beam to reach the photosensitive layer and to replace the lost electrons, so that current flows from the electron gun to the photosensitive layer as a function of the luminance of the image as the electron beam scans the picture: the flow

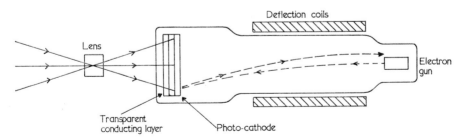

Fig. 17.3(a). Ordinary orthicon (C.P.S. Emitron) camera tube. Full lines: light; broken lines: electrons.

343

of this current causes changes in the voltage on the transparent conducting layer, from which the image signal is derived. This type of tube does not suffer from local tone-distortions which occur in iconoscopes, but its sensitivity is rather too low for effective use in colour cameras. It has an almost linear relationship between signal and luminance, which means that the signal must be adjusted (*gamma-corrected*) before being applied to a receiver; the range of tones over which the response is linear is such as to make its use for deriving television signals from photographic film (where its low sensitivity is less important) rather marginal.

17.3 Tubes suitable for colour

In Fig. 17.3(b) the main features of the *image-orthicon* tube are illustrated. This tube combines the low-energy scanning beam of the orthicon, with the electron-image stage of the image-iconoscope, and adds an electron-multiplier stage for increased sensitivity. The image is formed on a photosensitive layer,

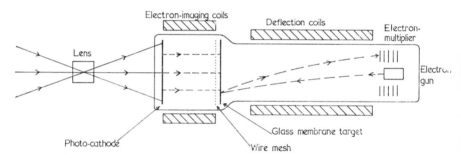

Fig. 17.3(b). Image-orthicon camera tube. Full lines: light, broken lines: electrons.

and the photo-electrons produced from this photo-cathode are focussed in an imagewise way on the 'target'. The target consists of an extremely thin glass membrane with a fine metal mesh spaced very closely parallel to it on the side from which the photo-electrons are incident. The photoelectrons cause secondary electrons to be emitted from the glass membrane and these are collected on the wire mesh; the glass is so thin that the resulting charge pattern on the glass appears on both sides of it. When the glass is scanned by a low-energy electron beam, electrons therefore reach the target only as a function of the luminance of the image of the scene, as in the ordinary orthicon. Changes in image luminance therefore cause changes in the electron beam current, which on returning from the target enters the first stage of a five stage electron-multiplier tube.

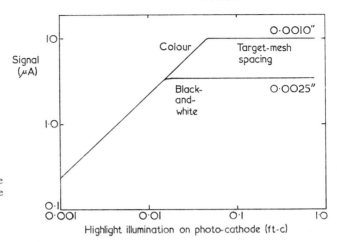

Fig. 17.4. Response
characteristic for image
orthicon tubes.

The sensitivity of image-orthicon tubes is very high, enabling good black-and-white pictures to be obtained at illumination levels down to a few foot-candles. Like the orthicon, the image-orthicon has a linear response; but, as the luminance level is raised, a point is reached where the wire mesh is unable to collect many more secondary electrons and the response then flattens out as shown in Fig. 17.4 (Neuhauser, 1956), and the secondary electrons not collected by the mesh fall back on to the target and produce areas of negative charge which result in black halos appearing around very bright objects such as light sources. For colour work these distortions being, in general, different in the three pictures, would produce intolerable spurious colours, so the tubes must be operated below the bend, or 'knee', of their characteristics. By reducing the mesh spacing the knee can be raised, as shown in Fig. 17.4, and this is usually done for tubes intended for colour. The range of tones over which a colour image-orthicon tube operates linearly is about 90 to 1, expressed as the ratio of peak-signal to R.M.S.-noise; in log-units this amounts to 1.95, or in decibels of signal amplitude 39 dB.[1] In practice, however, the need for gamma correction and *aperture-correction* (increasing the amplitudes of the high frequencies in the signal so as to offset fine-detail contrast-reduction caused by finite size or 'aperture' of the electron spots, see Section 17.9) usually reduce the peak signal-to-noise ratio, below this level.

[1] In electrical engineering, power is proportional to the *square* of the voltage (or current) so that the decibel is defined as twenty times (not ten times) the change in $\log_{10}$ voltage. In television the (un-gamma-corrected) voltages are considered as *directly* proportional to the amount of light, so that a given change in signal voltage or current expressed in decibels must be divided by twenty to obtain the corresponding change in $\log_{10}$ of the amount of light. Conversely, changes in $\log_{10}$ of the amount of light must be multiplied by twenty to obtain the corresponding change in current or voltage in decibels.

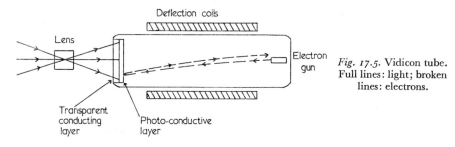

Fig. 17.5. Vidicon tube. Full lines: light; broken lines: electrons.

In Fig. 17.5 the main features of the *vidicon* tube are shown. The image of the outside scene is formed on a thin layer of photo-conductive material which has in contact with it (on the incident-light side) a transparent conducting layer which is kept at a voltage positive with respect to that of a low-energy electron gun on the other side of the layer. The result is that, in the absence of light, the photo-conductive layer acts as an insulator and prevents current flowing from the gun to the transparent conducting layer; but when light falls on the device, the photo-conductive layer becomes conducting, so that electrons move towards the transparent conducting layer, and hence the potential of the surface of the photo-conductive layer rises as a function of the light intensity; then the electron beam, as it scans the image area, deposits electrons so as to reduce the charge once more, and hence a current flows to the transparent conducting layer, in accordance with the luminance of the image, to provide the required signal.

It is clear that the vidicon is a somewhat simpler device than the image orthicon but it is less sensitive, requiring illumination levels of around 50 foot-candles for good black-and-white pictures. The response characteristics of the vidicon are like the iconoscope's, the signal being roughly proportional to the square root of the incident light so that no gamma correction is needed; but unlike the iconoscope's, the vidicon's response is not affected by local luminance variations. Unlike the orthicon, the tone range handled without distortion is very adequate, signal to noise ratios of 300 to 1 (50 dB) being quoted, although aperture correction often causes a reduction to more like 100 to 1 (40 dB). In Fig. 17.6 response curves for a typical vidicon (Neuhauser, 1956) are shown on a log-log plot, so that straight lines of gamma (slope) equal to about 0.5 are obtained; the gammas of typical vidicon tubes usually fall in the range 0.5 to 0.6. The different lines in Fig. 17.6 were obtained simply by altering the voltage difference between the transparent conducting layer and the electron gun, and this provides a very convenient sensitivity adjustment (in a colour camera it can be used to equalize the three signals given by white). The vidicon has very low and stable dark current and this is important in colour cameras, otherwise shadows and blacks may be reproduced coloured; in fact all its tonal transfer characteristics are very stable and linear (on a log-log plot), being free from any 'knees' such as occur

346

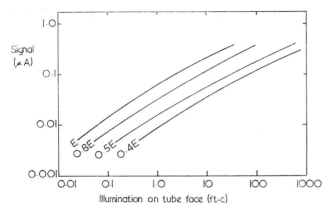

Fig. 17.6. Response characteristics for vidicon tube at various voltage differences (E, 0.8E, 0.5E, and 0.4E, where E is the maximum possible) between the transparent conducting layer and the electron gun.

with the image-orthicons. But in addition to limited sensitivity the vidicon does possess one further disadvantage: it has a time lag which can cause slight smearing of the picture; however, the lag is dependent on the light level, and above 100 foot-candles it is fairly negligible. The vidicon, with its wide stable range of tone reproduction, is well suited to deriving television signals from photographic film images. Vidicon tubes are smaller than image-orthicons and therefore enable smaller colour cameras to be constructed.

The *plumbicon* tube (De Haan and Van Doorn, 1964) operates on exactly the same principles as the vidicon tube but the photo-conductor, instead of being antimony sulphide (Sb_2S_3) or Selenium (Se) is lead monoxide (PbO).

The sensitivity of the plumbicon is intermediate between that of the image-orthicon and the vidicon, good black-and-white images being obtained

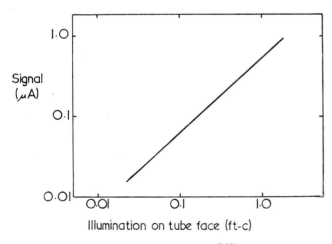

Fig. 17.7. Response characteristic for plumbicon tube.

347

down to about 10 foot-candles. The gamma of the response curve, as shown in Fig. 17.7, is about 1.0 (on a log-log plot) so that gamma correction is required. The range of tones reproduced without distortion is about 80 to 1 or 38 dB at 150 foot-candles, and about 65 to 1 or 36 dB at 25 foot-candles. The image area used is very small, 12 × 16 mm., so that high aperture lenses can be used without serious loss of depth of focus, and very compact colour cameras can be made. The dark current is very low and the tone characteristics are very reproducible and linear, and are independent of light level, local luminance differences in the image, operating voltage, and ambient temperature. The plumbicon does not suffer from any appreciable time-lag effects (except at very low light levels).

17.4 Spectral sensitivities of television camera tubes

It is obviously necessary that camera tubes used for colour should have sensitivity throughout the visible spectrum, but the exact form of the spectral sensitivity curve is relatively unimportant because the desired curves (see Section 16.13) can usually be closely enough approximated by means of suitable filtration. In Fig. 17.8 the spectral sensitivities of typical image-orthicon, vidicon, and plumbicon tubes are shown for comparison. It is clear that all of the tubes have relatively more sensitivity in the blue than in the red regions of the spectrum; but blue filters are usually less efficient than red, and conditions of dim illumination often occur with tungsten lighting which is particularly poor in blue content. Hence it is usually found that in colour cameras the red and blue channels have similar effective sensitivities, with the green somewhat more sensitive. The sensitivity of the ordinary plumbicon tube is too restricted in the red to give proper rendering of colours which

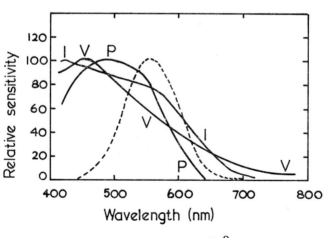

Fig. 17.8. Spectral response curves for various tubes. I = image orthicon; V = vidicon; P = plumbicon; broken line = the eye.

have important changes in spectral reflectance beyond 640 nm; however, by matrixing this can be corrected to a useful degree for the colours which are most likely to occur in practice (Monteath, 1966). Experimental plumbicon tubes with increased far-red sensitivity have been described (De Haan and Van Doorn, 1965).

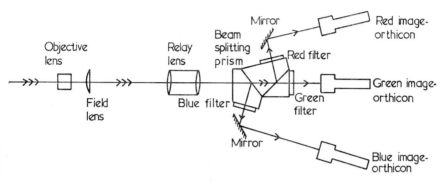

Fig. 17.9. Camera using three image-orthicon tubes.

17.5 Camera arrangements

For closed circuit television, where the signals travel entirely by cable, the simple field-sequential system of colour television can be used: in this case a red, green, and blue filter wheel rotating in front of what is essentially a black-and-white camera (but with the frame frequency suitably increased) is all that is needed. But for broadcast colour television the need to transmit mixtures of the red, green, and blue signals requires that they be present simultaneously, and hence different arrangements are necessary for both the cameras and the receivers. Three different types of camera are shown diagrammatically in Figs. 17.9, 17.10, and 17.11.

In Fig. 17.9 a camera employing three image-orthicon tubes is shown (Bertero, 1963). The objective lens forms an image in the plane of its associated field lens and a relay lens then forms secondary images on the three camera tubes. (The field lens, by forming an image of the objective lens in the relay lens, ensures that the latter collects all the light over the whole of the field.) The light is split by a dichroic (interference) prism assembly into red, green, and blue components before being imaged on to the three image-orthicon tubes. Colour filters are added to improve the approximation to the required spectral sensitivity curves, and neutral density filters may also be added to equalize the signals produced by white. The adjustable iris diaphragm of the camera is mounted in the relay lens. Focussing is carried out by altering the position of the objective lens along its axis.

Fig. 17.10 shows the main features of a colour camera which employs three vidicon tubes (James, 1959). In this camera a relay lens is avoided by using a telephoto lens system and inserting the dichroic beam splitting mirrors between the front (negative) part of the lens and the rear (positive) part; the rear lens, being situated after the beam is split into three, has to be triplicated, of course. By a suitable choice of focal lengths the angles of the beams of light between the front and rear lenses is kept down to $\pm 4\frac{1}{2}°$ which makes the optics easier to design.

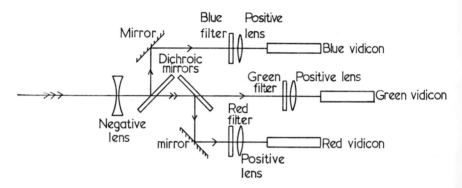

Fig. 17.10. Camera using three vidicon tubes.

Fig. 17.11 depicts a plumbicon camera arrangement. A very compact dichroic prism arrangement, situated between the lens and the tube faces, is used to split the beam into three, and this, combined with the small size of the plumbicon tubes, results in a very neat camera arrangement (Van Doorn, De Lang, and Bouwis, 1966).

17.6 Image equality in colour cameras

In a colour camera it is necessary for the three images to be identical in tone reproduction, and, to achieve this, care has to be taken at several stages. First, the flare characteristics of the three optical paths should be closely similar. Secondly, each of the three tubes should have uniform sensitivity and tone reproduction characteristics all over its image area or colour shading over the picture will occur (although some correction for non-uniformity over the picture can be provided subsequently electronically). Finally the tone reproduction characteristics of the three tubes should be closely similar to one another, or a grey scale will be reproduced coloured at some densities.

The camera tubes used in colour television are normally capable of providing all the definition required by the television system being used, but unless the images formed on the three tubes are geometrically identical and in exact registration with respect to the electron scanning, poor definition, and colour fringing, occur. Very precise optical and electronic components are therefore required and the optics have to be mounted very rigidly. In the image-orthicon cameras it is also necessary for the electron-imaging sections of the three tubes to be identical. These requirements present formidable problems in camera construction.

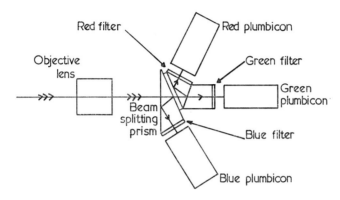

Fig. 17.11. Camera using three plumbicon tubes.

17.7 R-Y-B cameras

The problems of definition are somewhat alleviated in the case of the blue tube because the blue contribution to the high definition luminance signal usually amounts to only about 10 % of the total, and the colour difference signals, where the blue contribution is much more important, are of low definition. From the point of view of definition alone, the ideal camera would be one in which the three signals produced were not red, green, and blue, but red, luminance, and blue. Optically this is not difficult to arrange, requiring only that the green filter be broadened to admit a little red and blue light so as to result in that channel having a spectral sensitivity similar to the $\bar{y}_\lambda$ function. The registration problems would then be alleviated because all the high definition would be confined to one of the three images, and lack of registration with the other two would only show up if it was so large as to be resolved by the low definition colour-difference signals. The advantage, however, is not found in practice to be as large as might be expected, because the eye seems to be very sensitive to colour fringes around edges in a picture: the mis-registration tolerances in an R-Y-B camera are therefore only about twice as great as for an R-G-B camera, instead of four times as might be expected from band-width considerations.

351

The production of a separate luminance signal in the camera leads to a rather complicated situation regarding gamma correction. The luminance signal, E_Y, would have to be gamma-corrected to $E_Y^{1/\gamma}$ before transmission, and would therefore be related to the red, green, and blue signals E_R, E_G, and E_B, thus:

$$E_Y^{1/\gamma} = (lE_R + mE_G + nE_B)^{1/\gamma}$$

where l, m, and n are the usual luminance factors. The other two signals available at the receiver would be $E_R^{1/\gamma} - E_Y^{1/\gamma}$ and $E_B^{1/\gamma} - E_Y^{1/\gamma}$, and although $E_R^{1/\gamma}$ and $E_B^{1/\gamma}$ are easily recovered (by adding $E_Y^{1/\gamma}$ to each), the recovery of $E_G^{1/\gamma}$ is a very complicated business, requiring the signals first to be raised to the power γ, then added and subtracted, and then raised to the power $1/\gamma$. The added complexity that this would call for in the receiver (involving extra cost and loss of signal-to-noise ratio) has prevented R-Y-B types of camera from being used in this way.

Various schemes have been suggested for recovering an approximate $E_G^{1/\gamma}$ signal by less complicated procedures at the receiver: for instance, if the circuits used were the same as those for use with the normal luminance signal ($E_Y' = l E_R^{1/\gamma} + m E_G^{1/\gamma} + n E_B^{1/\gamma}$) then the actual green signal recovered, $E_g^{1/\gamma}$ would be given by (remembering that $l+m+n = 1$, see Section 16.9)

$$E_g^{1/\gamma} = E_Y^{1/\gamma} - \frac{l}{m}(E_R^{1/\gamma} - E_Y^{1/\gamma}) - \frac{n}{m}(E_B^{1/\gamma} - E_Y^{1/\gamma})$$

$$= \frac{1}{m}E_Y^{1/\gamma} - \frac{l}{m}E_R^{1/\gamma} - \frac{n}{m}E_B^{1/\gamma}$$

$$= E_G^{1/\gamma} + \frac{1}{m}(E_Y^{1/\gamma} - E_Y').$$

For greys $E_Y^{1/\gamma} - E_Y'$ is zero, but for colours it is always positive. Hence the green signals are distorted by being increased as saturation increases: thus green colours would be increased in saturation, but red and blue colours would be desaturated and altered in hue. These errors can be reduced by subtracting from $E_g^{1/\gamma}$ a signal which is a suitable function of colour saturation, and this could be obtained by rectifying the chrominance signal (James and Karowski, 1962), but only at the cost of complicating the receiver.

Because of the above receiver complications it is preferable with an R-Y-B camera for a low definition E_G signal to be recovered from the E_R, E_B, and E_Y signals at the transmitter; in the next section it is shown that by suitable processing of these signals before transmission the correct signals can be recovered without any extra complications at the receiver, and without losing the advantages of having a separate high definition luminance signal produced by the camera.

17.8 Four-tube cameras

The difficulties over recovering the green signal properly when an R-Y-B camera is used, appear in a somewhat different form if a separate luminance signal is derived in addition to all three colour signals by using four camera tubes. In such an R-G-B-Y camera, the two colour-difference signals are derived from the red, green, and blue tubes in the usual way, by first forming the E_Y' signal

$$E_Y' = lE_R{}^{1/\gamma} + mE_G{}^{1/\gamma} + nE_B{}^{1/\gamma}$$

and then subtracting this signal from $E_R{}^{1/\gamma}$ and $E_B{}^{1/\gamma}$ to obtain

$$E_R{}^{1/\gamma} - E_Y'$$

and

$$E_B{}^{1/\gamma} - E_Y'$$

The fourth tube is then used to provide a true gamma-corrected luminance signal $E_Y{}^{1/\gamma}$. As usual, only the luminance signal is of high definition, so that the red, green, and blue tubes which contribute only to the colour-difference signals can be of lower definition and require less precise registration. The receiver then attempts to recover the required colour signals $E_R{}^{1/\gamma}$, $E_G{}^{1/\gamma}$, and $E_B{}^{1/\gamma}$, but, because in general E_Y' and $E_Y{}^{1/\gamma}$ are not equal, all three colour signals are now only recovered in modified form, $E_{MR}{}^{1/\gamma}$, $E_{MG}{}^{1/\gamma}$, and $E_{MB}{}^{1/\gamma}$, thus:

$$E_{MR}{}^{1/\gamma} = E_R{}^{1/\gamma} - E_Y' + E_Y{}^{1/\gamma} = E_R{}^{1/\gamma} + (E_Y{}^{1/\gamma} - E_Y')$$

$$E_{MB}{}^{1/\gamma} = E_B{}^{1/\gamma} - E_Y' + E_Y{}^{1/\gamma} = E_B{}^{1/\gamma} + (E_Y{}^{1/\gamma} - E_Y')$$

$$E_{MG}{}^{1/\gamma} = E_Y{}^{1/\gamma} - \frac{l}{m}(E_R{}^{1/\gamma} - E_Y') - \frac{n}{m}(E_B{}^{1/\gamma} - E_Y')$$

Remembering that $E_Y' = lE_R{}^{1/\gamma} + mE_G{}^{1/\gamma} + nE_B{}^{1/\gamma}$, the last expression reduces to:

$$E_{MG}{}^{1/\gamma} = E_G{}^{1/\gamma} + (E_Y{}^{1/\gamma} - E_Y')$$

Thus it is seen that, whereas in the R-Y-B camera only the green signal was distorted, in the four-tube camera all three colour signals are distorted, and this might at first sight seem to be a worse situation. But the distortion now consists of an equal addition to all three signals and this is equivalent to a small addition of white light, which is usually a fairly unimportant defect. Hue errors are thus largely avoided, and it is found in practice that the errors caused by a four-tube camera are appreciably less noticeable than those produced by an R-Y-B camera (Abrahams, 1963). It must be remembered also that, even with a basic R-G-B camera, colours of high colour saturation are reproduced too dark in small areas because of gamma-correction effects, so that the extra luminance resulting from the use of the fourth camera tube will operate in the direction of correcting this defect.

However, it is possible to process the signals from a four-tube camera so as to produce truly correct signals for transmission, at least for large areas. The procedure is to form an additional low-definition true luminance signal from the three colour tubes, thus:

$$E_{YC}{}^{1/\gamma} = (lE_R + mE_G + nE_B)^{1/\gamma}$$

This then has subtracted from it the low-definition E_Y' signal to obtain a low-definition luminance correcting signal

$$E_{YC}{}^{1/\gamma} - E_Y'.$$

This low-definition correcting signal is then subtracted from the high definition true-luminance signal $E_Y{}^{1/\gamma}$ to give a corrected luminance signal for transmission:

$$E_Y{}^{1/\gamma} - (E_{YC}{}^{1/\gamma} - E_Y').$$

When the receiver adds this signal to its colour difference signals, in large areas, where $E_Y{}^{1/\gamma} = E_{YC}{}^{1/\gamma}$, the correct colour signals are obtained thus:

$$E_R{}^{1/\gamma} - E_Y' + E_Y{}^{1/\gamma} - (E_{YC}{}^{1/\gamma} - E_Y') = E_R{}^{1/\gamma}$$

$$E_G{}^{1/\gamma} - E_Y' + E_Y{}^{1/\gamma} - (E_{YC}{}^{1/\gamma} - E_Y') = E_G{}^{1/\gamma}$$

$$E_B{}^{1/\gamma} - E_Y' + E_Y{}^{1/\gamma} - (E_{YC}{}^{1/\gamma} - E_Y') = E_B{}^{1/\gamma}$$

Circuits performing these operations are feasible and since all the extra complication is at the transmitter and none at the receiver, the use of luminance correcting signals of this type is a practicable procedure.

The four-tube camera makes it possible to run the colour signals at a higher gamma than the luminance signal, and in this way colour saturation can be increased to overcome system deficiencies which tend to lower saturation (such as neglect of the negative lobes of the theoretical sensitivity curves, or the addition of the unwanted white signal described earlier, if this is not corrected by a luminance correcting signal).

Fig. 17.12 illustrates the arrangement in a four-vidicon camera (Abrahams, 1963). This type of camera is well suited to deriving colour television signals from colour film (see Chapter 20). A four-tube camera employing an image-orthicon for the luminance signal and three vidicons for the colour signals has also been described (James, 1963); and four-tube cameras employing four plumbicons are made (Underhill, 1967; Parker-Smith, 1967).

17.9 Aperture correction

In camera pick-up tubes, even if the optical and electric-charge images are perfectly sharp, the picture-signal produced by the tube corresponds to an image whose sharpness is reduced by being scanned by an electron spot of finite size or *aperture*. This results in a basic limitation in the number of lines per picture-width which can be resolved, and also in a reduction in contrast across vertical edges; the contrast across vertical edges can, however, be increased again, a technique known as *horizontal aperture correction*. One way of achieving this type of correction is to delay the signal for a time comparable with that taken to scan a distance similar to the effective aperture of the electron spot, and then to subtract from it a correcting signal which is a function of the average of the undelayed signal and a signal delayed twice as long; in this way a sort

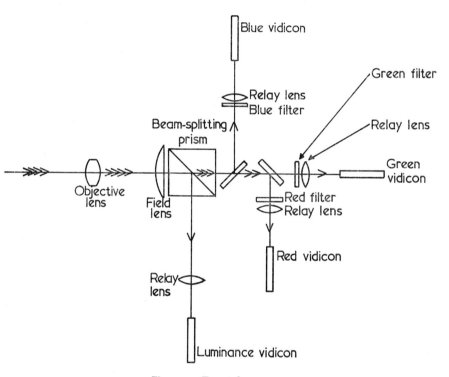

Fig. 17.12. Four-tube camera.

of unsharp masking effect can be achieved (see Section 13.2). The correcting signal is less sharp than the main signal, and is also made less contrasty; the result of subtracting it from the main signal is therefore to reduce contrast except in fine detail. Hence, upon increasing the overall contrast of the composite signal, the contrast of the coarse detail is restored, but that of the fine detail is enhanced.

In a similar way it is possible to introduce *vertical aperture correction* to correct for some of the effects of any tendency for the aperture of the electron spot in the camera pick-up tube to be greater than the spacing between neigh-bouring picture-lines. In this case the main signal has to be delayed by a time equal to that taken to scan one *line*, and the correcting signal is then a function of the average of the undelayed signal and a signal delayed twice as long. In this case the unsharpness of the 'mask' is equivalent to about 2 field-lines or 4 picture-lines.

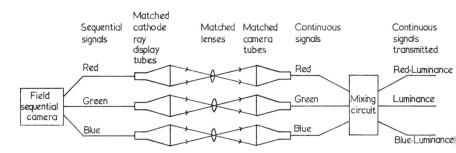

Fig. 17.13. Principle of the chromacoder: continuously available red, green, and blue signals are obtained from field-sequential camera signals.

In three- and four-tube cameras, the advantages of aperture correction are only fully realized if the registration of the images is very good, because of the high sensitivity of the eye to colour fringing. It is, however, possible to derive a common 'masking' signal from *one* of the camera tubes and to use it as the correcting signal for *all* the main signals. When this is done in three-tube cameras, some of the advantages of four-tube cameras are obtained because the enhancement of contrast across edges, being derived from a single camera-tube, cannot be affected by camera mis-registration and therefore cannot contribute to colour fringing. This is known as the *contours out of green* technique, because the green camera-tube (having the spectral sensitivity most similar to that corresponding to a true luminance signal) is generally the preferred source for the correcting signal (De Vrijer, Tan, and Van Doorn, 1966).

17.10 Single-tube cameras

Ideally, of course, the simpler the camera the better, and if only one pick-up tube was needed a really simple camera could be envisaged. The field-sequential system not being permissible for broadcast colour television, some thought has been given to the problem of producing simultaneous signals from a single tube. Tubes with vertical stripes, having sensitivities to red, green, and blue light only, have been described (Weiner, Grey, Borgan, Ochs, and Thompson, 1955) but so far none of these has been successfully reduced to practice.

Because of the great simplicity of field-sequential cameras, attempts have been made to obtain simultaneous signals from them. In one such device, called the *Chromacoder* (James, 1955; Kell, 1950) the successive red, green, and blue signals from a field-sequential camera are displayed on three very carefully matched cathode-ray tubes, the decay time of the phosphor on the tubes being made long enough to provide substantially continuous pictures on each display tube. In its simplest form, as shown diagrammatically in Fig. 17.13, such a Chromacoder displays the red, green, and blue signals on its three cathode-ray tubes, and these are then imaged optically on to three camera tubes carefully matched for scan-register and response-curve; thus continuous E_R, E_G, and E_B signals are available, from which the $E_R^{1/\gamma} - E_Y'$, $E_B^{1/\gamma} - E_Y'$, and E_Y' signals are obtained in the usual way. The advantage of this system is that in a television transmitting station, signals from any number of field-sequential cameras, scattered around the various studios, can be handled one after another by a single Chromacoder situated in one central place; and only the Chromacoder needs three matched tubes, it being permissible for the individual camera tubes to vary amongst themselves.

REFERENCES

Abrahams, I. C., *J. Soc. Mot. Pic. Tel. Eng.*, **72,** 594 (1963).
Bertero, E. P., *J. Soc. Mot. Pic. Tel. Eng.*, **72,** 602 (1963).
De Haan, E. F., and Van Doorn, A. G., *J. Soc. Mot. Pic. Tel. Eng.*, **73,** 473 (1964).
De Haan, E. F., and Van Doorn, A. G., *J. Soc. Mot. Pic. Tel. Eng.*, **74,** 922 (1965).
De Vrijer, F. W., Tan, A. L., and Van Doorn, A. G., *J. Soc. Mot. Pic. Tel. Eng.*, **75,** 1080 (1966).
James, I. J. P., *British Kinematography*, **26,** 5 (1955).
James, I. J. P., *J. Brit. Inst. Radio Engrs.*, **19,** 165 (1959).
James, I. J. P., private communication (1963).
James, I. J. P., and Karowski, W. A., *J. Brit. Inst. Radio Engrs.*, **23,** 297 (1962).
Kell, R. D., U.S. Patent 2,545,957 (1950).
Monteath, G. D., *Television Soc. J.*, **11,** 109 (1966).
Neuhauser, R. G., *J. Soc. Mot. Pic. Tel. Eng.*, **65,** 636 (1956).
Parker-Smith, N. N., *Brit. Kinematography Sound and Tel.*, **49,** 100 (1967).
Underhill, W. T., *J. Roy. Television Society*, **11,** 167 (1967).
Van Doorn, A. G., De Lang, H., and Bouwis, G., *J. Soc. Mot. Pic. Tel. Eng.*, **75,** 1002 (1966).
Weiner, P. K., Grey, S., Borgan, H., Ochs, S. A., and Thompson, H. C., *Proc. Inst. Radio Engrs.*, **43,** 370 (1955).

Display Devices for Colour Television

18.1 Introduction

THE earliest television systems, which depended on a mechanical or optical device for breaking the picture up into lines, such as the rotating disc shown in Fig. 17.1, used similar non-electronic devices for displaying the picture at the receiver. The advent of high definition television, with the invention of the iconoscope, required much more rapid means of 'writing' the picture, and the required means was found in the cathode-ray tube, the principle of which is to produce light by exciting a fluorescent layer with a beam of electrons moved rapidly over its surface.

The main features of a cathode-ray tube of the type used in television are shown diagrammatically in Fig. 18.1(a). A *cathode* is coated with a suitable electron-emitting material, and hence when its temperature is raised by a heater a supply of electrons is provided. The cathode is housed in an evacuated glass envelope, so that the electrons can be accelerated towards an *anode* which is kept at a highly positive potential relative to the cathode; the accelerated electrons strike a *screen,* consisting of a layer of phosphor coated on the inside of the glass envelope, and thus light is produced. The amount of light produced is regulated by altering the voltage difference between the cathode and the *modulator-grid* (sometimes called the *control-grid* or often just the *grid*). The position at which the light is produced on the screen is regulated by *focusing* devices and by *deflection* devices. The focusing devices, which produce suitable magnetic or electrostatic fields in the neck of the envelope, result

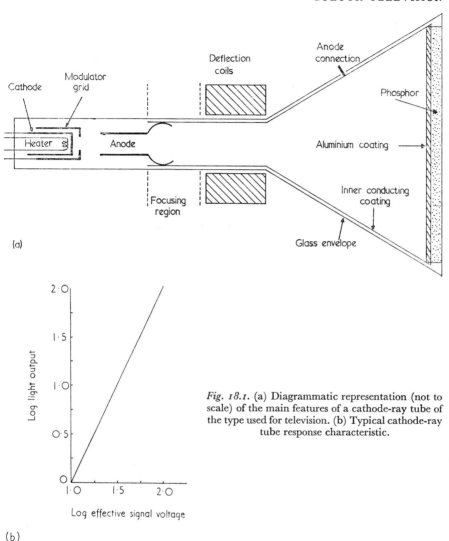

Fig. 18.1. (a) Diagrammatic representation (not to scale) of the main features of a cathode-ray tube of the type used for television. (b) Typical cathode-ray tube response characteristic.

in the electrons being imaged on the phosphor as a small spot, instead of as a large patch. The deflection devices usually consist of coils producing magnetic fields (electro-static deflection is generally used only in oscilloscopes); these magnetic fields cause the electron spot to be moved very rapidly across the face of the tube so as to produce the picture by scanning the phosphor line by line in the required manner. Accurate scanning is facilitated by coating the inside of the conical part of the tube with a conducting layer which is held at the same voltage as the anode thus providing for the moving electron beam a volume virtually free of any electrostatic fields. The phosphor usually has coated on its inner side a very thin layer of aluminium which is also held at anode voltage and this not only assists in eliminating electrostatic fields, but also prevents secondary emission of electrons from the phosphor, and avoids waste of light by reflecting forwards in a useful direction the light emitted by the phosphor backwards (towards the cathode) which would otherwise be lost.

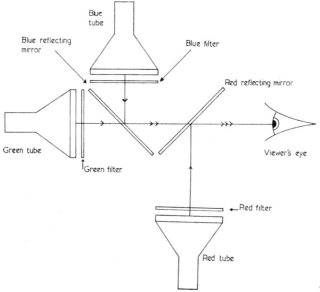

Fig. 18.2. The Trinoscope.

Typical operating values for cathode-ray tubes used for television, are as follows. Anode voltages range from about 16 kV (kilo-volts) for black-and-white tubes to 25 kV for colour tubes and 100 kV for projection tubes. The difference between the modulator-grid and the cathode voltages may range from some tens of volts negative (modulator-grid voltage *below* cathode voltage) when all the electrons are prevented from reaching the phosphor and black is produced, to some tens of volts positive when maximum luminance (*peak-white*) is being produced. The voltage difference which produces black is referred to as the *black-out bias* or *black-sit* (adjustment of which on a domestic receiver is sometimes labelled 'brightness'). It is convenient to express the modulator-grid to cathode voltage-difference as a difference from the black-out bias, and when this is done it may be referred to as the *effective signal voltage* or the *drive* (adjustment of the amplification of which on a domestic receiver is sometimes labelled '*contrast*'). The amount of current flowing in the electron beam (the *beam current*) usually varies from zero when black is being reproduced to some hundreds of micro-amps when peak-white is being reproduced. The luminance at which peak-white is produced is usually about 20 to 80 foot-lamberts for ordinary viewing, but may be as high as several hundred foot-lamberts for projection tubes operated at anode voltages as high as 100 kV. These high luminances would be unsatisfactory for direct viewing because the 50 or 60 cycle-per-second flicker in television pictures is only unobtrusive at the lower luminance levels.

The actual tubes used in practice are more elaborate than indicated in Fig. 18.1(a), and extra grids and electrodes may be included: thus a *screen-grid* at a few hundred volts above the cathode voltage, and focusing electrodes at a few thousand volts above the cathode voltage, may be used, in which case the electrons are accelerated through a series of voltage steps between the cathode and the anode.

When the effective signal voltage, E, is zero, the beam current, by definition, is also zero. As E is increased, the beam current, I, increases, and the effect is analogous to opening the iris diaphragm on a lens. If the effective diameter of the electronic iris is roughly proportional to E, the area of the iris will be proportional to E^2, and hence the beam current, I, will be roughly proportional to E^2. The power in the beam is equal to the current multiplied by the accelerating voltage, V, and hence is equal to VI. The accelerating voltage, V, is equal to the anode voltage relative to the cathode voltage, and although the latter may vary as E is varied, its maximum variation is usually only about 100 volts and this is negligible compared to the anode voltage of tens of thousands of volts. The accelerating voltage, V, may therefore be regarded as constant, so that the power is proportional to the beam current, I. If the phosphor is such that the amount of light produced is proportional to the power, and hence proportional to the beam current, I (such phosphors are often referred to as being *linear*), then, since I is proportional to E^2, the amount of light produced by this hypothetical tube will also be proportional to E^2.

The tone reproduction characteristics of real cathode-ray tubes are such that the light output is approximately proportional to a function intermediate between the square and the cube of the effective signal voltage. When the logarithm of the light output is plotted against the logarithm of the effective signal voltage, a straight line is therefore obtained, as shown in Fig. 18.1(b). For the sake of standardization a slope (or *gamma*) of 2.2 for this line has been agreed upon for colour television. The range of tones which a cathode-ray tube can display when no ambient light is allowed to fall on the face of the tube, depends on the amount of 'spill-over' light in the tube itself, and this may be low enough to enable the range to reach 100 to 1 (corresponding to 40 dB); but in practice the ambient lighting in the viewing situation usually lightens the blacks to the point where they have a luminance of at least 2%

of that of the maximum luminance, so that the range of tones is not more than 50 to 1 (34 dB); if the ambient and spill-over light amounts to about 5%, then the range becomes 20 to 1 (26 dB) and this is equivalent to a log range of only 1.3, which is less than that of typical reflection prints (Hunt, 1965), and much less than the figure of 2.2 log units typical of out-door scenes (Jones and Condit, 1941). Practical figures are generally regarded to be within the 2% to 5% range (Wentworth, 1955).

The application of the cathode-ray tube principle (fluorescence caused by electron bombardment) to the specific problems of colour television display devices has been the subject of intense technological effort and enormous ingenuity has been expended in trying to arrive at inexpensive reliable receivers for domestic use; some of these display devices will now be described, together with others for more special applications.

18.2 The Trinoscope

The principle of the *Trinoscope*, perhaps the least sophisticated colour television display device, is illustrated in Fig. 18.2. The three colour images are displayed on three separate cathode-ray tubes, and images of two of them are then combined with the third by means of semi-reflecting dichroic mirrors. To obtain maximum efficiency, special red-emitting, green-emitting, and blue-emitting phosphors can be used in the three tubes; colour trimming filters can be used in addition if necessary. The main problem in the Trinoscope is to get exact geometric registration, and matching tone reproduction characteristics, of the three images all over the picture area, and it is evident that in this respect the device has problems similar to those of colour cameras. It is therefore necessary to use very high quality cathode-ray tubes and ancillary gear, and very precise mirrors rigidly mounted in exact position relative to the tubes. This makes it a costly device, but it has the virtue of giving images of higher luminance than most other display devices. Its main use is as a high luminance monitor and as a device from which tele-recordings on film can be made; it is far too expensive, as well as being too bulky, to be considered for use as a domestic receiver.

18.3 Triple projection

When projection television devices are being used, it is possible to use the triple projection principle by having three projection television tubes arranged so as to throw red, green, and blue images onto a single reflecting screen. The usual problems of registration have to be overcome, but when the final display is wanted in projected form, the method is usually the best to adopt (unless field-sequential displays can be used). Triple projection has been used for the display of colour television pictures in cinemas, and for displaying the terrain in flight-simulators used for training the crew of aircraft.

18.4 The shadow-mask tube

The undesirable bulk and registration problems of the Trinoscope and triple projector are avoided in the *shadow-mask tube*, by incorporating all three electron-guns in the same cathode-ray tube. Electronic registration is still required, of course, but, by having the three guns in the same tube, the same magnetic fields can be used for moving the three electron beams throughout the scanning sequence for each field of the picture. This is a considerable help, but there are many residual problems caused by the fact that because the three electron beams do not originate from the same place they do not in fact scan the picture identically. Thus when the beams are scanning the corners of the picture they have further to travel to the screen than when they are scanning

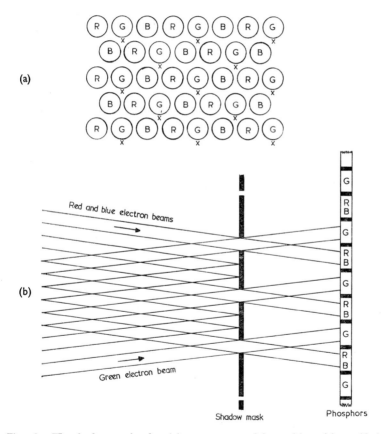

Fig. 18.3. The shadow-mask tube: (a) arrangement of dots, with positions of holes in the shadow mask marked thus: X. (b) Electron beam paths in a vertical plane: the red and blue electron beams and phosphors are separated horizontally.

the centre; hence if their convergence is correct for the centre it will be too great for the corners, and so the magnetic fields have to be altered during the scanning by means of special current wave-forms applied to the electromagnets.

Before reaching the screen the three beams meet a metal plate with about 357,000 holes in it, situated about $\frac{3}{4}$ inch from the phosphors. The three phosphors are laid down as dots (see Figs. 3.1 and 18.3), and the geometry of the electron beam directions, the positions of the holes, and the positions of the dots, is such that all the red-phosphor dots are irradiated only by the gun to which the red signal is applied, the green-phosphor dots by the green-signal gun, and the blue-phosphor dots by the blue-signal gun. The rows of dots do not have to be aligned with the lines of the picture, but *moiré patterns* caused by beats between the line structure and the dot pattern arise at certain angles; and as these are worst at $\pm 30°$ and negligible at $0°$ it is arranged for the lines of the picture and the lines of the dots to be more or less parallel.

The 357,000 holes provide about 520 lines of holes with about 690 holes in each line, so that the maximum definition of the tube amounts to about 345 black-and-white pairs along a line and 260 black-white pairs vertically. If the three electron beams were small enough to irradiate, on the average, not more than one line of holes and its associated triad of phosphor dots then the tube would not restrict the definition much, even in a 625-line system, but this would be a rather critical condition in which to operate and each electron beam normally irradiates two or three lines of holes and their associated triads of dots; there is therefore some theoretical loss of definition, but other factors, such as interlacing, may make the loss unimportant in practice (Jesty, 1958).

The shadow-mask tube is capable of giving pictures of very good colour quality and is widely used both for high quality monitors and for domestic receivers. Very great care has to be taken in manufacture to see that the pattern of phosphor dots exactly coincides with the pattern of the holes in the metal plate, otherwise colour contamination occurs and produces serious errors of hue. The holes in the metal plate are therefore etched by photo-engraving using a master negative to ensure absolutely correct geometry. The inside of a tube is then coated with a photo-resist containing the red-phosphor, and then its metal plate is mounted in position and a light source placed in the position from which the electron beam carrying the red signal will finally appear to emanate. The light passing through the holes in the metal plate then causes the photo-resist to form hardened dots of phosphor; the metal plate is then removed and the unhardened phosphor washed away leaving the required pattern of dots. The same metal plate is then replaced in exactly the same position and the green-phosphor dots formed in a similar way, and finally the blue-phosphor dots are formed similarly. In a 21 inch tube the distance between adjacent dots is only about 0.015 inch so that it can be seen that very great accuracy is required in carrying out all these operations.

18.5 The Gabor tube

In an attempt to make a three-gun tube which is less critical for registration, and which is a much more convenient shape, the Gabor tube has been conceived (Gabor, Stuart, and Kalman, 1958), the lay-out of which is shown in Fig. 18.4. In this tube the three electron beams travel first vertically downwards, and are then turned forwards and vertically upwards by means of an electronic reversing lens, whereupon they enter a 'scanning array'. This consists of a series of horizontal, individually insulated, metal strips, which, by becoming negatively charged progressively from the top strip downwards, automatically

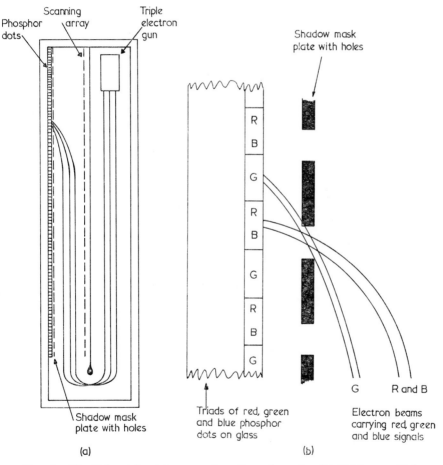

Fig. 18.4. The Gabor tube: (a) cross-section of complete tube; (b) highly magnified cross-section showing electron paths.

365

13B

move the beam downwards line by line. At the appropriate height for each line of the picture the three beams are turned forwards by suitable fields and pass through a shadow mask so as to fall on to red, green, and blue phosphor dots. The advantages claimed for this arrangement, in addition to the convenient shape of the device, are that the three electron beams are always automatically focused together, and that the shadow mask can be near enough to the phosphors to be integral with them (this is because the angle between the beams as they pass through the shadow mask can be about 20° instead of only a few degrees as in the conventional shadow-mask tube).

18.6 Lawrence tubes

Another form of the three-gun type of tube is the three-gun Lawrence tube (Dressler, 1953). In this tube the red, green, and blue phosphors are arranged in stripes; and the electron beams are guided to them by means of cylindrical electrostatic lenses. These electrostatic lenses are formed by means of wires running parallel to the stripes a short distance away from them, as shown in Fig. 18.5(a). The phosphor stripes can be horizontal or vertical, but the triads of stripes must be fine enough to reproduce the system definition.

There are very great advantages in reducing the number of electron guns from three to one in a colour tube, because practically all the problems of geometric registration and equalization of tone reproduction between the three images then disappear. The Lawrence tube can be made in single-gun form (Dressler, 1953). In this case the potential on the wires is switched to have one of three patterns: either equal potential on all wires, or relatively positive and negative potential on alternate wires, or a similar alternation but with the opposite potential on each wire; in this way three different patterns of electron lenses are formed as shown in Fig. 18.5(b). Hence, as the single electron beam scans the phosphors, it can be made to produce either red, or green, or blue light at will. The technique is therefore to select one at a time from continuously available red, green, and blue signals, using some suitable frequency, and to switch the voltages on the wires at the same frequency so as to produce light of the corresponding red, green, or blue colour. Again, the phosphor stripes can be horizontal or vertical in such an arrangement. The frequency of selection of the red, green, and blue signals as the electron beam 'writes' a line must of course be high enough to give adequate definition and must be such as to avoid producing undesirable beats with any residual ripple along the line from the chrominance sub-carrier frequency (the chrominance sub-carrier frequency is usually such as to provide about 250 cycles per line). For equal horizontal and vertical definition the luminance signal should be able to resolve about 350 cycles per line (for example $525 \times \frac{1}{2} \times \frac{4}{3}$ black-white pairs in a system having 525 actual picture lines); the number of triads of vertical lines required is therefore ideally not less than about 700, but, as in the shadow-mask tube, smaller numbers can be used without too much apparent loss of definition because the actual visual appearance is complicated by inter-lacing and various other factors (Jesty, 1958).

18.7 Decoding tubes

One solution to the problem of avoiding beats, in a single-gun tube, between the switching frequency and the chrominance sub-carrier frequency is to make them the same; if this is done, then the possibility exists of recovering the red, green, and blue signals from the composite luminance-chrominance signal actually in the tube itself, without using any demodulating circuits.

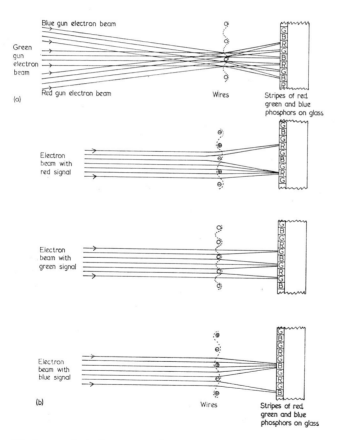

Fig. 18.5. Electron paths in Lawrence tubes (a) with three electron guns (b) with one electron gun. Broken line indicates shape of electron 'lens'.

Suppose that the luminance signal were composed of equal amounts of the three colour signals so that:

$$E_Y = \tfrac{1}{3}E_R + \tfrac{1}{3}E_G + \tfrac{1}{3}E_B$$

and suppose that the two colour difference signals $E_B - E_Y$ and $E_R - E_Y$ were amplified by a factor of $2/\sqrt{3}$ and combined with the luminance signal on a sub-carrier with a phase difference of $120°$ between them. The total *colour* signal could then be represented by the equation:

$$E_C = \frac{2}{\sqrt{3}}(E_B - E_Y)\sin(\omega t + 30°) + \frac{2}{\sqrt{3}}(E_R - E_Y)\cos \omega t$$

where ω is the phase angle and t the time. Then on adding the luminance signal E_Y to this colour signal in the receiver, the result is that at one phase

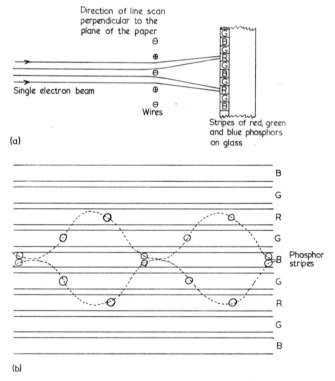

Fig. 18.6. Decoding tubes: (a) electron paths at the instant when the red phosphor is being excited; (b) showing the tracks of the electron spots over the phosphors.

angle in each cycle the signal is equal to E_R, at another angle to E_G, and at a third angle to E_B. This can be shown as follows. When $\omega t = 90°$, $\sin(\omega t+30°)$

$= \dfrac{\sqrt{3}}{2}$ and $\cos \omega t = 0$, hence

$$E_Y+E_C = E_Y+E_B-E_Y = E_B$$

When $\omega t = 210°$, $\sin(\omega t+30°) = -\dfrac{\sqrt{3}}{2}$ and $\cos \omega t = -\dfrac{\sqrt{3}}{2}$, hence

$$E_Y+E_C = E_Y-E_B+E_Y-E_R+E_Y = 3E_Y-E_B-E_R = E_G$$

When $\omega t = 330°$, $\sin(\omega t+30°) = 0$ and $\cos \omega t = \dfrac{\sqrt{3}}{2}$, hence

$$E_Y+E_C = E_Y+E_R-E_Y = E_R.$$

If therefore the red, green, and blue phosphor stripes were scanned in the correct order, at the right phase, and at the right frequency, then the red, green, and blue lights could be obtained simply by 'gating' the electron beam so that it only irradiated the phosphors in three 'instantaneous' bursts at the three phase angles. One convenient arrangement for doing this is shown in Fig. 18.6. Stripes of red, green, and blue phosphor in a Lawrence type tube are arranged in this case to run parallel to the picture lines, and the potential on the wires is made to vary sinusoidally so as to move the spot to and fro across the triads of stripes as shown, the red, green, and blue signals being pulsed in at the appropriate times on each cycle.

This approach leads to considerable simplification of the receiver circuitry, but unfortunately the usual types of composite luminance and chrominance signals are not of the form:

$$E_Y+E_C = E_Y+\frac{2}{\sqrt{3}}(E_B-E_Y)\sin(\omega t+30°)+\frac{2}{\sqrt{3}}(E_R-E_Y)\cos \omega t$$

where $E_Y = \tfrac{1}{3}E_R+\tfrac{1}{3}E_G+\tfrac{1}{3}E_B$, but of the form:

$$E_Y+E_C = E_Y+b(E_B-E_Y)\sin \omega t+r(E_R-E_Y) \cos \omega t$$

where $E_Y = 0.299E_R+0.587E_G+0.114E_B$ and b and r are usually less than one. The direct application of this type of signal to such a tube therefore produces pictures with distorted colour reproduction. By means of a monochrome correction circuit (Loughlin, 1954) the composition of the E_Y signal can be altered so as to have the required equal weight given to the three colours and this reduces the errors appreciably; full correction, however, requires, in addition, the use of circuits to provide the proper phase and amplitude relationships. (Jackson, 1961.)

369

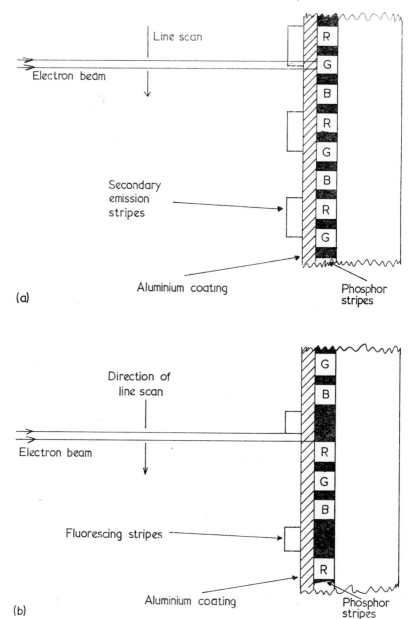

Fig. 18.7. Indexing tubes: (a) the Apple tube; (b) the Zebra tube.

18.8 Indexing tubes

Considerable simplification in the single-gun type of tube is achieved if the normal scanning operation is used to achieve the 'switching' from one strip of phosphor to the next. The simplest way of achieving this is to have vertical stripes of phosphor on the tube so that the normal horizontal line-scan results in the electron beam traversing each colour of each triad of stripes in turn, as shown in Fig. 18.7. A big advantage of these tubes is the ease with which they can display a monochrome picture: for by selecting the relative luminances and areas of the three phosphors appropriately a good black-and-white picture is obtained simply by applying a normal monochrome signal to the tube. To produce a colour picture it is, of course, necessary to have some means of indicating whether the beam is on a red, a green, or a blue stripe, and then ensuring that the signal of that colour is applied to the electronic beam at each instant. It is this requirement which has led to the name *index tube*: the tubes have the means of indexing the signals so that they are applied at the right times.

The tube must have several hundred triads of phosphors in order to provide adequate definition and hence the indexing must be extremely rapid. In the 'Apple' tube (Barnett, Bingley, Parsons, Pratt, and Sadowsky, 1956) each triad of phosphors has coated over part of it, on the electron-gun side, a strip of material giving high secondary-electron emission (such as magnesium oxide) as shown in Fig. 18.7(a). As the electron beam scans the triads, a burst of secondary electrons occurs each time a new triad is reached and this burst of secondary electrons is used to switch in the correct colour signals: because the electron beam intensity depends on the luminance and disappears for blacks, a second electron beam is provided especially for indexing purposes.

In the Zebra tube (Graham, Justice, and Oxenham, 1961) the indexing is carried out by means of the emission of light instead of the emission of secondary electrons. Each triad of red, green, and blue phosphor has associated with it on the electron-gun side a strip of phosphor which emits light, when the electron beam passes over it as shown in Fig. 18.7(b). This intermittent light signal is not mixed with the red, green, and blue light emitted by the phosphors of the triads because the triads are backed by the usual thin layer of aluminium; a photo-multiplier tube is used to detect the indexing light. The use of light has the advantage that it avoids the delay caused by the time taken for the secondary electrons to travel to their detector in the Apple tube.

Index tubes clearly have the attractions of being simple in construction and (like the single-gun Lawrence tube) of avoiding the registration and tone-reproduction matching problems of three-gun tubes. Their main problem is to maintain good separation of the three signals into their proper phosphor stripes at the very high switching frequencies required. It is, of course, necesary for the electron beam to be irradiating only *one* of the three phosphors each time it is pulsed and the size of the cathode ray tube spot must therefore be smaller than the width of the stripes. Bands of dark non-fluorescent material

371

are usually placed between the stripes of phosphor to allow some latitude in the spot size, as this varies with beam current and with position in the picture area.

Index tubes, as well as single-gun Lawrence tubes, can function as decoding tubes, provided that the chrominance signals are in the proper phase and frequency relationship with the traversing of the phosphors by the electron beam. In fact, index tubes are usually conceived as decoding tubes, because only then is full advantage taken of their basic approach.

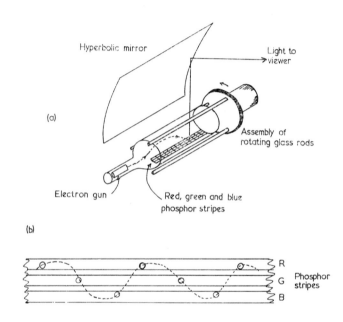

Fig. 18.8. The Banana tube: (a) general view (b) showing the track of the electron spot across the phosphors.

18.9 The Banana tube

The Banana tube, so called because of its shape and to distinguish it from the Apple tube, may be thought of as a one-gun Lawrence type of tube in which the electron beam traverses continually up and down only one triad of phosphor stripes, the vertical spacing of the lines of each field of the picture being obtained optically (Schagen, 1961). The device is illustrated in Fig. 18.8. The general direction of the electron beam is along the phosphor stripes until it is deflected down on to them, the point of deflection moving along at the line-scan speed; at the same time the spot oscillates sinusoidally from side to side so as to irradiate the three different phosphors in turn. The frequency of this oscillation is the same as that of the chrominance sub-carrier so that the device can be made to operate as a decoding tube.

Around the tube, and co-axial with it, a cylinder is mounted carrying three glass rods: by rotating the cylinder, each glass rod, acting as a cylindrical lens, results in the apparent position of the phosphor stripes gradually moving down throughout the period of time corresponding to one frame; at this point one glass rod disappears at the bottom of the picture and the next glass rod appears at the top of the picture to produce the next frame. The light from the glass rods travels upwards on to a large hyperbolic mirror which directs it forwards for viewing.

The Banana tube is clearly very ingenious and has a number of commendable features, such as the employment of only one triad of phosphor stripes to produce the entire picture. Its disadvantages include the necessity for an accurate rapidly-moving part (the rotating cylinder), and an angle of view which is somewhat restricted because of the optical arrangements.

18.10 The Eidophor

The Eidophor, invented by Fischer of Zurich, was developed primarily as a solution to the problem of showing television pictures to a large audience (Baumann, 1952; Sponable, 1953). This problem calls for a projection system, and the Eidophor is particularly interesting in that the image is formed by the light from a conventional carbon or xenon arc source, and not by fluorescence caused by electron bombardment.

The principles of the Eidophor are illustrated in Fig. 18.9. Light is picked up by a high aperture concave mirror and reflected horizontally so as to produce an enlarged aerial image of the source; a lens then further magnifies this image to the extent that, after being reflected downwards from a plane mirror, it fills another concave mirror, on which the image is formed. This second concave mirror sends the light back up through some slots in the plane mirror, through an objective lens, on to a second plane mirror, and so horizontally to the screen. The first plane mirror is situated so that its centre is at the centre of curvature of the second concave mirror. Its slots are so arranged that, in the absence of any image on the second concave mirror, all the light is returned back to the source: this is achieved because the image of each slot formed by the second concave mirror falls exactly on another slot, and each reflecting strip (between the slots) on another reflecting strip. The optical system is therefore a 'Schlieren' system in which all the direct light is just blocked and only when some disturbance is introduced, does any light reach the screen. The disturbance in this case is provided by the second concave mirror being covered with a very thin film of oil on which ripples are produced: the effect of a ripple is to deflect some of the light off the reflecting bars and through the slots, and so on to the screen. The ripples are produced by scanning the surface of the oil with an electron beam whose intensity is modulated according to the image to be reproduced. As the electron beam scans the surface, electrons are deposited and an image of electrical charge is built up. Where this charge is present. electrostatic forces deform the surface, and as the deformation increases with the charge, so the light on the screen is modulated in accordance with the intensity of the electron beam; hence an image is produced. The conductivity and viscosity of the oil are chosen so that the deformation at each spot does

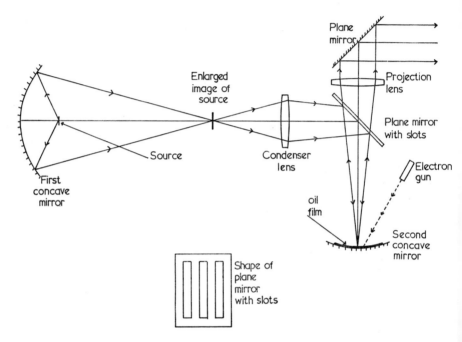

Fig. 18.9. The Eidophor.

not fully decay until the electron beam is just about to traverse the spot again: in this way each part of the image is emitting light on to the screen for most of the time, giving a very considerable gain over the cathode-ray tube, each point of which, even with its afterglow, is emitting appreciably for only a small percentage of the time. One of the disadvantages of using an optical system depending on Schlieren principles is the very critical nature of the optics, but the ripples on the oil are made small enough relative to their distance from the slots in the plane mirror, for their refractive effect to be accompanied by diffraction; the slots are then made smaller than the reflecting strips and the alignment is rendered less critical.

The Eidophor has been used for a number of successful demonstrations of field sequential colour television, but for simultaneous systems (using a single Eidophor) three different ripple patterns would have to be impressed on the oil surface by three separate electron beams and then illuminated separately, and this presents some very formidable problems. Alternatively three separate Eidophors can be used as a triple-projector.

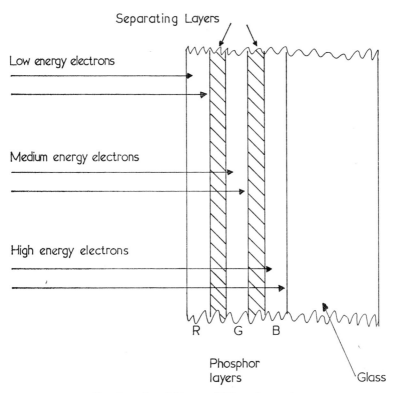

Fig. 18.10. A multi-layer additive tube coating.

18.11 Multi-layer additive receivers

It has been found possible to evaporate layers of red, green, and blue phosphors on top of one another as shown in Fig. 18.10, and if they could be excited separately a very neat colour receiver could be designed. It is necessary to use electrons of higher velocity to reach the phosphor in the middle layer than in the top layer, and of higher velocity still to reach the phosphor in the bottom layer, because of the retarding effects of the overlying layers;

but it is found that the energy required to excite each phosphor layer is quite specific and that if three appropriate electron velocities are chosen it is possible substantially to excite each layer separately. Cathode-ray tubes which can 'write' in three colours are therefore possible, but their application to colour television is hindered by the immense difficulty of making three electron beams of different velocities scan the picture in register with one another.

18.12 Electro-luminescent panels as receivers

It is possible to make electro-luminescent panels with one set of parallel conducting stripes on one side of them, and another set of parallel conducting stripes, which are at right angles to the first set, on the other side. The panel can then be made to light up only at the point where two energized conductors cross, and hence by applying suitable circuits to the conductors a television type of picture can be formed. Three such panels, emitting red, green, and blue light, and superimposed either optically as in the Trinoscope, or physically if they were sufficiently transparent, would make a colour receiver. At present, however, the maximum luminance obtainable from these panels is far too low to be adequate if they are only energized during the small fraction (about $1/100,000$) of the complete picture-scan which they represent. A continuous supply of energy to each point, at a level re-set every time each point is scanned, is therefore required; no method of doing this has yet been published.

18.13 Subtractive receivers

The success of subtractive methods of colour reproduction in colour photography, where they have completely replaced the earlier additive methods, has caused a search to be made for subtractive methods for colour television. What is required is a means of controlling, at each point in the picture, the absorption of the reddish, the greenish, and the bluish, parts of a white illuminant. If the phosphor of a cathode-ray tube is replaced by certain salts, the electron beam can be made to produce a darkening in proportion to the beam current, and if this darkening in three different salts is such as to result in separate darkening to reddish light only, to greenish light only, and to bluish light only, then a subtractive system of colour television would be possible, if the white light could be made to pass through the three layers in succession: one way of doing this (Rosenthal and Scophony, 1938) is shown in Fig. 18.11(a). Another suggestion is to display on a conventional monochrome tube, using a white phosphor, a signal which at each point corresponds to the lightest of the three colours; the appropriate absorptions of the cyan, magenta, and yellow images would then be added by viewing the tube through three electronically modulated colour cells as shown in Fig. 18.11(b). (Jesty, 1955.) So far, none of these subtractive proposals has been successfully reduced to practice.

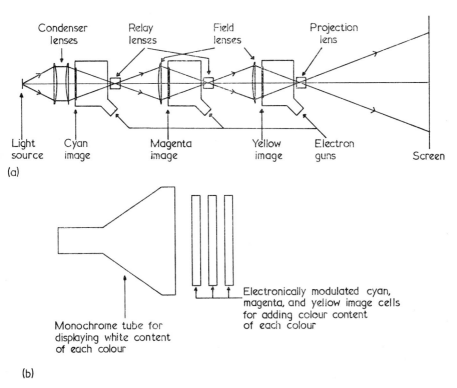

Electronically modulated cyan,
magenta, and yellow image cells
for adding colour content
of each colour

Monochrome tube for
displaying white content
of each colour

(b)

Fig. 18.11. Subtractive colour television systems: (a) by successive imaging (b) by multilayer imaging.

18.14 Phosphors for additive receivers

In the early days of colour television the phosphors used were cadmium borate for the red, zinc silicate for the green, and calcium magnesium silicate for the blue, but in 1951 new red and blue phosphors were discovered, so that the following set became established:

Red: zinc phosphate ($x = 0.674$, $y = 0.326$; $u = 0.485$, $v = 0.352$)
Green: zinc silicate ($x = 0.218$, $y = 0.712$; $u = 0.078$, $v = 0.384$)
Blue: zinc sulphide ($x = 0.154$, $y = 0.068$; $u = 0.175$, $v = 0.116$)

The N.T.S.C. standards were drawn up assuming the receiver colours:

Red:	$x = 0.67$	$y = 0.33$	$u = 0.477$	$v = 0.352$
Green:	$x = 0.21$	$y = 0.71$	$u = 0.076$	$v = 0.384$
Blue:	$x = 0.14$	$y = 0.08$	$u = 0.152$	$v = 0.130$

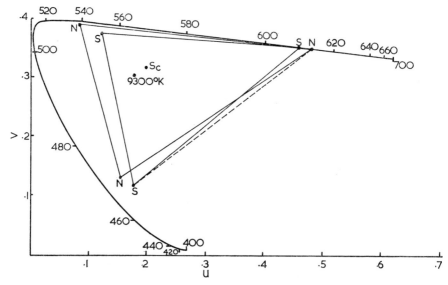

Fig. 18.12. Chromaticities of the sulphide phosphors, S, and of the N.T.S.C. receiver colours, N, together with those of standard illuminant C, S_C, and a white of colour temperature 9300°K.

The N.T.S.C. colours are thus similar in chromaticity to the set of phosphors available in 1951. The luminance of the pictures obtained with these phosphors was rather limited, however, and in 1961 the green and the red phosphors were changed and the following set of 'sulphide phosphors' became established:

Red: zinc cadmium
   sulphide   ($x = 0.663$, $y = 0.337$; $u = 0.464$, $v = 0.354$)
Green: zinc cadmium
   sulphide   ($x = 0.285$, $y = 0.595$; $u = 0.119$, $v = 0.373$)
Blue: zinc sulphide   ($x = 0.154$, $y = 0.068$; $u = 0.175$, $v = 0.116$)

The chromaticities of these phosphors are shown by the points marked S in Fig. 18.12; those of the N.T.S.C. receiver colours, marked N, are also shown for comparison. It is seen that the red sulphide phosphor is more orange than the red N.T.S.C. colour, the green is more yellow and less saturated, but the blue is less green and of similar saturation. Although the loss of colour gamut for blue-green and green colours is appreciable with the sulphide phosphors, the luminance of the picture is doubled, the efficiency with which a white is produced in a shadow-mask tube being increased from about 1 lumen per watt to about 2 lumens per watt, and experiments have shown that the effects of the gain in luminance more than offset the effects of the lower purity (see Section 9.4 (Matthews, 1963)). If the receiver white corresponds in chromaticity

378

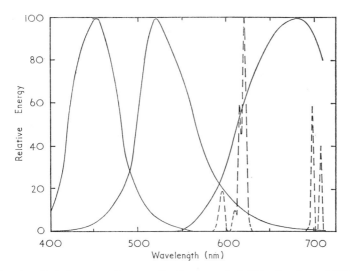

Fig. 18.13. Relative spectral energy distributions of sulphide phosphors, full lines, and of europium yttrium vanadate phosphor, broken line.

to that of a full radiator at a colour temperature of 9300°K, instead of to that of Standard Illuminant C (colour temperature approximately 6500°K), as specified in the N.T.S.C. standards, the efficiency rises to about 2.6 lumens per watt.

In 1964 it was discovered that the rare earth, yttrium vanadate, activated with europium, provided a red phosphor superior in both chromaticity and efficiency to the red sulphide phosphor, and this enabled a 9300°K white to be produced at an efficiency of 2.9 lumens per watt. The usual phosphor set thus became:

Red: europium yttrium
    vanadate   ($x = 0.675$, $y = 0.325$; $u = 0.182$, $v = 0.351$)
Green: zinc cadmium
    sulphide   ($x = 0.285$, $y = 0.595$; $u = 0.119$, $v = 0.373$)
Blue: zinc sulphide   ($x = 0.154$, $y = 0.068$; $u = 0.175$, $v = 0.116$)

The chromaticity of the new red phosphor is very close to that of the N.T.S.C. red receiver colour, so that the gamut of reproducible colours is represented in Fig. 18.12 by the triangle formed by the green and blue S-points and the red N-point; the line connecting the blue S-point to the red N-point is shown broken to indicate the increase in gamut obtained, with this red phosphor.

In Fig. 18.13 the relative spectral energy curves of the sulphide phosphors are shown by the full lines, and that of the europium yttrium vanadate phosphor by the broken line.

18.15 The chromaticity of reproduced white

As mentioned in Sections 5.7 and 16.9, it is usually arranged that television cameras produce equal red, green, and blue signals for a standard white surface, whatever the colour of the taking illuminant. This arrangement has the advantage that it imitates the adapting effects of the eye, which largely compensate for changes in illuminant colour so as to maintain the appearance of whites approximately constant; it also has the advantage of keeping the magnitudes of the chrominance signals to a minimum by making them zero for whites, greys, and blacks, whatever the illuminant colour.

But what effect does the above practice have on the best chromaticity to choose for the display of white on the receiver? In the N.T.S.C. system the luminance signal is compounded on the assumption that equal red, green, and blue signals produce the chromaticity of Standard Illuminant C on the display. Therefore the equalization of the red, green, and blue signals for the standard white in the taking illuminant may be thought of as roughly equivalent to filtering the light of the taking illuminant so that it always has approximately the same correlated colour temperature as Standard Illuminant C.

In monochrome displays the relative luminances of objects will therefore always be similar to those in Standard Illuminant C (they would be identical if the filtering effect of equalizing the red, green, and blue signals was equivalent to using the appropriate energy-converting filter; see Section 8.3). The relative increase in the luminances of reddish objects in tungsten light, for instance, is therefore lost; but this type of effect is probably not very important (it has been shown that in black-and-white photography a spectral sensitivity broader than that required for producing correct luminances is preferable; Mouchel, 1963).

In colour displays, if (as assumed by the N.T.S.C. system) the receiver reproduces equal-signal white at a chromaticity equal to that of Standard Illuminant C, then the reproduced chromaticities in the picture will approximate to those which the scene would have had if it had been illuminated by light of Illuminant C quality. The *appearance* of these chromaticities will, however, depend on the conditions under which the display is viewed: in tungsten light, the picture will appear bluish, in clear north-sky light it will appear yellowish. It might be argued that, since television pictures are viewed more in the evenings than in the day time, the equal-signal white should be reproduced at a correlated colour temperature typical of tungsten light, say 2850°K, but, if this is done, the picture becomes intolerably yellow in ambient daylight illumination. On the other hand, if the equal-signal white is reproduced at an ambient daylight chromaticity (6500°K, for instance) the picture does not appear intolerably bluish in ambient tungsten light illumination because the latter is often, or can be made to be, of sufficiently low intensity for the receiver to dominate the adaptation of the eye. This is why black-and-white receivers are usually made so as to have correlated colour temperatures of not less than 6500°K.

The higher the luminance of the television picture the greater is the extent to which it can dominate the adaptation, and since blue-emitting phosphors usually have higher efficiencies than those emitting light of longer wavelengths, the luminance of television pictures generally increases as the correlated colour temperature of the reproduced white is increased. In black-and-white television, correlated colour temperatures as high as 9300°K are therefore almost always used, and this chromaticity is also sometimes used for equal-signal white in colour television displays, where the higher luminance not only assists the picture to dominate the adaptation but also results in increased apparent colour saturation (see Section 7.8).

The best chromaticity at which to reproduce equal-signal white is thus affected by several factors, but in colour displays it is found that, for most ambient conditions met with in domestic situations, correlated colour temperatures in the range 6500 to 9300°K are acceptable. The use of a chromaticity different from that of Standard Illuminant C, however, should really involve a change in the proportions of the red, green, and blue signals in the luminance signal, but the departures from the constant luminance principle (see Section 16.8) caused by not making such a change are probably too small to be of any importance.

It should be borne in mind that there is a case for compensating somewhat less than completely for changes in illuminant colour at the camera, because this is also true of the eye (see Section 7.8). Thus, the camera should produce signals such that the standard white is reproduced slightly yellowish when the illuminant is tungsten light, for example. Even further departures from the conditions for which whites are reproduced as whites may be desirable if special 'moods' are required for artistic reasons.

18.16 The luminance of reproduced white

With phosphors giving an efficiency of 2.9 lumens per watt (see Section 18.14) in shadow-mask tubes when white is reproduced, it is possible for the peak-white luminance to reach about 50 foot-lamberts. For, if each electron gun produces a beam current of about 300 micro-amps, the composite beam current amounts to about 1 milli-amp, so that with an anode voltage of 25 kilo-volts, the power involved (current multiplied by voltage) is about 25 watts. With an efficiency of 2.9 lumens per watt, it is thus possible to produce about 75 lumens and if this is spread over a picture area of 1½ square feet the light-output amounts to about 50 lumens per square foot. Hence, assuming that the cathode-ray tube radiates its light equally in all forward directions, the luminance on its face will be 50 foot-lamberts.

REFERENCES

Barnett, G. F., Bingley, F. J., Parsons, S. L., Pratt, G. W., and Sadowsky, M., *Proc. Inst. Radio Engrs.*, **44**, 1108 (1956).

Baumann, E., *J. Brit. Inst. Radio Engnrs.*, **12**, 69 (1952).

Dressler, R., *Proc. Inst. Radio Engrs.*, **41**, 851 (1953).

Gabor, D., Stuart, P. R., and Kalman, P. G., *Proc. Inst. Elec. Engnrs.*, **105B**, 581 (1958).

Graham, R., Justice, J. W. H., and Oxenham, J. K., *Proc. Inst. Elec. Engnrs.*, **108B**, 511 (1961).

Hunt, R. W. G., *J. Phot. Sci.*, **13**, 108 (1965).

Jackson, R. N., *Proc. Inst. Elec. Engnrs.*, **108B**, 613 (1961).

Jesty, L. C., *J. Television Society*, **7**, 508 (1955).

Jesty, L. C., *Proc. Inst. Elec. Engnrs.*, **105B**, 425 (1958).

Jones, L. A., and Condit, H. R., *J. Opt. Soc. Amer.*, **31**, 651, (1941).

Loughlin, B., *Proc. Inst. Radio Engnrs.*, **42**, 299 (1954).

Matthews, J. A., Private communication (1963).

Mouchel, P., *J. Phot. Sci.*, **11**, 291 (1963).

Rosenthal, A. H., and Scophony, British Patent No. 514,776 (1938).

Schagen, P., *Proc. Inst. Elec. Engnrs.*, **108B**, 577 (1961).

Sponable, E. I., *J. Soc. Mot. Pic. Tel. Eng.*, **60**, 337 (1953).

Wentworth, J. W., *Colour Television Engineering*, McGraw Hill, New York, p. 153 (1955).

CHAPTER 19

The N.T.S.C. and Similar Systems of Colour Television

19.1 Introduction

THE National Television Systems Committee (N.T.S.C.) of the U.S.A. recommended a system of transmitting colour television signals which involves both band-sharing and carrier-sharing (Loughren, 1953), and in 1953 this system was adopted by the U.S.A. Federal Communication Commission (F.C.C.) for general use in that country. In this Chapter we shall examine the N.T.S.C. system to show how its features are related to its basic premises; the colorimetric calculations involved are therefore given in sufficient detail to enable the inter-relation of each feature with the others to be fully appreciated. Modifications of the N.T.S.C. system, such as the P.A.L. and S.E.C.A.M. systems, will also be considered.

19.2 N.T.S.C. chromaticities

The N.T.S.C. system is intended to be used with receiver colours having the following chromaticity co-ordinates (the original specifications were given in the XYZ system but the corresponding values in the approximately uniform chromaticity system UVW are also given for convenience):

	x	y	z	u	v	w
Red (R)	0.67	0.33	0.00	0.477	0.352	0.171
Green (G)	0.21	0.71	0.08	0.076	0.384	0.541
Blue (B)	0.14	0.08	0.78	0.152	0.130	0.718
White (S_C)	0.310	0.316	0.374	0.201	0.307	0.492

The positions of these stimuli in the u, v diagram are shown in Fig. 19.1.

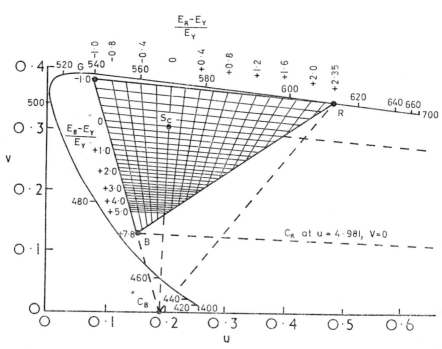

Fig. 19.1. The triangle formed by the points R, G, B representing the chromaticities of the red, green, and blue receiver stimuli in the N.T.S.C. system. S_C represents standard illuminant C, the stimulus matched by equal amounts of (R), (G), and (B). C_R, S_C, and C_B represent the stimuli corresponding to the variables $R-L$, L, and $B-L$, where $L = 0.299R + 0.587G + 0.114B$. The lines drawn from C_B represent $(R-L)/L$ constant, those from C_R represent $(B-L)/L$ constant. Since E_R, E_G, E_B, E_Y are proportional to R, G, B, L respectively, these are also lines of constant $(E_R-E_Y)/E_Y$ and $(E_B-E_Y)/E_Y$, the values of which are given in the figure.

19.3 The luminance signal

A luminance signal, E_Y, and two chrominance signals, E_R-E_Y and E_B-E_Y, are used,* and it is arranged that the two chrominance signals are both zero

---

* The need for gamma-correction is ignored for the moment; the complications it introduces will be considered later.

for Standard Illuminant C (S_C). This has the advantage that for whites, greys, and blacks illuminated by daylight, the band-width restricted chrominance signals are little used. The choice of the chromaticity for which the chrominance signals are zero, together with that of the chromaticities of the red, green, and blue reproduction stimuli, fixes the values of l, m, and n in the expression

$$E_Y = lE_R + mE_G + nE_B$$

where $l+m+n = 1$ (see Section 16.9).

If $E_R - E_Y$ and $E_B - E_Y$ are zero for illuminant C, then as shown in Section 16.9,

$$E_R = E_G = E_B = E_Y$$

for illuminant C. l, m, n must therefore be the luminances of unit quantities of the receiver stimuli (R)(G)(B), when the units used for the latter are such that equal quantities of (R), (G), and (B) are needed to match illuminant C, and when their units are also such that their luminances sum to unity.

These luminances can be evaluated by using the laws of colour mixture in any convenient chromaticity diagram: we will use the u, v diagram, but the same answer would be obtained in the x, y or any other diagram. We proceed as follows.

The luminances L_U and L_W of unit quantities of (U) and (W) are both zero and so the luminance L_V of unit quantity of (V) may be set arbitrarily at unity. With the amounts of (R) (G) and (B) measured in luminance units, a fact we indicate by using the symbols (R_L), (G_L), (B_L), we may therefore write:

$$0.352(R_L) \equiv 0.477(U) + 0.352(V) + 0.171(W)$$

$$0.384(G_L) \equiv 0.076(U) + 0.384(V) + 0.541(W)$$

$$0.130(B_L) \equiv 0.152(U) + 0.130(V) + 0.718(W)$$

But the units in which the amounts of (R), (G), and (B) are measured are such that

$$(S_C) \propto 0.333(R) + 0.333(G) + 0.333(B)$$

But when (R), (G), and (B) are measured in luminance units this becomes

$$0.333(l+m+n)(S_{CL}) \equiv 0.333l(R_L) + 0.333m(G_L) + 0.333n(B_L)$$

where (S_{CL}) indicates that the amount of (S_C) is also measured in luminance units. But the units in which the amounts of (R), (G), and (B) are measured are also such that $l+m+n = 1$. Therefore the equation for (S_{CL}) reduces to:

$$1.0(S_{CL}) \equiv l(R_L) + m(G_L) + n(B_L)$$

Hence by substitution:

$$1.0(S_{CL}) \equiv (0.477l/0.352)(U) + l(V) + (0.171l/0.352)(W)$$
$$+ (0.076m/0.384)(U) + m(V) + (0.541m/0.384)(W)$$
$$+ (0.152n/0.130)(U) + n(V) + (0.718n/0.130)(W)$$

But we also have, with the amount of (S_G) written in luminance units:

$$0.307(S_{GL}) \equiv 0.201(U) + 0.307(V) + 0.492(W)$$

$$\therefore \qquad 1.0(S_{GL}) \equiv (0.201/0.307)(U) + 1.0(V) + (0.492/0.307)(W)$$

By comparing the two equations for 1.0 (S_{GL}) we obtain

$$0.477l/0.352 + 0.076m/0.384 + 0.152n/0.130 = 0.201/0.307$$
$$l \qquad + \qquad m \qquad + \qquad n \qquad = 1.0$$
$$0.171l/0.352 + 0.541m/0.384 + 0.718n/0.130 = 0.492/0.307$$

These three simultaneous equations may be solved for l, m, and n in the normal way to obtain the result:

$$l = 0.299 \qquad m = 0.587 \qquad n = 0.114$$

Hence the luminance signal E_Y in the N.T.S.C. system is made up thus:

$$E_Y = 0.299E_R + 0.587E_G + 0.114E_B$$

19.4 (R)(G)(B) to (U)(V)(W) transformation equations

The evaluation of l, m, and n also enables the transformation equations between the (R), (G), (B) and (U), (V), (W) systems to be obtained. We have:

$$0.299(R_L) \equiv 1.0(R)$$
$$0.587(G_L) \equiv 1.0(G)$$
$$0.114(B_L) \equiv 1.0(B)$$

Therefore:

$$0.352(R_L) \equiv (0.352/0.299)(R) \equiv 0.477(U) + 0.352(V) + 0.171(W)$$

Hence:

$$1.0(R) \equiv (0.299/0.352)(0.477(U) + 0.352(V) + 0.171(W))$$

Similarly:

$$1.0(G) \equiv (0.587/0.384)(0.076(U) + 0.384(V) + 0.541(W))$$
$$1.0(B) \equiv (0.114/0.130)(0.152(U) + 0.130(V) + 0.718(W))$$

Which simplify to:

$$1.0(R) \equiv 0.405(U) + 0.299(V) + 0.145(W)$$
$$1.0(G) \equiv 0.116(U) + 0.587(V) + 0.827(W)$$
$$1.0(B) \equiv 0.133(U) + 0.114(V) + 0.627(W)$$

19.5 The effects of variations in chrominance-signal magnitude

The way in which variations in the magnitudes of the two chrominance signals $E_R - E_Y$ and $E_B - E_Y$ differ in their effects on the chromaticities of the reproduced colours can be seen by constructing the grid of lines shown in Fig. 19.1. This construction is facilitated by plotting the positions of the stimuli (S_C), (C_R), and (C_B) corresponding to the variables E_Y, $E_R - E_Y$, and $E_B - E_Y$ of the N.T.S.C. system. To find the positions of (S_C), (C_R), and (C_B) we proceed as follows.

The relationships between the signals may be written:

$$E_R = (1.0)(E_R - E_Y) + (1.0)E_Y + 0(E_B - E_Y)$$

$$E_G = -\frac{l}{m}(E_R - E_Y) + (1.0)E_Y - \frac{n}{m}(E_B - E_Y)$$

$$E_B = 0(E_R - E_Y) + (1.0)E_Y + (1.0)(E_B - E_Y)$$

Therefore, assuming for the moment that the optical signals R, G, B, and L are proportional to the electrical signals E_R, E_G, E_B, and E_Y respectively, we may write $R = kE_R$, $G = kE_G$, $B = kE_B$, and $L = kE_Y$, where k is a constant. Hence:

$$R = (1.0)(R - L) + (1.0)L + 0(B - L)$$

$$G = -\frac{l}{m}(R - L) + (1.0)L - \frac{n}{m}(B - L)$$

$$B = 0(R - L) + (1.0)L + (1.0)(B - L)$$

Hence the corresponding equations connecting the stimuli (see Section 7.4) may be written down by inspection as follows:

$$1.0(C_R) \equiv 1.0(R) - \frac{l}{m}(G) + 0(B)$$

$$1.0(S_G) \equiv 1.0(R) + 1.0(G) + 1.0(B)$$

$$1.0(C_B) \equiv 0(R) - \frac{n}{m}(G) + 1.0(B)$$

Therefore, using the (R) (G) (B) to (U) (V) (W) transformation equations,

$$1.0(C_R) \equiv 0.405(U) + 0.299(V) + 0.145(W)$$
$$-(0.299/0.587)(0.116(U) + 0.587(V) + 0.827(W))$$

$$1.0(S_G) \equiv (0.405 + 0.116 + 0.133)(U) + (0.299 + 0.587 + 0.114)(V)$$
$$+(0.145 + 0.827 + 0.627)(W)$$

$$1.0(C_B) \equiv -(0.114/0.587)(0.116(U) + 0.587(V) + 0.827(W))$$
$$+0.133(U) + 0.114(V) + 0.627(W)$$

These equations simplify to

$$1.0(C_R) \equiv 0.346(U) + 0.000(V) - 0.276(W)$$
$$1.0(S_G) \equiv 0.653(U) + 1.000(V) + 1.599(W)$$
$$1.0(C_B) \equiv 0.110(U) + 0.000(V) + 0.467(W)$$

The values of u and v are obtained in the usual way by dividing by $U + V + W$; the corresponding values of x and y can be obtained from u and v by formula or by nomogram, with the following results:

	x	y	z	u	v	w
(C_R)	1.070	0	−0.070	4.981	0	−3.981
(S_G)	0.310	0.316	0.374	0.201	0.307	0.492
(C_B)	0.131	0	0.869	0.191	0	0.809

The positions of these stimuli in the u, v diagram are shown in Fig. 19.1.

These values show that (S_C) is located at the position of Standard Illuminant C, as was to be expected. For (C_R) and (C_B) the values of y (and v) are zero, and this shows that, like the stimuli (X), (Z), (U), and (W), the stimuli (C_R) and (C_B) affect colour but not luminance. That this must be so can be seen by considering the equation:

$$1.0(C_R) \equiv 1.0(R) - \frac{l}{m}(G)$$

which when (R) and (G) are measured in luminance units becomes:

$$1.0(C_R) \equiv l(R_L) - \frac{l}{m}m(G_L) \equiv l(R_L) - l(G_L)$$

Therefore the luminance of 1.0 (C_R) is equal to $l - l = 0$. Similarly:

$$1.0(C_B) \equiv -\frac{n}{m}m(G_L) + n(B_L) \equiv n(G_L) - n(B_L)$$

Hence the luminance of 1.0 (C_B) is also zero.

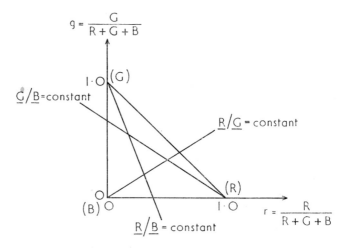

Fig. 19.2. The properties of straight lines through points representing the three matching stimuli.

It is clear from Fig. 19.1 that (C_B) lies on the line $(G)(B)$ produced; this feature stems from the fact that the position of (C_B) corresponds to the case where $E_R - E_Y$ and E_Y are both zero, in which case E_R must be zero, and this means that (C_B) must therefore be a mixture of (G) and (B) only; hence it lies on the line $(G)(B)$ or $(G)(B)$ produced. Similarly (C_R), which corresponds to $E_B - E_Y$ and E_Y both being zero, so that E_B is also zero, must be a mixture of (R) and (G) only; although (C_R) is located too far to the right in Fig. 19.1 to be plotted, it does in fact lie on the line (G)(R) produced.

By drawing a fan of lines from the point (C_B) the loci of changes in chromaticity corresponding to variations in $E_B - E_Y$ only are obtained. The fan of lines radiating from (C_R) has also been drawn and shows the loci of changes in chromaticity corresponding to variations in $E_R - E_Y$ only. The full significance of the fans of lines passing through these points can be seen by referring to any colour triangle such as that shown in Fig. 19.2. It is clear from this figure that for any line passing through (B), r is proportional to g, and hence, where s is the slope of the line,

$$g = sr$$

Hence all the points on any line passing through (B) have the property that r/g is constant. But since $r = R/(R+G+B)$ and $g = G/(R+G+B)$ it is also true that if r/g is constant then R/G is constant. For lines passing through (R)

$$g = s(1-r)$$
$$= s(r+g+b-r)$$
$$= sg+sb$$

Hence:
$$G/B = g/b = s/(1-s)$$

Similarly for lines passing through (G)

$$B/R = b/r = (1-s)/s$$

Thus lines radiating from (R) have G/B constant, lines radiating from (G) have R/B constant, and lines radiating from (B) have R/G constant. In an exactly similar way, considering the $R-L$, L, $B-L$ system and a colour triangle in which $(R-L)/(R-L+L+B-L)$ is plotted against $(B-L)/(R-L+L+B-L)$ it can be shown that lines radiating from (C_R) have $(R-L)/L$ constant, and hence $(E_R-E_Y)/E_Y$ is also constant, lines radiating from (C_B) have $(B-L)/L$ constant, and hence $(E_B-E_Y)/E_Y$ is also constant, and lines radiating from (S_C) have $(R-L)/(B-L)$ constant, and hence $(E_R-E_Y)/(E_B-E_Y)$ is also constant.

These general properties of lines passing through mixture stimuli are not changed by linear transformation to a different colour triangle and it is thus possible to assign to each line in each fan in Fig. 19.1 its value of $(E_R-E_Y)/E_Y$ or $(E_B-E_Y)/E_Y$. It is seen that the lines passing through (S_C) both have a value of zero as required. The values of the other lines can be determined by calculating the positions along the line joining (R) and (G) of various values of $(E_R-E_Y)/E_Y$ and the positions along the lines joining (G) and (B) of various values of $(E_B-E_Y)/E_Y$. Along the line joining (R) and (G), $E_B = 0$ and hence using $E_Y = 0.299E_R+0.587E_G+0.114E_B$ we have:

$$\frac{E_G}{E_R} = 1.704 \bigg/ \left(\frac{E_R-E_Y}{E_Y}+1\right) - 0.509.$$

389

Points on the line joining (R) and (G) will divide it, in accordance with the Centre of Gravity Law (see Section 7.6), in the same ratio as the centre of gravity of weights Rl/v_R and Gm/v_G, where v_R and v_G are the v-co-ordinates of (R) and (G) respectively. Since $R = kE_G$ and $G = kE_B$ the same result is obtained with weights $E_R l/v_R$ and $E_G m/v_G$. The ratio of the two weights therefore reduces to:

$$\frac{v_R m E_G}{v_G l E_R} = \frac{0.352}{0.384} \times \frac{0.587}{0.299} \times \frac{E_G}{E_R} = 1.80 \frac{E_G}{E_R}$$

If l_{RG} is the length of the line joining (R) and (G), the distances from (R) corresponding to various mixtures of E_R and E_G are then given by:

$$\frac{1.80 E_G/E_R}{1 + 1.80 E_G/E_R} \times l_{RG}$$

The positions corresponding to various values of $(E_R - E_Y)/E_Y$ can therefore be determined. Similarly, when $E_R = 0$

$$\frac{E_G}{E_B} = 1.704 \bigg/ \left(\frac{E_B - E_Y}{E_Y} + 1 \right) - 0.194$$

and points on the line joining (G) and (B) will divide it in the same ratio as the centre of gravity of weights having the ratio:

$$\frac{v_B m E_G}{v_G n E_B} = \frac{0.130}{0.384} \times \frac{0.587}{0.114} \times \frac{E_G}{E_B} = 1.75 \frac{E_G}{E_B}.$$

If l_{GB} is the length of the line joining (G) and (B) the distances from (B) corresponding to various mixtures of E_R and E_G are then given by:

$$\frac{1.75 E_G/E_B}{1 + 1.75 E_G/E_B} \times l_{GB}.$$

The positions corresponding to various values of $(E_B - E_Y)/E_Y$ can therefore be determined.

19.6 Effect of gamma correction on $E_R - E_Y$ and $E_B - E_Y$

The signals actually transmitted in practical colour television systems have to be gamma corrected as described in Section 16.14. It is therefore of interest to see how gamma correction affects the relation between the chromaticity of the reproduced colour and the values of the chrominance signals. In Fig. 19.3 a grid of lines is shown for constant values of $(E_R' - E_Y')/E_Y'$ and $(E_B' - E_Y')/E_Y'$ where

$$E_R' = E_R^{1/2.2}$$
$$E_G' = E_G^{1/2.2}$$
$$E_B' = E_B^{1/2.2}$$
$$E_Y' = 0.299 E_R' + 0.587 E_G' + 0.114 E_B'$$

It is only legitimate to draw such lines if for each pair of values of $(E_R'-E_Y')/E_Y'$ and $(E_B'-E_Y')/E_Y'$ there is a unique chromaticity. This is so, because these voltages produce ratios of stimuli amounts $(R-L)/L$ and $(B-L)/L$ and these variables correspond to unique lines on a chromaticity diagram for the variables $R-L$, L, $B-L$.

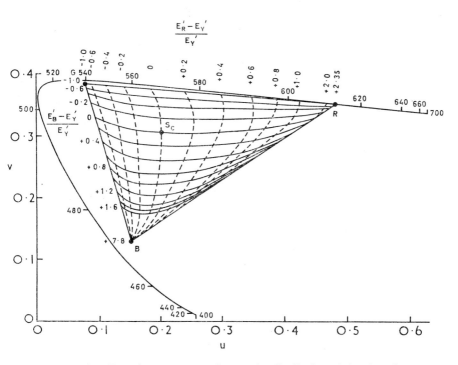

Fig. 19.3. The effect of gamma correction on the distribution of the chrominance signals in the chromaticity diagram. Lines of constant $(E_R'-E_Y')/E_Y'$ and $(E_B'-E_Y')/E_Y'$ are shown where $E_R' = E_R{}^{1/2.2}$, $E_B' = E_B{}^{1/2.2}$, $E_G' = E_G{}^{1/2.2}$ and $E_Y' = 0.299E_R'+0.587E_G'+0.114E_B'$.

The lines which form the grid in Fig. 19.3 are fairly straight around the (S_C) point, but elsewhere they are quite curved, and the two grids of lines of Figs. 19.1 and 19.3 are by no means the same. However, the differences do not represent errors in colour reproduction but only the way in which the effects of gamma correction alter the relationships between the electrical and the optical signals. Large areas of colour will be reproduced normally by a receiver operating at a gamma of 2.2.

If a pattern is transmitted for which the variations in $E_R'-E_Y'$ are too fine to be resolved, then the result on the display will be an average value of $E_R'-E_Y'$, together with the variations produced by the $E_B'-E_Y'$ signal which will result in chromaticity changes along one of the broken lines of Fig. 19.3 (or a similar parallel line); upon this will be superimposed the usual luminance difference produced by the E_Y' signal (provided that this does not call for a negative amount of green light, see Section 16.8). Similarly, if a pattern is transmitted for which the $E_B'-E_Y'$ variations are too fine to be resolved, the chromaticity displayed will comprise that produced by the average $E_B'-E_Y'$ value, together with variations in chromaticity lying along one of the full lines of Fig. 19.3 (or along a similar parallel line), upon which the usual luminance difference will again be produced by the E_Y' signal. The above arguments apply to chromaticity differences in the horizontal direction in the picture (along the lines of the display); the reproduction of chromaticity differences in the vertical direction depends only on the line structure of the picture.

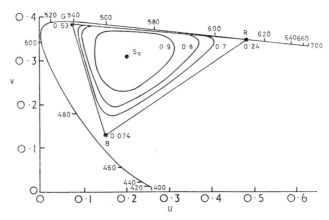

Fig. 19.4. The way in which $(E_Y')^{2.2}/E_Y$ varies over the RGB triangle. Although this ratio falls to less than 0.1 at the point B, over by far the greater part of the triangle it is above 0.8.

19.7 The effect of gamma correction on E_Y

In Fig. 19.4 the effect of gamma correction on the E_Y' signal is shown by plotting $(E_Y')^{2.2}/E_Y$ in the u, v diagram and drawing contours at the 0.9, 0.8, and 0.7 levels. The three effects noted in Section 16.14 resulting from the use of an E_Y' signal instead of a true E_Y signal were, first, that the constant luminance principle would be violated, so that the luminance would be in error (too low) in areas of fine detail, and noise in the chrominance signals would affect luminance; secondly, that coloured areas would be displayed too dark on monochrome receivers; and thirdly that definition in small coloured areas would suffer, because of the restricted band-width of the luminance content carried by the chrominance signals. It is clear from Fig. 19.4, however, that although the values of $(E_Y')^{2.2}/E_Y$ at the corners of the triangle (R)(G)(B) are only 0.24 at (R), 0.53 at (G), and 0.074 at (B), over by far the greater part of the triangle the ratio does not fall below 0.80. Since the extreme corners and edges of the triangle represent colours which are not used very often in typical scenes the effects of transmitting the E_Y' signal instead of a true luminance signal are likely to be quite small in practice.

19.8 The P.A.L. and S.E.C.A.M. systems

The P.A.L. and S.E.C.A.M. versions of the N.T.S.C. system transmit the signals E_Y', $E_R'-E_Y'$, and $E_B'-E_Y'$ (Roizen and Lipkin, 1965). (We consider these versions before the normal N.T.S.C. version because the latter, although historically earlier, involves additional signal-coding operations.) The E_Y' signal is transmitted at full band-width, and the $E_R'-E_Y'$, and $E_B'-E_Y'$ signals at about a quarter of the E_Y' band-width. Carrier-sharing is used so that some means of distinguishing between the two chrominance signals is required.

In the S.E.C.A.M. (Sequence and Memory) system, this is achieved by transmitting $E_R'-E_Y'$ and $E_B'-E_Y'$ on alternative lines of each field, together with a suitable identifying signal so that the receiver knows which of the two signals is being transmitted on each line. A circuit which delays a signal for a time exactly equal to that taken to scan one line, known as a *delay line*, is then used to provide the chrominance signal of the previous line of the field. In this way, although at any one time only one of the two chrominance signals is being transmitted, both are available for producing the colour picture. There is, however, a loss of definition of the chrominance information in the vertical direction, because the delay-line technique results, in effect, in an averaging over pairs of successive field lines, which is equivalent to groups of four picture-lines. But the resultant vertical chrominance resolution is no worse than the horizontal chrominance resolution, and hence the loss is of no great consequence. By alternating the order of the transmission of the $E_R'-E_Y'$ and $E_B'-E_Y'$ signals on successive pictures (pairs of fields) the vertical chrominance resolution for stationary or slowly moving objects is improved.

The S.E.C.A.M. system uses frequency modulation instead of the more usual amplitude modulation for the $E_R'-E_Y'$ and $E_B'-E_Y'$ signals; but the E_Y' signal is amplitude-modulated, and this difference in modulating method further aids the receiver in correctly distinguishing between chrominance and luminance.

In the P.A.L. (Phase Alternation Line) system $E_R'-E_Y'$ and $E_B'-E_Y'$ are transmitted simultaneously on the same carrier, using amplitude-modulation, but with a quarter of a cycle difference in phase between the two signals; the two signals are then distinguished at the receiver by virtue of their different phases. However, the phase of one of the two signals, say $E_R'-E_Y'$, is altered by half a cycle between successive field lines so that the signals transmitted on two successive lines of a field are:

$$\text{Line 1} \qquad E_R'-E_Y' \quad E_B'-E_Y'$$
$$\text{Line 3} \quad -(E_R'-E_Y') \quad E_B'-E_Y'$$

The signals from line 1 are then passed through a delay-line so that an average for the two lines can be obtained; since the $E_R'-E_Y'$ signals are half a cycle out of phase with one another on the two lines, they cancel one another out and hence $E_B'-E_Y'$ is obtained on its own, thus:

$$\tfrac{1}{2}(E_R'-E_Y')+\tfrac{1}{2}(E_B'-E_Y')-\tfrac{1}{2}(E_R'-E_Y')+\tfrac{1}{2}(E_B'-E_Y') = E_B'-E_Y'$$

By also passing the signals from line 3 through a circuit which alters the phase by half a cycle, and then taking an average with the delayed signal from line 1, $E_R'-E_Y'$ is recovered thus:

$$\tfrac{1}{2}(E_R'-E_Y')+\tfrac{1}{2}(E_B'-E_Y')+\tfrac{1}{2}(E_R'-E_Y')-\tfrac{1}{2}(E_B'-E_Y') = E_R'-E_Y'$$

As in the S.E.C.A.M. system it is necessary for the transmission to include a signal which enables the receiver to know which of the two types of signal is being transmitted on each line: in this case the difference is in the phase of the chrominance signals and hence a signal carrying a reference phase, called a *colour-burst signal* is usually used.

A feature of the P.A.L. system is that if there is a slight phase error in the relationship between the reference signal and the chrominance signals, the fact that the phase is reversed on alternate lines, results in the error being cancelled out and the system is thus fairly insensitive to slight phase shifts (such as may occur in transmissions over long links).

It is possible to make receivers for the P.A.L. system which do not have the delay lines. In this case the receiver has a phase-sensitive detector, and demodulates the two chrominance signals separately, at their two phases separated by a quarter of a cycle. With this arrangement, if there is a phase error in the detection of the chrominance signals, they will produce errors in hue in the display; but these errors will be in opposite directions on successive lines of each field, and therefore if they are fairly small the eye is able to average them out and obtain an approximately correct result; if the errors are large enough to be visible they appear as a coarse coloured line structure, often referred to as *Hanover bars* because they were first observed at Hanover.

19.9 The N.T.S.C. system

The N.T.S.C. system uses carrier-sharing with the two chrominance signals transmitted simultaneously a quarter of a cycle out of phase with one another, but, unlike the S.E.C.A.M. and P.A.L. systems, the signals are treated in the same way on every line. A colour burst signal provides a reference phase, and the receiver, which is provided with a phase-sensitive detector, recovers the two chrominance signals correctly by virtue of their different phases. A higher degree of accuracy in the phase identification is necessary in the N.T.S.C. system than in the P.A.L. system, however, because phase errors are not now cancelled out: thus phase must be held to about $\pm 5°$ in N.T.S.C. signals, but only to about $\pm 25°$ in P.A.L. signals.

For accurate separation of the two chrominance signals by means of their phase difference it is desirable for them both to be transmitted with both side-bands present: but, to accommodate about a quarter of the luminance band-width both above and below the sub-carrier frequency, requires the sub-carrier frequency being nearer that of the main carrier than is desirable. The N.T.S.C. system overcomes this problem by transmitting its two chrominance signals at different band-widths: one at about a quarter of the luminance band-width, and the other at only about a tenth. The higher definition chrominance signal then has *double* side-bands over the band-width where *both* signals are operating, but only a *single* side-band over the rest of its frequency range. In this way the two signals can be distinguished satisfactorily, and the chrominance sub-carrier kept well-spaced from the main carrier. To operate successfully with one chrominance signal having a band-width equal to only about one-tenth of that of the luminance signal, the N.T.S.C. system uses not only band-sharing and carrier-sharing but also blue-saving (see Section 16.7).

19.10 Blue-saving in the N.T.S.C. system

As has already been pointed out, the eye is much less able to detect fine blue detail than fine red or green detail. Fine patterns of blues and yellows of the same luminances are confused and invisible to the eye, a phenomenon known as *foveal tritanopia* (Willmer, 1944; Willmer and Wright, 1945; Thomson and Wright, 1947; Wright, 1952). It would therefore seem reasonable to transmit the $E_B' - E_Y'$ signal with less band-width than that used for the $E_R' - E_Y'$ signal.

In Fig. 19.5 are shown lines connecting the points representing colours which are most readily confused when seen in small areas (Thomson and Wright, 1953). Comparison with Fig. 19.3 shows that the directions of the lines of Fig. 19.5 are roughly similar to those representing variations in $E_B' - E_Y'$ only, and this would seem to confirm that the $E_B' - E_Y'$ signal would be the appropriate one to restrict in band-width. However, the restriction in the N.T.S.C. system is not applied in quite this way; instead, it is applied so that, when that fineness of detail is reached such that only one chrominance signal is operating, the colour range remaining is not parallel to the reddish to greenish direction of the $E_R' - E_Y'$ signal, but approximately parallel to the orange to blue-green direction. This has been found preferable in practical tests. It was also found by Middleton and Holmes that, using pieces of coloured papers subtending very small angles to the eye, there was a tendency for the normal range of colour discrimination to degenerate into orange to blue-green differences only (Middleton and Holmes, 1949).

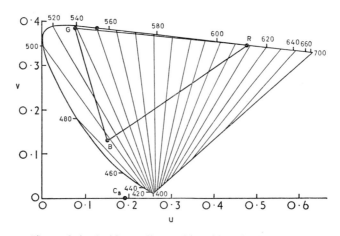

Fig. 19.5. The confusion loci for small-area vision Any pair of colours whose chromaticities fall on the same line will tend to be confused when seen at small angles of view
(Thomson and Wright, 1953).

An understanding of the way in which this shift in the axis of restriction is achieved in the N.T.S.C. system is facilitated by considering a diagram in which $E_R - E_Y$ is plotted against $E_B - E_Y$ as shown in Fig. 19.6. (The effects of gamma correction will be brought in later.) In this diagram the origin represents all colours having the same chromaticity as standard illuminant C, whatever their luminance, so that blacks, greys, and whites plot in this vicinity. The distance of a point, such as P, from the origin represents the purity multiplied by the luminance of the colour concerned. The way in which colours are distributed in this diagram can be seen by considering the cases where E_R, E_G, and E_B are allowed to have values of either 0 or 1, as given in Table 19.1. These colours are plotted in Fig. 19.6. Because, in the N.T.S.C. system, 1 volt is generally the maximum value allowed for E_R, E_G, or E_B at the camera, the colours considered are those of maximum saturation and luminance if the axes are considered to represent camera voltages.

In the N.T.S.C. carrier-sharing system, the sub-carrier wave is amplitude-modulated with two separate signals a quarter of a cycle out of phase with one another. For any given colour, the combined result of the two separate modulations can be considered as a single amplitude modulation at a particular

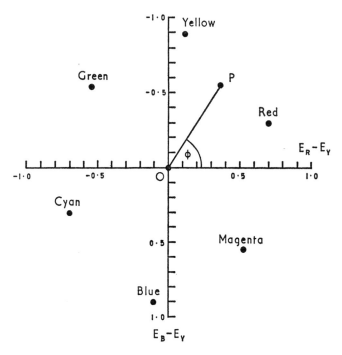

Fig. 19.6. The distribution of colours for which E_R, E_G, E_B equal zero or unity on a plot of E_R-E_Y against E_B-E_Y. The length of a line such as OP is proportional to the purity multiplied by the luminance of the colour plotting at P. The angle ϕ of the line OP is a function of the hue of the colour represented by P.

phase; the amplitude is then proportional to the product of luminance and purity, while the phase indicates the dominant wavelength. Thus in Fig. 19.6 the colour, P, in this carrier-sharing system, would be transmitted by an amplitude represented by OP at a phase represented by the angle ϕ. In the N.T.S.C. system this correlation between phase and dominant wavelength is used to alter the directions of the axes representing the colour difference signals. But, as will be explained more fully later, in order to avoid over-loading the transmitter when the chrominance signals are transmitted at maximum amplitude, they are first reduced in amplitude by factors of 1.14 for E_R-E_Y and 2.03 for E_B-E_Y. It is therefore necessary to replot the data of Fig. 19.6 using $\dfrac{E_R-E_Y}{1.14}$ and $\dfrac{E_B-E_Y}{2.03}$ as variables, as shown in Fig. 19.7. The two chrominance signals used, E_I and E_Q are then shifted in phase by an angle of $33°$ relative to the E_R-E_Y and E_B-E_Y axes as shown. The E_I signal is an In-phase component of the sub-carrier, while the E_Q signal is a Quadrature component

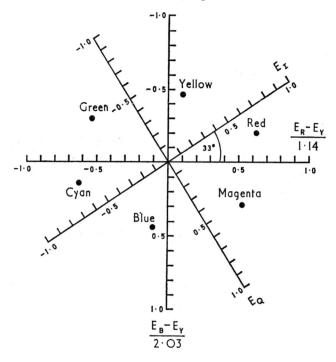

Fig. 19.7. The colours of Fig. 19.6 replotted using $(E_R-E_Y)/1.14$ and $(E_B-E_Y)/2.03$ as co-ordinates. Relative to these axes, the axes of E_I and E_Q are rotated through an angle of 33°.

of the sub-carrier, a quarter of a cycle out of phase with E_I. The two sets of signals are related to one another (in accordance with the usual equations for the rotation of co-ordinate axes) thus:

$$E_I = \frac{E_R-E_Y}{1.14}\cos 33° - \frac{E_B-E_Y}{2.03}\sin 33°$$

$$E_Q = \frac{E_R-E_Y}{1.14}\sin 33° + \frac{E_B-E_Y}{2.03}\cos 33°$$

which (to three significant figures) reduce to:

$$E_I = 0.736(E_R-E_Y) - 0.268(E_B-E_Y)$$
$$E_Q = 0.478(E_R-E_Y) + 0.413(E_B-E_Y)$$

These two signals E_I and E_Q are used together with the same luminance signal as before, E_Y.

398

The values for E_I and E_Q for the colours considered previously are given in Table 19.2.

The equations relating E_Q and E_I with $E_R - E_Y$ and $E_B - E_Y$ enable the positions of the stimuli (C_Q) and (C_I) corresponding to the signals E_Q and E_I to be located in the chromaticity diagram. Thus, solving for $E_R - E_Y$ and $E_B - E_Y$ we obtain

$$E_R - E_Y = 0.956E_I + 0.621E_Q$$
$$E_B - E_Y = -1.106E_I + 1.703E_Q$$

from which:

$$E_R = 0.956E_I + 1.000E_Y + 0.621E_Q$$
$$E_B = -1.106E_I + 1.000E_Y + 1.703E_Q$$

and using $E_Y = 0.299E_R + 0.587E_G + 0.114E_B$ we obtain:

$$E_G = -0.272E_I + 1.000E_Y - 0.647E_Q$$

If we put $I = kE_I$, $L = kE_Y$, and $Q = kE_Q$, where k is a constant, we have

$$R = 0.956I + 1.000L + 0.621Q$$
$$G = -0.272I + 1.000L - 0.647Q$$
$$B = -1.106I + 1.000L + 1.703Q$$

The corresponding equations relating to the stimuli are therefore:

$$1.0(C_I) \equiv 0.956(R) - 0.272(G) - 1.106(B)$$
$$1.0(S_C) \equiv 1.000(R) + 1.000(G) + 1.000(B)$$
$$1.0(C_Q) \equiv 0.621(R) - 0.647(G) + 1.703(B)$$

Using the $(R)(G)(B)$ to $(U)(V)(W)$ transformation equations we obtain:

$$1.0(C_I) \equiv 0.956(0.405(U) + 0.299(V) + 0.145(W))$$
$$-0.272(0.116(U) + 0.587(V) + 0.827(W))$$
$$-1.106(0.133(U) + 0.114(V) + 0.627(W))$$

Calculating 1.0 (S_C) and 1.0 (C_Q) similarly, and simplifying the results we obtain:

$$1.0(C_I) \equiv 0.208(U) + 0.000(V) - 0.780(W)$$
$$1.0(S_C) \equiv 0.653(U) + 1.000(V) + 1.599(W)$$
$$1.0(C_Q) \equiv 0.403(U) + 0.000(V) + 0.623(W)$$

It is useful for some purposes to re-write these equations in the corresponding form connecting the amounts of the stimuli:

$$U = 0.208I + 0.653L + 0.403Q$$
$$V = 1.000L$$
$$W = -0.780I + 1.599L + 0.623Q$$

From the equations for (C_I), (S_C), and (C_Q) in terms of (U), (V), and (W), their positions in the u, v diagram (and in the x, y diagram) can be calculated in the usual way with the following results:

	x	y	z	u	v	w
(C_I)	−0.333	0	1.333	−0.365	0	1.365
(S_C)	0.310	0.316	0.374	0.201	0.307	0.492
(C_Q)	0.245	0	0.755	0.393	0	0.607

The positions of these stimuli in the u, v diagram are shown in Fig. 19.8. It is clear that (C_I) and (C_Q) are also stimuli which affect colour but not luminance, because their values of y (and v) are zero. Lines drawn through (C_I) have constant Q/L and therefore E_Q/E_Y is also constant; lines drawn through (C_Q) have constant I/L and therefore E_I/E_Y is also constant. It should be noted that as the value of E_I/E_Y increases the chromaticity moves away from (C_I) instead of towards it.

In Fig. 19.8 the fans of lines radiating from (C_I) and (C_Q) are shown and it is seen that the transformation has rotated the axes as required, variations in E_I now running roughly parallel to the orange-red to cyan direction. The band-width restriction is therefore applied to the E_Q signal, which is transmitted at about $\frac{1}{2}$ Mc/s band-width while the E_I signal is transmitted at about $1\frac{1}{2}$ Mc/s. The exact band-widths vary slightly according to the number of lines used in the system: for 525 and 625 line systems the E_Q signal has about 0.4 Mc/s and the E_I signal about 1.3 Mc/s; for a 405 line system E_Q has about 0.3 Mc/s and E_I about 1.0 Mc/s. Some idea of the restriction in definition can be gauged from the fact that 0.3 Mc/s corresponds to a blurring of about 6 mms. along a line of a 21 inch receiver picture.

The values of the lines of Fig. 19.8 are indicated and are calculated from the equations for E_I and E_Q in terms of E_R-E_Y and E_B-E_Y, remembering that $E_Y = 0.299E_R + 0.587E_G + 0.114E_B$.

When $E_B = 0$

$$\frac{E_G}{E_R} = \frac{1.253}{E_I/E_Y+0.468} - 0.509$$

The positions on the line joining (R) to (G) corresponding to various values of E_I/E_Y can therefore be calculated using as before:

$$\frac{1.80E_G/E_R}{1+1.80E_G/E_R} \times l_{RG}$$

to give the distance from (R). (The values of these lines are actually marked on the line joining (R) to (B) in Fig. 19.8 for convenience.)

When $E_R = 0$

$$\frac{E_G}{E_B} = \frac{0.704}{E_Q/E_Y+0.891} - 0.194$$

and the positions on the line joining (G) to (B) corresponding to various values of E_Q/E_Y can therefore be calculated using as before:

$$\frac{1.75E_G/E_B}{1+1.75E_G/E_B} \times l_{GB}$$

to give the distance from (B).

It is clear from Fig. 19.8 that the grid of lines corresponding to variations in E_I/E_Y and E_Q/E_Y covers the (R)(G)(B) triangle in the u, v chromaticity diagram in a fairly uniform manner, particularly around (S_C), and is rather better in this respect than the lines of constant $(E_R-E_Y)/E_Y$ and $(E_B-E_Y)/E_Y$. This means that variations in the magnitude of E_I/E_Y and E_Q/E_Y will be of approximately equal visual importance for colours of low or moderate purity.

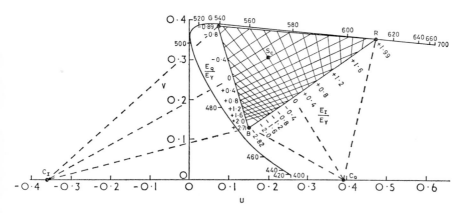

Fig. 19.8. C_I, S_C, and C_Q represent the N.T.S.C. stimuli corresponding to the variables I, L, and Q respectively, where

$$I = 0.736(R-L)-0.268(B-L) \text{ and}$$
$$Q = 0.478(R-L)+0.413(B-L).$$

The lines drawn from C_Q represent I/L constant, those drawn from C_I represent Q/L constant. Since I, L, Q are proportional to E_I, E_Y, E_Q respectively, these are also lines of constant E_I/E_Y and E_Q/E_Y, the values of which are given in the figure.

19.11 Gamma correction in the N.T.S.C. system

We must now consider the effects of gamma correction on the N.T.S.C. signals. Without gamma correction we have:

$$E_I = 0.736(E_R-E_Y)-0.268(E_B-E_Y)$$
$$E_Q = 0.478(E_R-E_Y)+0.413(E_B-E_Y)$$

But because of gamma-correction the signals actually transmitted are

$$E_I' = 0.736(E_R^{1/\gamma} - E_Y') - 0.268(E_B^{1/\gamma} - E_Y')$$
$$E_Q' = 0.478(E_R^{1/\gamma} - E_Y') + 0.413(E_B^{1/\gamma} - E_Y')$$

where
$$E_Y' = 0.299E_R^{1/\gamma} + 0.587E_G^{1/\gamma} + 0.114E_B^{1/\gamma}$$

The changes in chromaticity produced when the fineness of detail is such that only one chrominance signal is transmitted will now correspond to those caused by the E_I' signal instead of by the E_I signal. It is therefore instructive to consider how variations in E_I' and E_Q' affect chromaticity, and this can be done if, as before, E_I' and E_Q' are both divided by the third signal transmitted, which in this case is E_Y'; thus:

$$\frac{E_I'}{E_Y'} = 0.736\left(\frac{E_R^{1/\gamma}}{E_Y'} - 1\right) - 0.268\left(\frac{E_B^{1/\gamma}}{E_Y'} - 1\right)$$

$$\frac{E_Q'}{E_Y'} = 0.478\left(\frac{E_R^{1/\gamma}}{E_Y'} - 1\right) + 0.413\left(\frac{E_B^{1/\gamma}}{E_Y'} - 1\right)$$

The positions of lines of constant E_I'/E_Y' and E_Q'/E_Y' can be calculated by inserting various values of E_R, E_G, E_B in the above equations, plotting the corresponding values of E_I'/E_Y' and E_Q'/E_Y', and drawing the appropriate contours. This has been done in Fig. 19.9 for $\gamma = 2.2$ which is the value adopted in the N.T.S.C. system. It is seen that around the (S_C) point the grid of lines of constant E_I'/E_Y' and E_Q'/E_Y' is similar to that of the lines of constant E_I/E_Y and E_Q/E_Y in Fig. 19.8 and is again rather more equally spaced than for the $(E_R' - E_Y')/E_Y'$ and $(E_B' - E_Y')/E_Y'$ grid shown in Fig. 19.3. As the colour considered departs from (S_C) it is clear that considerable differences occur between the gamma-distorted and the undistorted signals. It is emphasized, however, that these differences only occur in the transmitted electrical signals; the colours displayed by a receiver operating at a gamma of 2.2 will be the same as those which would be displayed by a (hypothetical) receiver using the undistorted signals and operating at a gamma of unity. This is true for large areas of colour, but in detail which is too fine for the E_Q' signal to resolve, the E_Q' signal will assume the average value for the area and the chromaticities displayed in the horizontal direction of the picture will exhibit differences only in the direction of the full line corresponding to the particular average value of E_Q'/E_Y' concerned. Similarly, when the detail is too fine for the E_I' signal to resolve, the displayed chromaticity in the horizontal direction of the picture will correspond to the average values of both E_I' and E_Q' for the particular area, upon which will be superimposed fine detail luminance differences provided by the E_Y' signal. In the vertical direction of the picture, of course, the chromaticity is displayed normally throughout. It is seen that the directions of the lines corresponding to variations in E_I'/E_Y' are still mainly parallel to the orange to cyan direction, but curve towards red (at the orange end) and towards blue (at the cyan end).

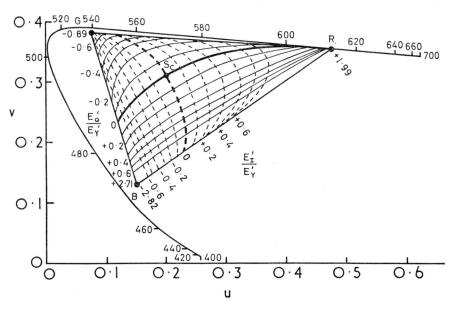

Fig. 19.9. The effect of gamma correction on the distribution of the I and Q signals in the chromaticity diagram. Lines of constant E_I'/E_Y' and E_Q'/E_Y' are shown where

$$E_I' = 0.736(E_R^{1/2.2} - E_Y') - 0.268(E_B^{1/2.2} - E_Y')$$

$$E_Q' = 0.478(E_R^{1/2.2} - E_Y') + 0.413(E_B^{1/2.2} - E_Y')$$

$$E_Y' = 0.299E_R^{1/2.2} + 0.587E_G^{1/2.2} + 0.114E_B^{1/2.2}$$

The full lines, representing E_Q'/E_Y' constant, show the directions of chromaticity changes available when the fineness of detail is such that only the E_Y' and E_I' signals are being transmitted.

19.12 Maximum signal amplitudes in the N.T.S.C. system

It was mentioned earlier that, to avoid over-loading the transmitter, it was necessary to reduce the magnitude of the $E_R - E_Y$ signal by a factor of 1.14 and that of the $E_B - E_Y$ signal by a factor of 2.03 before forming the E_I and E_Q signals. In Table 19.3 the values of the gamma corrected E_Y', E_I', and E_Q' signals which are actually produced are shown for the colours corresponding to E_R, E_G, E_B being equal to 0 or 1.0. Since 1.0 is the maximum value normally permitted for these signals, the values in Table 19.3 show the maximum which will have to be transmitted. The load on the transmitter will be a function of the combined amplitudes of the luminance signal and the chrominance signal and the maximum and minimum values are given by:

$$E_Y' \pm \sqrt{(E_I')^2 + (E_Q')^2}$$

403

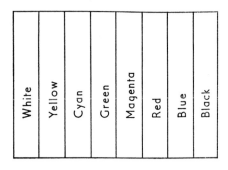

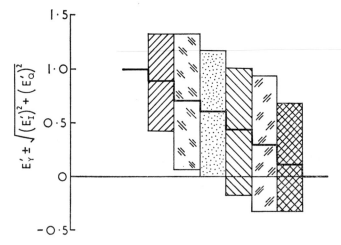

Fig. 19.10. The upper part of the figure depicts a typical 'colour bar' test pattern. The lower part shows the way in which the amplitude of the transmitted signal varies along a single line scan. The heavy line represents the amplitude of the luminance signal; the shaded rectangles represent the amplitude ranges of the combined luminance and chrominance signals.

It is seen that the weighting factors of 1.14 and 2.03 result in this combined signal being confined to the range −0.333 to +1.333, Strictly speaking, to avoid all over-loading, the permitted range should be from 0 to 1.0 but since large values of the chrominance signal occur only for very short times in typical scenes the slightly wider range is permissible. The negative amplitude simply indicates that the signal is using a region of amplitudes normally reserved for the receiver synchronizing signals.

In Fig. 19.10 the pattern of amplitudes of Table 19.3 is shown in diagrammatic form. The top half of the figure shows an array of vertical bars of different colours, known as the *colour bar test signal*. The colours in this test signal correspond to the eight colours for which E_R, E_G, and E_B have values of o or 1.0, and hence the corresponding signals have the values of Table 19.3. In the lower half of the figure the range of values from

$$E_Y' + \sqrt{(E_I')^2 + (E_Q')^2} \text{ to } E_Y' - \sqrt{(E_I')^2 + (E_Q')^2}$$

has been shown for each of the eight colours immediately below them. The result in the lower half of the figure is to depict the changes in amplitude of the transmitted signal during the scanning of a single line, the value at any instant being somewhere between the top and bottom of each of the hatched areas, according to the phase of the chrominance signal; the phases at which the extreme values occur are, of course, different for the different colours. If in fact the amplitude is displayed on an oscilloscope which is synchronized to the line scanning frequency then its appearance is similar to that shown in Fig. 19.10, the hatched area appearing as an area of very high frequency oscillations superimposed on the amplitude representing the luminance. If the signal were replaced by a scale of greys for which $E_R = E_G = E_B$ and E_Y' was the same as for the eight colours, then the display would consist simply of the heavy line in Fig. 19.10 representing the amplitude of the luminance signal, the chrominance signal being zero throughout.

19.13 Cross-talk between E_I' and E_Q'

In Fig. 19.11 and Table 19.4 the exact frequency arrangement is shown for the 525-line N.T.S.C. system and the 625 and 405 line adaptations of it. It is clear that the adoption of band-widths of $1\frac{1}{2}$ Mc/s for E_I' and $\frac{1}{2}$ Mc/s for E_Q', at the chrominance carrier frequencies shown, means that the E_I' signal has its upper side-band partially cut off by the upper limit of the total band; hence the E_I' transmission is not fully double-side-band. The effect of this on cross-talk (or interference) between the two signals is as follows: E_Q' is double side-band so does not cross-talk to E_I'; also E_I' is transmitted double side-band up to the band-width of E_Q', so these lower frequency E_I' components do not cross-talk to E_Q'; but above E_Q' cut-off, E_I' does cross-talk to E_Q', but if these frequencies are removed from the E_Q' channel by a filter which passes only frequencies up to the E_Q' limit, the result is effective freedom from cross-talk between E_I' and E_Q'.

19.14 The effect of the chrominance sub-carrier on the display

When a grey area is being transmitted, the chrominance signals are both zero, and therefore the colour sub-carrier has no effect on the picture either in colour or in black-and-white. But when a non-grey colour is displayed on a monochrome receiver, the chrominance carrier appears as a modulation of intensity along each line, the frequency being such as to produce $262\frac{1}{2}$, $227\frac{1}{2}$, or $283\frac{1}{2}$ 'dot-pairs' per line according to whether the system is, respectively, the 405, 525, or 625 line adaptation of the N.T.S.C. system; the dot-pairs are displaced along successive lines of each *field* by a distance equal to half a dot pair, and, because the total number of lines in each picture-system is odd, the dot pattern is reversed on successive complete pictures. The effect of the dots is therefore reduced by persistence of vision, but their presence can nevertheless be disturbing on monochrome pictures, particularly if they tend to 'crawl' in rows or columns.

When a colour-receiver displays a non-grey colour, the intensity of each of the three electron beams does not produce $262\frac{1}{2}$, $227\frac{1}{2}$, or $283\frac{1}{2}$ coloured dots along each line because the sub-carrier frequency is removed by means of a suitable electronic filter; the result is that the colour sub-carrier has a less disturbing effect on a colour display than it has on a monochrome display.

19.15 Comparison of the N.T.S.C., P.A.L., and S.E.C.A.M. systems

All three systems, N.T.S.C., P.A.L., and S.E.C.A.M., have been shown in practical tests to be capable of producing very similar and satisfactory results, and the differences between them can often be detected only by viewing the reproduced picture at viewing distances appreciably closer than normal. The main differences between the systems, may, however, be summarized as follows:

The P.A.L. and S.E.C.A.M. systems, by delaying chrominance information over a line-scan, reduce colour definition in the vertical direction; but since chrominance is severely band-width limited anyway, they do not make the vertical colour definition worse than that in the horizontal direction. The normal interlacing of the lines on successive fields helps to make the averaging of the colour information over successive lines more uniform, and, by interchanging which signal is transmitted on any given line on successive complete pictures, the definition and smoothness of the final result is further improved except for rapidly moving objects.

The N.T.S.C. and P.A.L. systems, for certain patterns, result in fine detail luminance signals being mis-interpreted as chrominance signals; thus certain black-and-white patterns are reproduced with spurious coloured fringes. The S.E.C.A.M. system avoids this defect by its use of frequency modulation for the chrominance signals. However, the N.T.S.C. and P.A.L. systems can be considerably improved in this respect by the use of a 'notch filter' which preferentially attenuates luminance signals of frequencies near those of the chrominance sub-carrier; curious edge effects are obtained if the notch filter has too strong an effect but useful advantages can be obtained at a proper compromise level.

Spurious 'crawling dot' or 'herring-bone' patterns can occur in all three systems, typical effects being as follows. In the N.T.S.C. system crawling dots occur on monochrome displays, but the colour displays are undisturbed. In the P.A.L. system, lines moving at 30° occur on monochrome displays, and

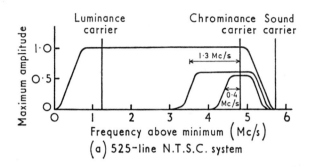

(a) 525-line N.T.S.C. system

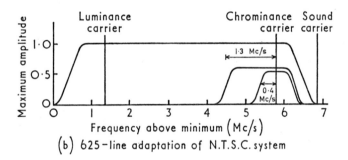

(b) 625-line adaptation of N.T.S.C. system

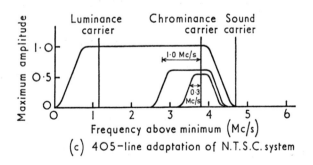

(c) 405-line adaptation of N.T.S.C. system

Fig. 19.11. The frequency arrangements adopted in the 525-line N.T.S.C. system, and in 625 and 405 line adaptations of it.

less obtrusively on colour displays. In the S.E.C.A.M. system herring-bone patterns occur on monochrome displays, and less obtrusively on colour displays.

The greater similarity between the N.T.S.C. and P.A.L. systems means that they can more easily be used together than either can with the S.E.C.A.M. system. Thus the P.A.L. system, in which phase changes matter far less than in the N.T.S.C. system, could be used for long distance transmission along co-axial cables; and then the N.T.S.C. system could be used for local broadcasting to avoid the necessity for incorporating delay circuits in the receivers.

19.16 Some useful graphical constructions

If reference is made to Fig. 19.12 it is clear that it must be possible to match a colour (M), whose chromaticity lies on the line joining (G) and (B), by a suitable mixture of (G) and (B), so that we can write

$$M(\mathrm{M}) \equiv G(\mathrm{G}) + B(\mathrm{B})$$

Similarly a colour (N), whose chromaticity lies on the line joining (M) and (R) can be matched by a suitable mixture of (M) and (R):

$$N(\mathrm{N}) \equiv M(\mathrm{M}) + R(\mathrm{R})$$

The exact position of the point representing (N) on the line joining (R) and (M) will be governed by the centre of gravity law, and will be the same as that of the centre of gravity of weights

$$\frac{L_{\mathrm{M}}M}{v_{\mathrm{M}}} = \frac{m.G + n.B}{v_{\mathrm{M}}} \qquad \text{placed at (R), and}$$

$$\frac{lR}{v_{\mathrm{R}}} \qquad \text{placed at (M).}$$

where L_{M} is the luminance of one unit of (M). The same result is obtained using weights

$$\frac{mE_{\mathrm{G}} + nE_{\mathrm{B}}}{v_{\mathrm{M}}} \qquad \text{and} \qquad \frac{lE_{\mathrm{R}}}{v_{\mathrm{R}}}$$

But $mE_{\mathrm{G}} + nE_{\mathrm{B}} = E_{\mathrm{Y}} - lE_{\mathrm{R}}$, therefore the weights can become

$$\frac{E_{\mathrm{Y}} - lE_{\mathrm{R}}}{v_{\mathrm{M}}} \qquad \text{and} \qquad \frac{lE_{\mathrm{R}}}{v_{\mathrm{R}}}$$

If (M) and (R) lie on a line of constant v so that $v_{\mathrm{M}} = v_{\mathrm{R}}$, then the weights can become

$$E_{\mathrm{Y}} - lE_{\mathrm{R}} \qquad \text{and} \qquad lE_{\mathrm{R}}$$

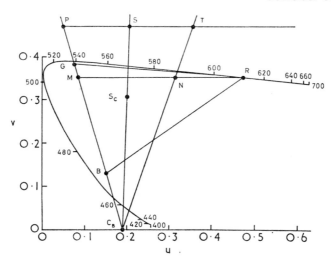

Fig. 19.12. Since the line joining R to M is a line of constant *v*, mixtures of R and M are represented by points equivalent to the centres of gravities of weights directly proportional to the luminances of R and M, placed at R and M. The proportion of R in the mixtures can therefore be represented by a uniform scale along MR, or along any line parallel to MR such as PT. A uniform scale along PT can therefore be used to find the values of R/L, and therefore of $(R-L)/L$, for lines of constant R/L drawn from the point C_B.

The distance from (M) of the point representing (N) is therefore given by

$$\frac{lE_R}{(E_Y - lE_R) + lE_R}\, l_{RM} = \frac{lE_R}{E_Y}\, l_{RM}$$

where l_{RM} is the length of the line joining (R) and (M).

Since l and l_{RM} are both constants, the distance of (N) from (M) is thus proportional to E_R/E_Y, and hence the line joining (R) and (M) can carry a linear scale of E_R/E_Y, which is easily converted to a linear scale of $(E_R - E_Y)/E_Y$ by subtracting 1.0 from each value. The construction can often be made more convenient by using a line parallel to (R)(M), such as PT in Fig. 19.12 (with P lying on (B)(G) or (B)(G) produced). If the line from (C_B) through (S_C) is produced to meet the line PT at S, and the position of the line PT is chosen so that PS = 1.0 on some convenient scale, then the other values can be very easily marked out directly. This arrangement gives the correct results because, at the point (S_C), $E_R = E_Y$, and therefore the line through (S_C) is the line for which $E_R/E_Y = 1.0$ (hence $(E_R - E_Y)/E_Y = 0$) and the line from (C_B) through (B) and (G) is the line for which $E_R = 0$, and therefore $E_R/E_Y = 0$ (hence $(E_R - E_Y)/E_Y = -1.0$).

In principle the same type of construction could be used for obtaining the fan of lines from (C_R). In this case the distances are given by:

$$n\frac{E_B}{E_Y}l_{BM}$$

where l_{BM} is the length of the line through (B), parallel to the u-axis, which meets (G)(R) produced at (M). Unfortunately the geometry of the u, v diagram is such that the method is impracticable for scaling E_B/E_Y but in some other chromaticity diagrams it can be used.

The method can also be used for obtaining the values of lines of constant E_Q/E_Y and E_I/E_Y. For since on the line joining (R) and (M) the distances are given by

$$l\frac{E_R}{E_Y}l_{RM},$$

by substituting for E_R/E_Y we obtain:

$$l_{RM}l(0.621\frac{E_Q}{E_Y}+0.956\frac{E_I}{E_Y}+1.0).$$

But for all points on the line joining (R) and (M) the value of v is constant and equal to v_R, the v co-ordinate of (R). Therefore

$$\frac{V}{U+V+W}=v=v_R$$

$$\therefore \qquad V=v_R(U+V+W)$$

$$\therefore \qquad V(1-v_R)/v_R=U+W$$

Using the equations relating U, V, W, with I, L, Q (Section 19.10), and inserting $v_R=0.352$ we obtain

$$L(1-0.352)/0.352=(0.208-0.780)I$$
$$+(0.653+1.599)L+(0.403+0.623)Q$$

Hence $\qquad 1.842L=1.026Q-0.572I+2.252L$

Therefore $\qquad 1.842E_Y=1.026E_Q-0.572E_I+2.252E_Y$

Which reduces to:

$$\frac{E_Q}{E_Y}=0.557\frac{E_I}{E_Y}-0.400$$

But the distances are given by:

$$l_{RM}l(0.621\frac{E_Q}{E_Y}+0.956\frac{E_I}{E_Y}+1.0).$$

Therefore, substituting for E_Q/E_Y, we have the distances given by:

$$l_{RM}l(0.621\times0.557\frac{E_I}{E_Y}-0.621\times0.400+0.956\frac{E_I}{E_Y}+1.0).$$

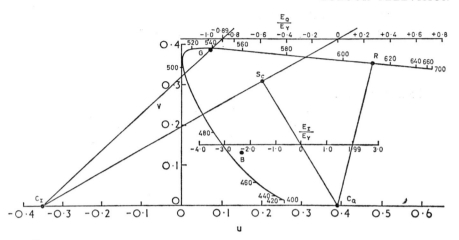

Fig. 19.13. Lines of constant v used to provide scales of uniform E_1/E_Y and E_Q/E_Y for finding the values of lines of constant E_1/E_Y drawn from C_Q and lines of constant E_Q/E_Y drawn from C_1.

Inserting $l = 0.299$ this reduces to

$$(0.389\frac{E_1}{E_Y}+0.225)l_{RM}.$$

Thus E_1/E_Y is linear along (R)(M) with the zero 22.5% away from (M). Similarly, by substituting for E_1/E_Y, we have the distances for E_Q/E_Y given by:

$$(0.699\frac{E_Q}{E_Y}+0.504)l_{RM}.$$

Thus E_Q/E_Y is linear along (R)(M) with the zero 50.4% away from (M).

Once again lines parallel to (R)(M) may be chosen instead of (R)(M) for more convenient scaling, as shown in Fig. 19.13. The lines through (S_C) correspond to the zero in each case, and the line from (C_Q) through (R) for which $E_1/E_Y = 1.99$ is used to fix the scale of E_1/E_Y; the line from (C_1) through (G) for which $E_Q/E_Y = -0.89$ is used to fix the scale of E_Q/E_Y.

19.17 Some useful equations

In this section are collected together various equations which will be found useful when it is necessary to perform calculations in the N.T.S.C. system.

(a) Connecting luminance and R, G, B.

$$E_Y = 0.299E_R + 0.587E_G + 0.114E_B$$
$$L = 0.299R + 0.587G + 0.114B$$

(b) Connecting R, G, B and U, V, W.

$$1.0(R) \equiv 0.405(U) + 0.299(V) + 0.145(W)$$
$$1.0(G) \equiv 0.116(U) + 0.587(V) + 0.827(W)$$
$$1.0(B) \equiv 0.133(U) + 0.114(V) + 0.627(W)$$

$$U = 0.405R + 0.116G + 0.133B$$
$$V = 0.299R + 0.587G + 0.114B$$
$$W = 0.145R + 0.827G + 0.627B$$
$$1.0(U) \equiv 2.432(R) - 1.519(G) + 1.440(B)$$
$$1.0(V) \equiv 0.332(R) + 2.083(G) - 2.823(B)$$
$$1.0(W) \equiv -0.576(R) - 0.057(G) + 1.803(B)$$

$$R = 2.432U + 0.332V - 0.576W$$
$$G = -1.519U + 2.083V - 0.057W$$
$$B = 1.440U - 2.823V + 1.803W$$

(c) Connecting $R-L$, L, $B-L$ and U, V, W.

$$1.0(C_R) \equiv 0.346(U) + 0.000(V) - 0.276(W)$$
$$1.0(S_C) \equiv 0.653(U) + 1.000(V) + 1.599(W)$$
$$1.0(C_B) \equiv 0.110(U) + 0.000(V) + 0.467(W)$$

$$U = 0.346(R-L) + 0.653L + 0.110(B-L)$$
$$V = \qquad\qquad 1.000L$$
$$W = -0.276(R-L) + 1.599L + 0.467(B-L)$$

$$1.0(U) \equiv 2.432(C_R) + 0.000(S_C) + 1.440(C_B)$$
$$1.0(V) \equiv -0.668(C_R) + 1.000(S_C) - 3.823(C_B)$$
$$1.0(W) \equiv -0.576(C_R) + 0.000(S_C) + 1.803(C_B)$$

$$R-L = 2.432U - 0.668V - 0.576W$$
$$L = \qquad\qquad 1.000V$$
$$B-L = 1.440U - 3.823V + 1.803W$$

(d) Connecting E_I, E_Y, E_Q and E_R, E_G, E_B.

$$E_I = 0.736(E_R-E_Y)-0.268(E_B-E_Y)$$
$$E_Q = 0.478(E_R-E_Y)+0.413(E_B-E_Y)$$

$$E_R-E_Y = 0.956E_I+0.621E_Q$$
$$E_B-E_Y = -1.106E_I+1.703E_Q$$

$$E_R = 0.956E_I+1.000E_Y+0.621E_Q$$
$$E_G = -0.272E_I+1.000E_Y-0.647E_Q$$
$$E_B = -1.106E_I+1.000E_Y+1.703E_Q$$

$$1.0(C_I) \equiv 0.956(R)-0.272(G)-1.106(B)$$
$$1.0(S_c) \equiv 1.000(R)+1.000(G)+1.000(B)$$
$$1.0(C_Q) \equiv 0.621(R)-0.647(G)+1.703(B)$$

$$E_I = 0.596E_R-0.274E_G-0.322E_B$$
$$E_Y = 0.299E_R+0.587E_G+0.114E_B$$
$$E_Q = 0.211E_R-0.523E_G+0.312E_B$$

$$1.0(R) = 0.596(C_I)+0.299(S_c)+0.211(C_Q)$$
$$1.0(G) = -0.274(C_I)+0.587(S_c)-0.523(C_Q)$$
$$1.0(B) = -0.322(C_I)+0.114(S_c)+0.312(C_Q)$$

(e) Connecting I, L, Q and U, V, W.

$$1.0(C_I) \equiv 0.208(U)+0.000(V)-0.780(W)$$
$$1.0(S_c) \equiv 0.653(U)+1.000(V)+1.599(W)$$
$$1.0(C_Q) \equiv 0.403(U)+0.000(V)+0.623(W)$$

$$U = 0.208I+0.653L+0.403Q$$
$$V = 1.000L$$
$$W = -0.780I+1.599L+0.623Q$$

$$1.0(U) \equiv 1.403(C_I)+0.000(S_c)+1.757(C_Q)$$
$$1.0(V) \equiv 0.534(C_I)+1.000(S_c)-1.898(C_Q)$$
$$1.0(W) \equiv -0.907(C_I)+0.000(S_c)+0.470(C_Q)$$

$$I = 1.403U+0.534V-0.907W$$
$$L = 1.000V$$
$$Q = 1.757U-1.898V+0.470W$$

TABLE 19.1

Values of camera signals for saturated colours at maximum luminance

	White	Yellow	Cyan	Green	Magenta	Red	Blue	Black
E_R	1	1	0	0	1	1	0	0
E_G	1	1	1	1	0	0	0	0
E_B	1	0	1	0	1	0	1	0
E_Y	1.000	0.886	0.701	0.587	0.413	0.299	0.114	0
$E_R - E_Y$	0	0.114	−0.701	−0.587	0.587	0.701	−0.114	0
$E_B - E_Y$	0	−0.886	0.299	−0.587	0.587	−0.299	0.886	0

TABLE 19.2

Values of weighted camera signals for saturated colours at
maximum luminance

	White	Yellow	Cyan	Green	Magenta	Red	Blue	Black
E_R	1	1	0	0	1	1	0	0
E_G	1	1	1	1	0	0	0	0
E_B	1	0	1	0	1	0	1	0
E_Y	1.000	0.886	0.701	0.587	0.413	0.299	0.114	0
E_I	0	0.321	−0.596	−0.275	0.275	0.596	−0.321	0
E_Q	0	−0.312	−0.212	−0.523	0.523	0.212	0.312	0

TABLE 19.3

Values of gamma corrected signals for large area saturated colours at full luminance

	White	Yellow	Cyan	Green	Magenta	Red	Blue	Black
E_R	1	1	0	0	1	1	0	0
E_G	1	1	1	1	0	0	0	0
E_B	1	0	1	0	1	0	1	0
$E_R^{1/\gamma}$	1	1	0	0	1	1	0	0
$E_G^{1/\gamma}$	1	1	1	1	0	0	0	0
$E_B^{1/\gamma}$	1	0	1	0	1	0	1	0
E_Y'	1.000	0.886	0.701	0.587	0.413	0.299	0.114	0
$E_R^{1/\gamma} - E_Y'$	0	0.114	−0.701	−0.587	0.587	0.701	−0.114	0
$E_B^{1/\gamma} - E_Y'$	0	−0.886	0.299	−0.587	0.587	−0.299	0.886	0
E_I'	0	0.321	−0.596	−0.275	0.275	0.596	−0.321	0
E_Q'	0	−0.312	−0.212	−0.523	0.523	0.212	0.312	0
$\sqrt{(E_I')^2 + (E_Q')^2}$	0	0.447	0.632	0.591	0.591	0.632	0.447	0
$E_Y' + \sqrt{(E_I')^2 + (E_Q')^2}$	1.000	1.333	1.333	1.178	1.004	0.931	0.561	0
$E_Y' - \sqrt{(E_I')^2 + (E_Q')^2}$	1.000	0.439	0.069	−0.004	−0.178	−0.333	−0.333	0

TABLE 19.4

Frequencies used in N.T.S.C. systems

Number of lines	405	525	625
Number of complete pictures per second	25	29.97	25
Approximate band-width of picture, Mc/s	3	4	5
Frequency of chrominance carrier above luminance carrier, Mc/s	2.6578125	3.579545	4.4336875
Chrominance carrier frequency as a multiple of line frequency	262.5	227.5	283.5
Frequency of sound carrier above luminance carrier, Mc/s	3.54375	4.5	5.5
E_I' band-width (at 2 dB below max.)	1.0	1.3	1.3
E_Q' band-width (at 2 dB below max.)	0.3	0.4	0.4
Approximate frequency of luminance carrier above band minimum, Mc/s	1.15	1.25	1.35
Approximate total band-width used, Mc/s	5	6	7

REFERENCES

Loughren, A. V., *J. Soc. Mot. Pic. Tel. Eng.*, **60,** 321 and 596 (1953).
Middleton, W. E. K., and Holmes, M. C., *J. Opt. Soc. Amer.*, **39,** 582 (1949).
Roizen, J., and Lipkin, R., *Electronics*, **38,** 97 (March 22nd, 1965).
Thomson, L. C., and Wright, W. D., *J. Physiol.*, **105,** 316 (1947).
Thomson, L. C., and Wright, W. D., *J. Opt. Soc. Amer.*, **43,** 890 (1953).
Willmer, E. N., *Nature*, **153,** 774 (1944).
Willmer, E. N., and Wright, W. D., *Nature*, **156,** 119 (1945).
Wright, W. D., *J. Opt. Soc. Amer.*, **42,** 509 (1952).

GENERAL REFERENCES

Carnt, P. S., and Townsend, G. B., *Colour Television: N.T.S.C., Principles and Practice*, Iliffe, London (1961).
Fink, D. G., *Colour Television Standards*, McGraw Hill, New York, (1955).
Kaufman, M., and Thomas, H., *Introduction to Colour T.V.*, John F. Rider, New York (1954).
Proc. Inst. Radio Engnrs., **39,** 1124–1331 (1951).
Proc. Inst. Radio Engnrs., **41,** 838–858 (1953).
Proc. Inst. Radio Engnrs., **42,** 5–344 (1954).
Proc. Inst. Radio Engnrs., **43,** 742–748 (1955).
Theile, R., *J. Soc. Mot. Pic. Tel. Eng.*, **72,** 860 (1963).
Wentworth, J. W., *Colour Television Engineering*, McGraw Hill, New York (1955).

CHAPTER 20

The Use of Colour Film
in Colour Television

1. Introduction – *2*. Deriving television signals from colour film – *3*. Tele-recording – *4*. Electronic correction of signals derived from colour film – *5*. Overall transfer characteristics

20.1 Introduction

ALTHOUGH colour television programmes can be recorded on magnetic tape, the use of colour photographic film for this purpose is widespread for four reasons: first, film cameras are more convenient to use on location than television cameras and video tape-recorders; secondly, film can be edited more easily; thirdly, film is a cheaper means of long-term storage; and fourthly, film enables television signals to be obtained in the form required for any desired system (e.g. 525-line N.T.S.C., 625-line P.A.L., etc.), a feature termed *free standards conversion* which is important when the same programme is used in different countries.

If a programme is filmed live, there being no intermediate television link between the scene and the photographic camera, normal motion-picture techniques can often be used, and it is then only necessary for each television transmitting station to be provided with a print of the programme, having a contrast suitable for the televising equipment being used. If, however, it is required, for economic or artistic reasons for instance, that the film be made using television programming techniques, then either the film must be exposed to a television monitor tube, or it must be arranged that each television camera provides not only a picture in television but also one in film (the television pictures then being used only for editing the programme). Of these two arrangements the latter is preferable, because recording in colour from a monitor on to film is liable to introduce colour degradations. Equipment has therefore been designed in which a colour television camera and a film camera have been combined, such as is used in the *Electronicam* system (Caddigan and Goldsmith, 1956).

417

In order to avoid any parallax errors, the television and the film images are formed by the same objective lens, a beam-splitter (which can consist of a rotating sector with reflecting blades) separating the beams of light required for the two different parts of the camera. For economic reasons, the film is only run while each television camera is actually contributing to the programme; but, because the film-camera takes about five (photographic) frames to attain its true running speed (and to stop at the end of each take), the cutting from one camera to another occurs about a fifth of a second later in the film records than on the television monitor: however, this delay is usually quite acceptable. Editing of the films is carried out, either with the aid of special marks made to identify the correct sequence of the lengths of film corresponding to the programme, or a film recording from a television monitor is also made and used as a guide for assembling the final film.

The film used for the actual broadcasting is normally a print, and not, except in very unusual circumstances, the original camera film; this is because of the danger of damaging the original film, the undesirability of broadcasting a film with many splices, and the frequent need to supply several identical copies. The negative-positive film system is therefore very suitable, but the reversal-reversal system is also used for some applications, such as news-reel work, where having a positive image on the camera-film assists very rapid editing and also facilitates the exceptional use of the camera film itself for broadcasting.

It might be thought that, with the rather limited definition of all broadcast television pictures, it would be unnecessary to use 35 mm. motion-picture film for television, and that 16 mm. film would provide sharp enough pictures. It must be remembered, however, that in any system some losses of definition occur at frequencies well below the limiting frequency, and that these losses are multiplicative: thus if, for instance, a 16 mm. system, consisting of a photographic lens, a negative film, and a print film, resulted in a 25 % loss of contrast of detail spaced at 200 line-pairs per picture-width, and the television system also introduced a similar loss, the combined loss of televised 16 mm. film would be 44 % ($\frac{3}{4} \times \frac{3}{4} = 0.56$). Thus, although the 25 % loss might be unnoticeable in either the film or the television system on its own, the effect in the combined system might be quite noticeable, and 35 mm. films would then be necessary if the best results were desired.

20.2 Deriving television signals from colour film

Professional motion picture film is normally shot at 24 pictures per second; but, because a light interrupted at this frequency appears to flicker very noticeably, motion picture projectors usually provide two (or sometimes three) dark periods per picture instead of one, so as to raise the frequency to 48 (or 72) per second where flickering is much less noticeable. One of the dark periods is used to move the film in the gate from one picture to the next so that the sequence of events is as shown in Fig. 20.1(a), the picture being projected in flashes of about 1/96 second duration with dark periods of about 1/96 second in between. The sequence of events in a television picture is, however, rather different, as is indicated in Fig. 20.1(b). The television equivalent to the period when film is moved from one picture to the next (known as the *pull-down* time) is the time taken for the spot to move from the end of the bottom line of the picture to the beginning of the top line of

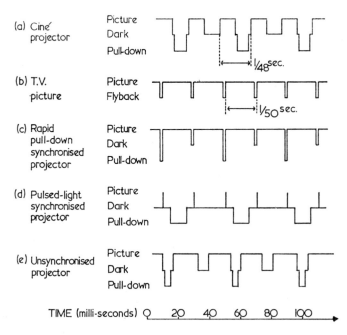

Fig. 20.1. Diagrammatic representation of the relation between film projected at 24 pictures per second and television displayed at 50 fields per second.

the picture (known as the *fly-back* time). This fly-back time can be very short indeed and the interval between the end of scanning one frame and the beginning of scanning the next is usually less than 10 % of one cycle of the frame frequency, that is, less than 1/500 second in 50 cycle systems or less than 1/600 second in 60 cycle systems. If, therefore, the light from an ordinary cine-projector were shone on to a television camera, the light would only be falling on to the pick-up tubes for roughly half the time occupying each scanned frame. Special devices have therefore had to be constructed for televising film, and they are usually referred to as *tele-cine* projectors.

It has been found possible in 16 mm. film equipment (but not in 35 mm. equipment) to design special very fast pull-down mechanisms, which can move the film on in about 1/750 second (Wheeler, 1963) so that the pull-down time can be confined to the fly-back time; alternatively the film may be run continuously and optical devices, such as drums of mirrors or rotating prism blocks, used to present the required series of stationary images with very short intervals between them. If such a projector is run at 25 pictures per second instead of the usual 24, the situation for a 50-frame per second television system is as shown in Fig. 20.1(c): satisfactory pictures are obtained if the projector pull-down is synchronized with the television fly-back. The slight change in picture-rate, from 24 to 25 per second, is not usually noticeable, but if the film is being shot specifically for television purposes the film-cameras can be run at the higher speed.

Simplifications are possible, however, because some television camera tubes, such as the vidicon, are able to store their images of electron charge between successive scans of the electron beam, and hence it is not necessary for the optical image to be present throughout the entire electron-beam scanning period. In fact it is possible to confine the optical image to a single flash during each fly-back period, as shown in Fig. 20.1(d), leaving plenty of time between the flashes for a normal pull-down mechanism to operate; (the flashes, of about 1/1000 second duration, can be given either by means of a rotating sector or by pulsing the light source electronically). With this type of television pick-up tube (capable of image storage) it is also possible to work without exact synchronization of the camera pull-down and television fly-back periods, but it is advisable in this case for the pick-up tube to be illuminated for at least 60% of the total time (otherwise those parts of the picture covered by the electron beam during the time when the light was on would be noticeably different from the rest); this type of arrangement is shown in Fig. 20.1(e), a slow drift in phase between the film pull-down and the television fly-back being unimportant.

When the television system operates at 60 frames per second, the situation is more complicated because the film cannot be speeded up from 24 to 30 pictures per second without obvious distortion of the portrayed motion. The film cannot be projected at 24 pictures per second on to a television camera with tubes capable of storing the electronic image, because the beating between the 24 pictures per second of the film and the 30 pictures per second of the television scan results in a pulsation of the television signal caused by the fact that the interval between successive television frames would alternate between including a whole dark interval, only part of one, and practically no dark interval at all (see Fig. 20.2(a) and (b)). It is therefore necessary to adopt one of the arrangements shown in Fig. 20.2(c), (d), and (e). In these arrangements each pair of pictures on the film provides five television frames: thus the first picture on the film provides two television frames, occupying 2/60 = 1/30 second, but the second picture provides three television frames occupying 3/60 = 1/20 second.

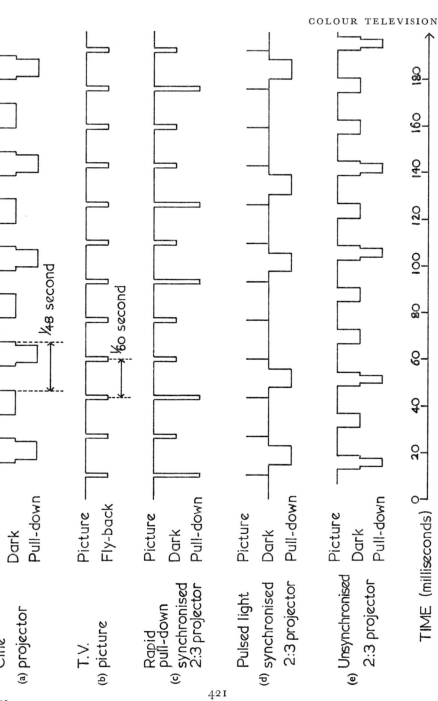

Cine
(a) projector

Dark
Pull-down

⅟₄₈ second

T.V.
(b) picture

Picture
Fly-back

⅟₆₀ second

Rapid
pull-down
(c) synchronised
2:3 projector

Picture
Dark
Pull-down

Pulsed light
(d) synchronised
2:3 projector

Picture
Dark
Pull-down

Unsynchronised
(e) 2:3 projector

Picture
Dark
Pull-down

TIME (milliseconds)

0   20   40   60   80   100   120   140   160   180

Fig. 20.2. Diagrammatic representation of the relation between film projected at 24 pictures per second and television at 60 fields per second.

15

421

The two pictures together therefore occupy $5/60 = 1/12$ second, as required to maintain an average of 24 pictures per second, but the television fields are produced at the rate of 60 per second as required.

An alternative method of deriving colour television signals from colour film is to use a *flying-spot scanner* (as shown in Fig. 20.3): in this case the image is broken up into its lines before the light is passed through the film instead of afterwards. An unmodulated (white all over) television raster is displayed on a cathode-ray tube having a very short after-glow; this raster of lines is imaged on to the film and the light is then split into red, green, and blue components and made to fall on three photo-multiplier tubes. The photo-multiplier tubes then generate three simultaneous signals which are functions of the red, green, and blue transmittances of the film at each point. The device has the great advantage that the registration of the three images depends only on the time responses of the three photo-multiplier tubes and their associated circuitry which can be made very similar to each other. For the method to work it is clearly essential for the film to remain stationary throughout the whole of the scan of each field, and therefore the device has to be used either with a rapid pull-down intermittent projector or with a continuous projector with optical devices for immobilizing images of the raster on the film. (If the field frequency is 60 cycles per second the 3 : 2 type of projector arrangements have to be used.) Alternatively the film can be moved at a uniform speed past an image of a single line produced on a cathode-ray tube operating with no vertical deflection; the movement of the film then provides the vertical scanning effect. The need for interlacing complicates the situation, however, and it is usually advisable to form pairs of images of rasters of lines on the film; although this is practicable for 50 fields-per-second operation very complicated arrangements are required for 3 : 2 type of operation (Whitehead, 1965).

Flying spot scanners are widely used for deriving colour television signals from colour transparencies: in this case there are no problems of pull-down or image immobilization, of course.

The four-tube camera principle (see Section 17.8) can be used in both projector-type and flying-spot tele-cine equipment: it is particularly advantageous in reducing registration problems in the former (Taylor, 1965).

20.3 Tele-recording

When it is required to record a programme from a television monitor display on to photographic film, the same problems of differences in frame frequencies and of pull-down are encountered as have just been discussed in connection with deriving television signals from film. It is therefore necessary with 60 frame-per-second television to use a 2 : 3 *exposing* sequence: that is, two television frames are used for $1/30$ second and three television frames for $1/20$ second; however, to avoid alternate pictures on the film having different densities because of different exposure times, it is necessary to make adjustments to the exposure levels. The pull-down problems can be solved in one of several ways. A quick pull-down camera (either mechanical-intermittent or continuous-optical) can be used. Or, by using phosphors with long afterglows on the monitor, a camera with only a moderately rapid pull-down need be used, the television signals being boosted during the part of the scan during which pull-down is taking place so as to give uniform intensity all over the image recorded by the film. Alternatively, at the sacrifice of definition, one of the two (or three) television frames in each film picture can be obscured and the film moved on in this time: this technique is known as *suppressed-field* tele-recording and gives results equivalent to rather better than half the full definition (because interlacing itself degrades definition to some extent, especially in the case of moving subjects).

In the interests of having adequate light for colour tele-recording on film, a trinoscope type of monitor display may have to be used.

Colour television signals can also be recorded on magnetic tape (Anderson and Roizen, 1959).

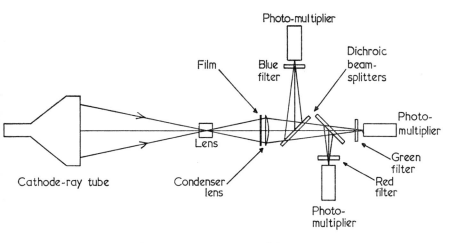

Fig. 20.3. Typical arrangements for a flying-spot scanner.

20.4 Electronic correction of signals derived from colour film

A motion picture film which, when projected in a dark auditorium, appears to be of perfectly satisfactory quality, may prove disappointing when transmitted on colour television. This may be for a number of reasons, but it is possible to apply very useful corrections to the pictures electronically.

For instance, if a motion picture print has a slight overall colour cast, this can easily pass unnoticed in a dark auditorium, but on a television set viewed in a room with considerable ambient light, the colour cast is often easily detected. However, by adjusting the relative amplitudes of the red, green, and blue signals produced by the tele-cine apparatus a colour cast of this nature is easily corrected. Mis-match of the *contrast* of the red, green, and blue pictures can also occur, either because of imperfect control of the motion-picture processes, or because of the spectral sensitivities of the three colour channels of the tele-cine apparatus being such as to evaluate the contrasts differently from the eye: this type of defect can also be corrected electronically, and in fact some control can even be exercised over variations of contrast mis-match at different density levels (Wood, Sanders, and Griffiths, 1965).

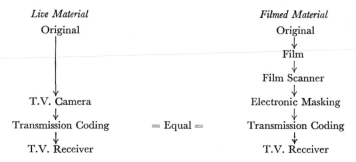

Fig. 20.4. Comparison of system sequences for live programmes and those derived from colour film.

Even when the colour balance, contrast match, overall contrast, and curve shape of a colour motion-picture film are all ideally suited to a colour television system, however, dissatisfaction with the final result may still be felt. This can be because both the film system and the television system introduce errors of colour reproduction, particularly losses of colour saturation, and while the errors introduced by either system on its own may be perfectly tolerable, the multiplicative effect of combining them can easily become intolerable. The problem becomes particularly acute if it is desired to include film and live sequences of the same subject matter in the same programme. Here again, electronic correction of the signals can provide a very useful improvement in the results, a step known as *electronic masking* (Burr, 1954; Brewer, Ladd, and Pinney, 1954; Wood and Griffiths, 1966).

If it is required that the colour and tone reproduction of the recorded and live parts of the programme should be as nearly alike as possible, it follows that, in the sequences of operations shown, in Fig. 20.4, the input to the transmission coding stages should be equal.

If the television camera and the film have different spectral sensitivities, exact equality of the final results is impossible, and a rigorous calculation of the optimum electronic masking requires the arbitrary selection and weighting of test colours and an evaluation of their reproduction errors which is relevant to overall picture quality. The selection, weighting, and evaluation of test colours can only be done very approximately, and approximate results can in fact be obtained by simpler means. It has, however, been shown (Evans, Hanson and Brewer, 1953) that the effects of altering the spectral sensitivities in colour reproduction systems are often of a fairly minor nature, and it is therefore to be expected that the optimum electronic masking can be calculated to a good approximation by ignoring the differences in spectral sensitivity between the television camera and the film. If this is done, simple calculations lead to results which are otherwise rigorous for colours which are filmed at density levels where the characteristic curves and inter-image effects are linear.

In order to evaluate the degree of the electronic masking required, it is necessary to know the relation between the optical input to the film camera and the electronic output of the tele-cine apparatus. This can conveniently be determined by varying the exposure of each layer of the film in turn by known amounts above and below a point representing an average medium grey. The rates of change of the logarithms of the red, green, and blue signals from the tele-cine apparatus, with respect to the logarithms of the film exposures, can then be determined, either directly, or by measuring the film on a densito-meter filtered so that its spectral sensitivities match those of the three channels of the tele-cine apparatus. As a result, nine rates of change, or gammas, are obtained as follows:

	Film exposure		*Tele-cine channel*	
Layer varied	*Layers held constant*	*Red*	*Green*	*Blue*
Red	Green and Blue	γ_{rr}	γ_{rg}	γ_{rb}
Green	Red and Blue	γ_{gr}	γ_{gg}	γ_{gb}
Blue	Red and Green	γ_{br}	γ_{bg}	γ_{bb}

If this block of gammas is represented by the matrix, M, and the logarithms of the exposures received by the three layers of the film by o_r, o_g, o_b, and the logarithms of the tele-cine output signals by p_r, p_g, p_b, then

$$(p_r \quad p_g \quad p_b) = (o_r \quad o_g \quad o_b)M$$

By inverting the matrix, M, we obtain

$$(o_r \quad o_g \quad o_b) = (p_r \quad p_g \quad p_b)M^{-1}$$

If, therefore, masking equivalent to the matrix M^{-1} is applied to the signals so that masked signals p_{rm}, p_{gm}, p_{bm} are obtained thus:

$$(p_{rm} \quad p_{gm} \quad p_{bm}) = (p_r \quad p_g \quad p_b)M^{-1}$$

then the input to the television transmission stage will be the same as that from the original scene viewed by the television camera, apart from the effects of

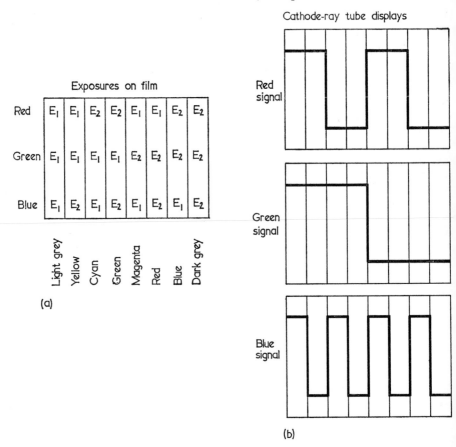

Fig. 20.5. (a) Exposure pattern on test-film to be used for setting electronic masking parameters. (b) Cathode-ray tube displays from the test-film when the masking is correctly adjusted.

differences in spectral sensitivities between the television camera and the camera film, and any non-linear portions of the characteristic curves used in the photographic steps.

Masking equivalent to the matrix M^{-1} can be set up by practical tests, instead of by calculation, if test film is exposed, as shown in Fig. 20.5(a), to give eight vertical stripes (two grey, and six coloured) in which the exposure of each layer is at one of two values, E_1 and E_2, representing suitable increments above and below a medium grey. The values of the masks are then set so that the magnitudes of the red, green, and blue signals, which can be displayed on cathode-ray tubes, as shown in Fig. 20.5(b), are all at the appropriate one of the two levels produced by the two grey stripes; the nine gammas of the electronic masks are then all proportional to the corresponding values in the matrix M^{-1}. By setting the overall contrast of the system correctly (an adjustment which will alter the two levels on the cathode-ray tubes) the masks can be made equal to the values of M^{-1}. Thus the correct masking can be set up without having to evaluate M^{-1} or calibrate the electronic masking controls.

Electronic masking can also be used to improve the results obtained when broadcasting from a tele-recording on colour film. Ideally the picture finally displayed on the receiver should look the same as if the signals had been transmitted directly without going through the camera-film, tele-cine chain. It therefore follows that in the sequences of operations shown in Fig. 20.6 the input at the transmission coding stages should be the same. Here, the original scene is photographed by a television camera in both cases and therefore the problem is confined to recovering the red, green, and blue signals from the film record; in this case, exact equality of the input to the transmission coding stage is theoretically possible.

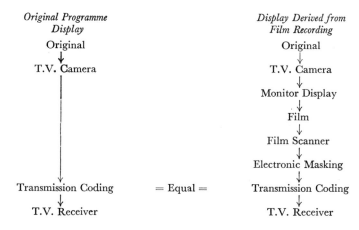

Fig. 20.6. Comparison of system sequences for live programmes and those derived from tele-recordings on film.

If the monitor display, and the spectral sensitivities of the layers of the film, are such that there is no cross-talk on to the film (in other words if the displayed record corresponding to the red camera signal is recorded only on the red layer of the film, and similarly for the green and blue channels) then the required electronic masking characteristics can be evaluated exactly as described above, and will be inaccurate only in so far as any non-linear portions of the characteristic curves (including inter-image effects) are used in the photographic steps. In order to maximize signal-to-noise ratio it is desirable that the electronic masking be kept as low as possible and hence monitor-to-film cross-talk should preferably be eliminated by physical means. If this is not possible then the effects of the cross-talk can be allowed for approximately by evaluating the matrix from exposures on the camera film made by light having the same spectral energy distributions as those of the red, green and blue displays of the monitor instead of through red, green and blue filters chosen to isolate the three layers of the film. The effects of cross-talk can only be counteracted approximately by electronic masks, because cross-talk causes extra signals at lower exposure levels (log exposure shifts) instead of altering contrasts (gamma changes); it is the latter which electronic masking can correct for exactly, but it can be used to provide approximate correction for the former also.

20.5 Overall transfer characteristics

The way in which the magnitude of the recorded signal is related to the magnitude of the optical image in a system is often referred to as the *transfer characteristic;* it is convenient to plot both these magnitudes on logarithmic scales, so that the slope of the transfer characteristic is the gamma of the system. The transfer characteristic of a typical television system is made up of a combination of the individual transfer characteristics of the taking lens, the pick-up tube, the transmission coding, the display device, and the effect of the ambient lighting on the viewed picture. When film or video-tape recordings are included then the transfer characteristics of these media and their associated recording and read-out equipments also contribute.

Because of the effects of flare light in lenses and equipment, and the addition of ambient lighting to the viewed picture, even if the transfer characteristics of all the rest of the systems were linear (on a log-log plot) the overall transfer characteristic would have curvature (Wentworth, 1955). The concept of the slope, or gamma, of the overall transfer characteristic is nevertheless helpful as a broad description of a system.

Black-and-white motion pictures intended for projection are usually made to an overall gamma of about 1.3 as measured densitometrically, but the actual operating figure is reduced by flare and ambient lighting. A comparable figure for black-and-white television is about 1.4 (without the effect of ambient light), so that, if the gamma of the cathode-ray tube is taken as 2.2,[1] we arrive at a figure of about 0.65 for the rest of the system: vidicon tubes provide about this amount of gamma reduction intrinsically, but image-orthicons, plumbicons, and flying-spot scanners, require special circuits in order to obtain it. When television signals are derived from film, care must be taken to see that the two gamma increases of 1.3 and 1.4 are not multiplied,

[1] This is the accepted N.T.S.C. figure; many cathode-ray tubes have a gamma of between 2.5 and 3.

for an overall gamma of 1.8 (1.3 × 1.4) would be too high. The use of special vidicon tubes with gammas of about 0.5 are helpful in keeping the gamma down in tele-cine equipment, or the film can be specially made so that the gamma of its pictures is lower than that which is customary for normal optical projection; this lower gamma can be obtained either by using less contrasty lighting conditions when exposing the camera film, or by making the print lighter than normal so that more of the subject matter is on the low-gamma toe of the print-film, or by using special low-contrast films if these are available. When film is used for tele-recording, three successive increases in gamma could occur: 1.4 on the television monitor display; 1.3 in the film-recording system; and 1.4 on the receiver display; to avoid an overall gamma of 2.5 (1.4 × 1.3 × 1.4) it is necessary to use monitor-displays or film systems (or both) having suitable reduced gamma characteristics.

When colour film is used for deriving television signals, these problems can be even more acute, because (as discussed in Section 12.16) in colour the combined gammas of the film system are often as high as about 1.6 in order to obtain increased colour saturation; flat lighting has therefore to be used to reduce the apparent contrast in order to obtain good tone rendering even for ordinary projection. Further reduction of the lighting contrast to obtain film suitable for television may not then be feasible, in which case one or more of the other methods of reducing contrast mentioned above must be used.

REFERENCES

Anderson, C. E., and Roizen, J., *J. Soc. Mot. Pic. Tel. Eng.*, **68**, 667 (1959).
Burr, R. P., *Proc. I.R.E.*, **42**, 192 (1954).
Caddigan, J. L., and Goldsmith, T. T., *J. Soc. Mot. Pic. Tel. Eng.*, **65**, 7 (1956).
Evans, R. M., Hanson, W. T., and Brewer, W. L., *Principles of Colour Photography*, p. 504, Wiley, New York (1953).
Brewer, W. L., Ladd, J. H., and Pinney, J. E., *Proc. Inst. Radio Engnrs.*, **42**, 174 (1954).
Taylor, D. M., *J. Soc. Mot. Pic. Tel. Eng.*, **74**, 930 (1965).
Wentworth, J. W., *Colour Television Engineering*, p. 156, McGraw Hill, New York (1955).
Wheeler, L. J., *Principles of Cinematography*, 3rd Edition, p. 60, Fountain Press, London (1963).
Whitehead, R. C., *Principles of Television Engineering*, Vol. 2, p. 15, Iliffe, London (1965).
Wood, C. B. B., and Griffiths, F. A., *Brit. Kinematography Sound and Television*, **48**, 74 (1966).
Wood, C. B. B., Sanders, J. R., and Griffiths, F. A., *J. Soc. Mot. Pic. Tel. Eng.*, **74**, 755 (1965).

GENERAL REFERENCE

Palmer, A. B., *J. Soc. Mot. Pic. Tel. Eng.*, **74**, 1069 (1965).

PART FOUR
COLOUR PRINTING

CHAPTER 21

Photomechanical Principles

1. Introduction – *2.* Letterpress – *3.* Lithography – *4.* Gravure – *5.* Super-imposed dye images – *6.* Superimposed dot images – *7.* Exact colour repro-duction with dot images – *8.* Colour correction by masking – *9.* Contact screens – *10.* Autoscreen film – *11.* Practical systems for preparing colour separations – *12.* A four-mask system – *13.* A multi-layer mask system – *14.* A direct screening system

21.1 Introduction

IF a large number of copies of a colour reproduction are required, the cheapest method is usually to transfer colorants from some surface containing the image to a less expensive surface such as mordanted cloth, paper, or gelatin-coated film base, the image-bearing surface then being re-coloured for subsequent transfers. Thus Technicolor films, as described in Chapter 10, are printed by successively transferring cyan, magenta, and yellow dye images from matrices consisting of gelatin relief-images to suitably prepared gelatin-coated film base. In the textile industries, except when the pattern is woven into the fabric, coloured designs are printed on to the material by rollers embossed with the required design and suitably loaded with dye. And it is the role of the printing industry to provide inexpensive multiple copies of colour reproductions for inclusion in magazines, books, posters, wrappers and the like.

The main methods adopted for colour reproduction by the printing trade have been developed from those used for many years in ordinary monochrome printing, known as Letterpress, Lithography, and Gravure. It is helpful to consider the characteristics of these three methods in monochrome printing before going on to a consideration of their application to colour reproduction.

21.2 Letterpress

Letterpress, as its name implies, is the method generally adopted for the reproduction of *letters*, and most (though not all) newspapers, books, and many magazines are Letterpress productions. The method originated in the hand engraving of wooden blocks so that the areas to be printed light were gouged out of the wood, while those to be printed dark were left untouched. Running an inky roller over such a surface resulted in the untouched parts being inked and the gouged out parts not being inked, as shown in Fig. 21.1(a). By pressing the paper into contact with a block inked in this way, the required pattern of ink was obtained on the paper. Movable type, whereby letters are carved on small blocks which can be arranged and rearranged to form different matter, was invented independently in China in the tenth century and by Gutenberg in Germany in the middle of the fifteenth century, and the Letterpress system, in its literal sense, was born.

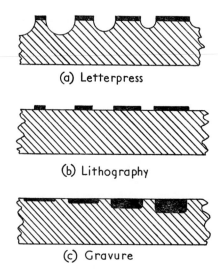

(a) Letterpress

(b) Lithography

(c) Gravure

Fig. 21.1. Diagrammatic representation of the difference between Letterpress, Lithographic, and Gravure methods of printing. Cross-sections of the three types of printing surface after inking are shown.

It is clear that the Letterpress system tends to be an all or nothing affair. An area is either inked or not inked, and hence either black (assuming black ink is being used) or white. Thus only two colours can be produced by this system, that of the ink and that of the support. For the printing of letters this is ideal, and results in the well-known clarity of Letterpress reading matter. But for printing black-and-white photographs it is necessary to reproduce not only black and white, but also all the tones of grey in between. The way in which this has been done in the Letterpress system is very ingenious. The same physiological property of the eye is utilized as in the mosaic processes of additive colour photography. As we have seen, in these processes, the fairly sharply defined limit below which the eye ceases to resolve fine detail results in the individual red, green, and blue areas blending into all the intermediate colours.

The Letterpress method of reproducing greys is to print them as mosaics of black and white dots which the eye blends into greys. The formation of the dots is achieved by photographing the original through a *screen* which is placed a short distance in front of the photographic negative plate or film being used. The screen consists of a glass plate on which have been ruled very fine opaque lines in two directions at right angles to one another, leaving square interstices as shown in the upper part of Fig. 21.2. These interstices can be thought of as being rough pinhole 'lenses' forming out-of-focus 'images' of the camera lens on the plate. An extremely high contrast film is used so that after development the image consists almost entirely of black dots and white spaces. Moreover, the pinhole images of the camera lens in areas light in the original, because they are bright, will produce larger areas of developable latent image than those in areas dark in the original. Thus, in areas light in the original, large black dots will be produced after development, but in areas dark in the original only small black dots will be formed. Hence the appearance of a negative, when highly magnified, is similar to that shown in Fig. 21.3. In areas very light in the original the black dots are so large as to overlap and leave the 'white-dot' pattern shown. This type of image structure is often referred to as *half-tone*, and the screens from which they are made as *half-tone screens*.

By various photomechanical processes which need not concern us here, screen-negatives are printed on to copper or zinc plates which are then treated so that the black areas of the dot-negatives result in copper being etched away, while the white areas leave it untouched. It is clear that upon inking such a copper plate a positive dot image (as shown in Fig. 21.4) is obtained which can be printed on to paper. If the dot pattern is sufficiently fine it will blend to form grey tones similar to those in the original photograph. From the point of view of successful blending into grey the finer the dot pattern the better. The fineness of the dot pattern is set by that of the screen and can be made as fine as 300 lines per inch. Unfortunately, however, dot patterns of this fineness can only be printed successfully on very smooth high quality paper, and 133 lines per inch are generally used for magazine work, while for newspaper work 65 or 85 lines per inch can be used, which is why the dot structure of newspaper photographs is somewhat obtrusive. Incidentally, the abrupt limit of resolution of the eye is well illustrated by moving gradually further and further away from a newspaper photograph: its dot structure will be found to vanish quite suddenly. If at this distance the photograph is rotated through 45 degrees it will be found that the dot structure at once reappears. The physiological reason for this is not fully known, but, because of the effect, the screen patterns in black-and-white dot reproductions are always arranged at 45° (as shown in Fig. 21.2) and not vertically-and-horizontally.

It will be realized that the method of forming grey tones by the Letterpress method is sufficiently complicated to induce distortions in the tone reproduction. Thus some greys will be too dark and others too light. Much of the skill in successful Letterpress reproduction lies in the careful choice of lens aperture, distance from screen to photographic material, and development, in making the screen-negative. In spite of every care at these and subsequent stages, however, hand-correction of important areas of the picture is often required. Plates 1 to 7, and Figs. 21.2 and 21.6, are all Letterpress reproductions. Plates 8 to 13 are Lithographic reproductions.

21.3 Lithography

In Lithography greys are again reproduced by means of physiological blending of dots of different sizes, but the printing plate is not etched as in the Letterpress system but is quite flat as shown in Fig. 21.1(b). The early stages of the process are the same as in the Letterpress method in that a screen-negative is produced. The screen-negative is then printed on to a plate in such a way that a greasy ink can be deposited in the interstices but not in the dot areas. (Alternatively, a screen-positive can be used with a plate such that a greasy ink is deposited only in the dot areas.) The method of keeping the greasy ink out of the interstices is generally to make them highly water-accepting and then to wet the surface immediately prior to inking. The printing cycle then consists of wetting, inking, printing, wetting, inking, printing, etc. It is customary to print from cylinders rather than flat plates, and the ink image is often transferred from the cylinder to a rubber-covered roller, which then prints it on to the paper, a technique known as *offset printing*.

21.4 Gravure

In contrast to the Letterpress and Lithographic methods, the Gravure method (in its conventional form) does not produce greys by means of varying the relative sizes of black dots and white interstices. The printing plate has hollows or *cells* filled with ink, while raised portions are left clear (Fig. 21.1(c)). Light or dark tones are then printed by transferring small or large quantities of ink from shallow or deep hollows respectively. At first sight, in such a system, there would seem to be no need for any screen pattern, there being no apparent need to break the image into dots. But it is essential in the Gravure method that the unetched areas be absolutely free from ink, and this can only be achieved by wiping them clean after the plate as a whole has been inked. But in the wiping operation, large etched areas would tend to be wiped clear of ink also. To avoid this a very fine screen, usually 175 lines per inch, and with interstices three times as wide as the lines, is generally used in making the plate in order to provide a fine honey-comb of unetched walls in the large etched areas. The purpose of this screen is thus quite different from those used in the Letter-

Fig. 21.2. Above: Small portion of a half-tone screen, highly magnified. *Below:* Distribution of light (highly magnified) obtained when a half-tone screen is placed a short distance away from the plate. This is also the appearance of a *contact screen*.

press and Lithographic methods where the object is to form dots of different sizes; in conventional Gravure the 'dots' are all the same size, and remain square at all densities. In colour Gravure there are practical difficulties in controlling the colour in the shallow hollows, and processes have been devised to try to overcome this by making the shallower hollows smaller, somewhat like the letterpress half-tone, but of course with the dots sunk into the surface instead of raised above it.

The Gravure method is well suited to paper of only medium smoothness, because there is no need for the 175-line screen to be sharply reproduced, since it has no image-producing function. For this, and other reasons, Gravure is widely used for printing fairly inexpensive weekly magazines, where good quality paper is precluded by its expense, but where the more costly Gravure etched printing cylinders are justified by the large circulation of the periodical. The use of gravure for newspaper work is precluded by the difficulty of making changes to the printing cylinders once they have been etched.

The different nature of the images produced by the Letterpress, Lithographic, and Gravure methods of printing is shown in Plate 11 (page 465).

21.5 Superimposed dye images

We have seen that in colour photography, the subtractive methods employ three superimposed dye images, of cyan, magenta, and yellow colours. In Section 10.5 we made reference to the microscopic nature of these images, and it is sometimes thought that they have no granular structure, but simply exhibit image-wise variations in dye-concentration over the entire area of the picture. It must be remembered, however, that black-and-white photographic images (from which all colour photographs are ultimately derived) are made up of minute crystals, or *grains* as they are usually called, of finely divided metallic silver. In some transfer processes, such as Technicolor and the Kodak Dye Transfer process, the dye diffuses somewhat and the granular structure of the original silver image (from which the dye image has been obtained) may be almost entirely blurred over. In such cases the process is a truly subtractive one. From the point of view of picture sharpness, however, such dye diffusion is undesirable, and most subtractive processes result in the three dyes being deposited in granular form, either closely following the structure of the parent silver image, as in the case of Kodachrome, for instance, or modifying it slightly by means of a superimposed coupler structure as in the case of Ektachrome and Kodacolor, for instance, as shown in Figs. 10.4, 10.5, and 10.6.

These discontinuities in photographic dye images are generally of so fine a pattern that to the naked eye they are quite invisible, and indeed for this reason some subtractive processes have carried a reputation of being 'grain-less'. A powerful microscope, however, soon reveals that the image has a granular structure, as is also the case with the random mosaic additive processes, which the subtractive processes have so effectively superseded.

439

Fig. 21.3. Half-tone negative, highly magnified.

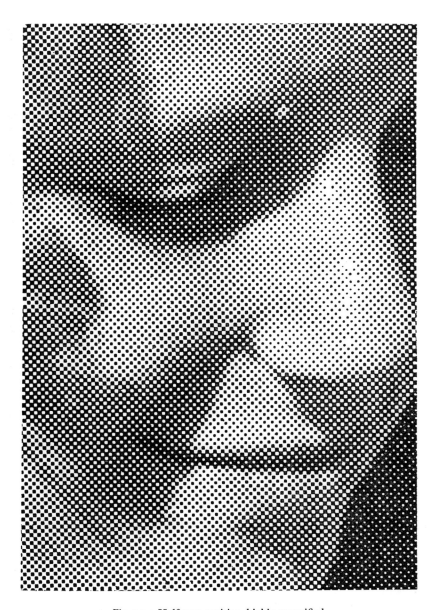

Fig. 21.4. Half-tone positive, highly magnified.

21.6 Superimposed dot images

It has been seen in the previous section that in practice subtractive photographic processes really consist mainly of superimposed granular dye patterns. Their success encourages the hope that, in printing, successful colour reproduction can be achieved simply by printing three dot images one on top of the other.[1] The three dot images would have to be made from red, green, and blue

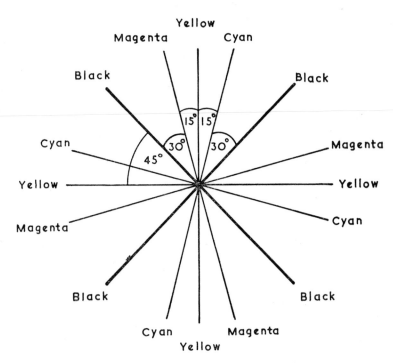

Fig. 21.5. The angles at which the screens are usually set in four-colour printing.

separation negatives and printed in cyan, magenta, and yellow inks. This, of course, is widely practised, although, as mentioned in Chapter 4, the colours are often termed blue, red, and yellow in the printing trade. Very frequently a black dot image is also printed, see Plate 9 (page 250), partly to make up for certain deficiencies in the colours of some printing inks which make a good black difficult to attain and partly for various other reasons. In order to avoid

[1] In fact, trichromatic colour reproductions depending on this principle were made by Jakob Christoffel LeBlon as long ago as the early 1700's.

undesirable patterns (*moiré patterns*) caused by superimposed parallel lines of dots of different colours, the dot images are always printed with the lines of dots running at different angles, and the usual arrangement is for the black ink to be printed at the least obtrusive angle, that is 45°, for the cyan to be printed at 30° to one side of the black, the magenta at 30° to the other side, and the yellow, being the colour for which the dots are least noticeable, midway between the cyan and magenta, that is vertically and horizontally, as shown in Fig. 21.5.

In conventional Gravure work the image is not broken into dots of different sizes, and since the original silver grain structure is generally far too fine to be obtrusive in the final reproduction, the process tends to be truly subtractive rather like the photographic transfer systems. In Letterpress and Lithographic colour reproduction, however, the result is a cross between a subtractive and a mosaic process. For, consider three dot images, cyan, magenta, and yellow, superimposed on one another.

A mosaic of eight different colours will be formed: white, where three gaps in the dot images coincide, black, where three dots are superimposed, cyan, magenta, and yellow, where the ink dots are seen against gaps in the other images, and red, where magenta and yellow dots are superimposed, green, where cyan and yellow dots are superimposed, and blue, where magenta and cyan dots are superimposed, as shown in Plate 11 (page 465).

In practice, the distortions in tone rendering and the deficiencies of the inks used in all three processes generally wreak such havoc with the colour reproduction that a great deal of etching (*retouching*) of individual colours is usually desirable. This is very costly and the remainder of this chapter, and the next, describe methods of correcting such errors automatically.

21.7 Exact colour reproduction with dot images

In 1937 Neugebauer (Neugebauer, 1937) treated the problem of eight-colour mosaics quite generally in the following way. Let c be the area of paper covered by the cyan dots, m the area covered by the magenta dots, and y the area covered by the yellow dots, per unit area of paper. It follows that the area not covered by cyan is $1 - c$, that not covered by magenta $1 - m$, and that not covered by yellow $1 - y$, per unit area of paper. The probability of any particular point on the paper being covered by a cyan dot is obviously equal to c, by a magenta dot, equal to m, and by a yellow dot, equal to y. Hence the probability of any particular point on the paper being covered by all three colours, is equal to the product cmy; hence the area covered by all three inks, which of course is the area that is black, is equal to cmy per unit area of paper. Similarly the probability of any particular point on the paper being not covered by any of the three colours is equal to $(1-c)(1-m)(1-y)$; hence the area that is white is equal to $(1-c)(1-m)(1-y)$ per unit area of paper. By similar reasoning the areas of each of the eight colours can be evaluated, and the results are as follows, the symbols in brackets preceding each colour name representing the C.I.E. tristimulus values for that colour:

$$(X_1, Y_1, Z_1)\text{White} \quad (1-c)(1-m)(1-y) = f_1$$
$$(X_2, Y_2, Z_2)\text{Cyan} \quad c(1-m)(1-y) = f_2$$
$$(X_3, Y_3, Z_3)\text{Magenta} \quad m(1-c)(1-y) = f_3$$
$$(X_4, Y_4, Z_4)\text{Yellow} \quad y(1-c)(1-m) = f_4$$
$$(X_5, Y_5, Z_5)\text{Red} \quad my(1-c) = f_5$$
$$(X_6, Y_6, Z_6)\text{Green} \quad cy(1-m) = f_6$$
$$(X_7, Y_7, Z_7)\text{Blue} \quad cm(1-y) = f_7$$
$$(X_8, Y_8, Z_8)\text{Black} \quad cmy = f_8$$

Now suppose we have some patch, P, of colour in our original, the tristimulus values of which were X_P, Y_P, Z_P. It is clear that exact colour reproduction would result if the reproduction had the same tristimulus values X_P, Y_P, Z_P. The conditions for this to be so can be set out quite simply as follows:

$$f_1 X_1 + f_2 X_2 + f_3 X_3 + f_4 X_4 + f_5 X_5 + f_6 X_6 + f_7 X_7 + f_8 X_8 = X_P$$
$$f_1 Y_1 + f_2 Y_2 + f_3 Y_3 + f_4 Y_4 + f_5 Y_5 + f_6 Y_6 + f_7 Y_7 + f_8 Y_8 = Y_P$$
$$f_1 Z_1 + f_2 Z_2 + f_3 Z_3 + f_4 Z_4 + f_5 Z_5 + f_6 Z_6 + f_7 Z_7 + f_8 Z_8 = Z_P$$

That these must be the conditions follows from the additivity of colour equations (see Section 6.4). For in our patch of superimposed dots we have f_1 units of white, and f_2 units of cyan, which add together thus:

$$f_1 \text{ units of white} \equiv f_1 X_1(X) + f_1 Y_1(Y) + f_1 Z_1(Z)$$
$$f_2 \text{ units of cyan} \equiv f_2 X_2(X) + f_2 Y_2(Y) + f_2 Z_2(Z)$$

Hence f_1 units of white additively mixed with f_2 units of cyan $\equiv$

$$(f_1 X_1 + f_2 X_2)(X) + (f_1 Y_1 + f_2 Y_2)(Y) + (f_1 Z_1 + f_2 Z_2)(Z)$$

It is clear, therefore, that the additive mixture of all eight colours will have as coefficients of (X), (Y), and (Z) the expressions given in the left hand sides of the set of three equations shown above. If, then, these coefficients are identical to X_P, Y_P, and Z_P, exact colour reproduction will have resulted.

But the three equations given above are really equations for c, m, and y, and if X_1, Y_1, Z_1; X_2, Y_2, Z_2, etc. and X_P, Y_P, Z_P are known they can be solved for c, m, and y. These values of c, m, and y are, then, the fractional areas of inks which must be printed in order to produce the colour of the original in the patch P. If therefore the original colours could all be analysed in terms of their tristimulus values X, Y, and Z, all the corresponding values of c, m, and y calculated, and the printing plates etched so that these amounts of ink were printed at each point of the reproduction, exact colour reproduction would be achieved. In spite of the obvious complexity of such a procedure, Hardy and Wurzburg (Hardy and Wurzburg, 1948) have invented a method of achieving this, which is described in Section 22.2.

Of course, some colours in the original may be too saturated to be matched by any mixture of the three inks being used, and in this case one or more of the values of c, m, and y will become negative. As it is impossible to print a negative amount of ink on the paper the best that can be done is to print no ink at all at these points, and this generally results in the correct hue at a lower saturation. Hardy and Wurzburg have also considered the case of four-colour printing, involving a black ink as well as the cyan, magenta, and yellow inks (Hardy and Wurzburg, 1948).

21.8 Colour correction by masking

The Hardy and Wurzburg method is of great interest for both its elegance and its theoretical possibilities, but its practical realization is obviously complicated. Simpler methods of obtaining some improvement in colour reproduction have therefore been sought, and, apart from tedious hand retouching of individual areas on the printing plates, the use of masking either manually or in scanners has been the method most widely used. For instance, Pollak, by making a few assumptions concerning the nature of the inks, has solved the Neugebauer equations and derived a system of masking based upon them (Pollak, 1955). So far, however, the methods most widely used have been worked out empirically, and some of them were described in Section 13.9. Further examples will be given in Sections 21.12, 21.13, and 21.14.

Much thought has been given to the validity of applying the continuous tone type of masking theory, dealt with in Chapter 13, to half-tone images. The topics discussed have included the additivity of half-tone densities, and the necessity of using non-linear mask characteristics (Pollak, 1955 and 1956; Yule and Clapper, 1955; Preucil, 1953; Pollak and Hepher, 1956).

21.9 Contact screens

An important device is the magenta contact screen (Yule, Johnston, and Murray, 1942) for the Letterpress and Lithographic methods. In normal practice in the Gravure method the screen is printed in contact with the photographic material, but its only function is to prevent large inked areas being wiped clean. In the Letterpress and Lithographic methods the screen is deliberately printed out of contact with the photographic material so that dots of different sizes can be produced.

At a given lens aperture, a screen at a given distance from the photographic material results in a certain distribution of light. If a film exposed under these conditions were developed in an ordinary developer, instead of in a very high contrast developer, and a positive made from the negative thus obtained, an approximate record of the original light distribution would result. If now this 'photographic screen' were placed in contact with a suitable film in a copying camera, the ordinary screen could be removed, for the photographic screen gives approximately the same light distribution on the film. The appearance of such a screen is as shown in the lower half of Fig. 21.2.

At first sight there may not seem to be any advantages in such a system,

445

but there are in fact several. First, the production of the conventional type of screen, by the traditional ruling methods, is a very costly process. A very large number of photographic screens can be produced from one ordinary screen used as a master screen.

Secondly, the fact that the photographic screen is used *in contact* with the photographic plate means that fine detail is reproduced more clearly. Thus with the conventional type of screen, which has to be used *out of contact*, a long fine line, for instance, can only be reproduced as a line of dots, all of which are approximately circular or square in shape. With a contact screen, however, a fine line will be reproduced as a line of dots, each of which is elongated in the direction of the line. The reproduction of the line will therefore be finer and less broken up than with the conventional screen method (Hepher, 1953). This is illustrated in Fig. 21.6.

Thirdly, by making the photographic screen a magenta dye-image instead of a black image a very simple method of controlling contrast is obtained. If such a magenta screen is viewed through a red filter, since magenta dyes absorb little or no red light, the screen pattern becomes virtually invisible. If it is viewed through a blue filter, the blue absorption which all magenta dyes exhibit enables the screen pattern to be seen at a low contrast. If it is viewed through a green filter, the magenta dye being a heavy absorber of green light, the screen pattern is seen at its maximum contrast. If, therefore, the magenta screen is used in conjunction with an orthochromatic film, which is sensitive to both blue and green light, the contrast can be varied by altering the colour of the exposing light from blue to green; and intermediate contrasts can be obtained by using blue-green filters or by giving part of the exposure through a blue filter and part through a green filter. (In practice, since orthochromatic films are insensitive to red light a magenta filter can be used instead of a blue filter, and a yellow instead of a green; magenta and yellow filters are in fact preferable because they are generally more efficient transmitters of the required light.)

Paradoxical as it seems, when this system is adopted it is the exposure to green light which gives low contrast, and that to blue light which gives high contrast. The reason for this can best be understood by referring to Fig. 21.7. In this figure the density of the screen along part of a line of dots is plotted for green light in the upper diagram and for blue light in the lower diagram. Two exposure levels E_1 and E_2 are indicated on both diagrams, together with the dot-sizes d_1 and d_2 which result from them in both cases. It is clear from the figure that it is the lower contrast screen (obtained by exposure to blue light) which results in the larger difference d_2-d_1 between the dot-sizes produced by the given exposure difference E_1-E_2. Hence the blue light exposure results in a higher contrast image than the green light exposure. This very simple means of controlling the contrast of half-tone images is obviously a very valuable tool in the hands of the colour printer, and properly handled can result in considerable improvement in quality.

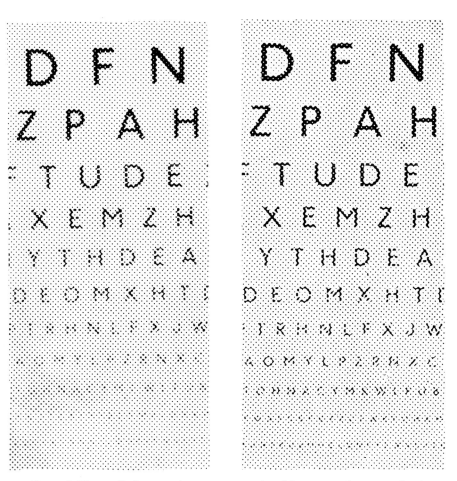

Fig. 21.6. The small charts at the top are reproduced by means of a conventional ruled screen (on the left), and a contact screen (on the right). The lower charts are photo-micrographs of parts of the upper charts and show that the contact screen reproduces more fine detail because fine lines are less broken into dots.

447

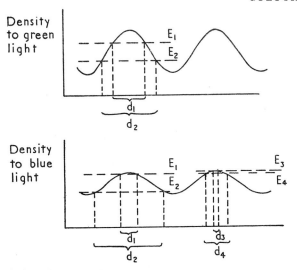

Fig. 21.7. Variation of contrast using magenta contact screen. *Above:* exposure to green light giving a high contrast screen and a low contrast image. *Below:* exposure to blue light giving a low contrast screen and a high contrast image.

In spite of the advantage of easy control of contrast offered by magenta contact screens, grey contact screens are widely used, the contrast then being controlled by 'flashing' (giving part of the exposure without the original, thus effectively reducing the contrast range of originals). When it is required to carry out colour separation by *direct screening* (see Section 21.14) of coloured originals magenta screens cannot be used, and grey screens are used with high contrast panchromatic films.

The fourth advantage of the contact screen is that, when it is used, highlights tend to be reproduced at a somewhat higher contrast and therefore gain in clarity and brilliance. This is because in the portions of the screen which are responsible for highlight rendering the modulating density pattern passes through a maximum and is therefore of very low contrast, resulting as before in contrasty reproduction. This is illustrated in Fig. 21.7 by the two highlight exposure levels E_3 and E_4, which although very similar result in a large difference $d_4 - d_3$ in dot-size.

The fifth advantage of contact screens is that, when no change in image-size is required, they can be used in vacuum contact-printing frames.

21.10 Autoscreen film

Another interesting device is the autoscreen film (Yule and Maurer, 1954). In this material the photographic sensitivity is not constant over its area, but varies in the same pattern as that of the light distribution from a half-tone screen. It is therefore possible, with this material, to use it in the camera or in a contact frame, without either a conventional or a contact screen, and to obtain a half-tone instead of a continuous-tone image. The Kodalith Autoscreen Ortho Film, for example, thus enables half-tone images to be obtained without the need for the skill necessary for the successful manipulation of half-tone screens (Maurer, 1956).

21.11 Practical systems for preparing colour separations

The use of standardized procedures to produce colour printing surfaces which require little or no hand-correction of local areas has for long been a goal in photomechanical processes. Amongst earlier attempts to solve the problems involved mention may be made of the Gresham-McCorquodale system (Gresham, 1952 and 1956) and the Kodak Short-Run system (Clark, 1952; Staehle, 1952; Yule, 1953). Three systems of more recent origin will now be described; they all assume that the 'original' to be reproduced is a reversal colour transparency, since the majority of photomechanical colour reproductions are in fact made from colour transparencies; similar methods can be used with reflection originals.

The use of scanners as an aid to preparing colour printing surfaces will be described in Chapter 22.

21.12 A four-mask system

In this system (Kodak, 1961) four masks are made: three of them are used to produce corrected separation negatives from which the cyan, magenta, and yellow printing surfaces are made; the fourth mask is used in making the negative from which the black printing surface is made. The functions of the masks are as described in Section 13.9 and Fig. 13.8. The procedure is as follows.

The transparency to be reproduced is placed in contact with a sheet of unexposed, low-contrast black-and-white masking film and exposed through an orange filter, such as Wratten 85B (together with a neutral density filter of density about 0.5 to make this exposure of similar length to the other mask-making exposures). The colour transparency is placed with its *base-side* (not *image-side*) in contact with the emulsion-side of the mask-film so as to introduce a small degree of unsharpness into the mask (this eases registration problems and increases the apparent sharpness of the final reproduction; see Section 13.2). After exposure, this mask material is removed for subsequent processing, and the second mask is exposed. The second mask is made using the same techniques and type of film as for the first mask, but with a magenta filter, such as Wratten 33; the third and fourth masks are made similarly using, respectively, a green filter, such as Wratten 58, and a narrow-cut yellow filter, such as two thicknesses of Wratten 90. The four masks are then processed together (to ensure uniform treatment).

The separation negatives and the 'black-printer' negative are then made as follows. The transparency is bound up in register with the mask made through the orange filter and printed by contact or by enlargement on to a sheet of unexposed black-and-white negative film of contrast suitable for making the separations. The exposure is made with red light, using an orange-red filter, such as Wratten 25. The various films are arranged so that the light passes through in the following sequence: mask-base, mask, transparency-base, transparency (then the lens if enlargement is being used) negative-emulsion, negative-base; this ensures that the mask is slightly unsharp but that the transparency prints (or enlarges) sharply on to the separation emulsion. After exposure, the sheet of separation film is removed for subsequent processing, and the mask made through the orange filter replaced by the one made through the magenta filter. Using the same techniques and type of film, the green separation is then exposed through a green filter, such as Wratten 58. The mask made through the magenta filter is then replaced by that made through the green filter, and the blue separation exposed through a blue filter, such as Wratten 47B. Finally the green-filter mask is replaced by the yellow-filter mask, and the black-printer separation exposed to white light (a pale green filter, such as a Kodak Colour Correcting filter CC50G, is sometimes used for this exposure). The four exposed negatives are then processed: it is usually necessary to develop them for slightly different times in order to obtain those contrasts which will result in a correctly matched grey scale in the final reproduction.

The corrected continuous-tone negatives obtained are then 'screened' in order to obtain half-tone positives or negatives from them, and the printing surfaces are then produced by conventional techniques.

21.13 A multi-layer mask system

Considerable simplification of the system just described is possible if masking is carried out using a special multi-layer colour film, such as Kodak *Tri-Mask* film (Kodak, 1964). As discussed in Section 13.10 and Fig. 13.10 this film produces low contrast dye-images of such colours and contrasts, and in such relation to the colour of the exposing light, that the functions of the masks made through the orange, magenta, and green filters, as described in the previous section, are all performed by the one film. Thus the function of the orange-filter mask is performed by a red-sensitive layer forming a very low contrast cyan image and a green-sensitive layer forming another very low contrast cyan image; the function of the magenta-filter mask is performed by a red-sensitive layer forming a low-contrast magenta image, and a blue-sensitive layer forming an extremely low contrast magenta image; and the function of the green-filter mask is performed by a green-sensitive layer forming a low-contrast yellow image. The Tri-Mask film, therefore, not only achieves the same functions as the masks made through the orange, magenta, and green filters, but actually provides more elaborate masking in that the correction is based on five mask images instead of on only three.

The procedure when using Tri-Mask film is as follows. The transparency to be reproduced is placed in contact with a sheet of unexposed Tri-Mask film and exposed with white light; as before, the transparency is placed with its base-side in contact with the Tri-Mask film so as to make the mask slightly unsharp. The Tri-Mask film is processed and then re-registered with the transparency. Separation negatives are then made by printing (by contact or by enlargement) the masked transparency on to black-and-white negative film of suitable contrast using red, green, and blue filters, such as Wratten 25 (plus a neutral filter of density 1.0 for exposure equalization) for the red, Wratten 58 (plus a neutral filter of density 0.5) for the green, and Wratten 47B for the blue; the black separation is exposed by giving a fourth piece of film a suitable composite exposure through each of the three filters successively. As before the separations are then developed for different times to obtain the desired contrasts, for subsequent screening.

The advantages of the Tri-Mask system over the four-mask system are as follows. First, a more elaborate degree of colour correction is provided; secondly, only one exposure is necessary to produce all the masks; thirdly, registration problems are reduced because only one mask requires registering with the transparency; fourthly, all four separations are made from the same transparency-mask combination, thus eliminating tiresome manipulations between the exposure of each separation; fifthly, because of the smaller number of separate films involved colour balance and tone reproduction are more easily controlled. The use of Tri-Mask film is illustrated in Plate 9 (page 250).

21.14 A direct screening system

Further simplifications to the process of obtaining corrected printing surfaces result if the corrected separation negatives are already 'screened', so that a separate screening step does not have to be introduced subsequently. A major reason why the introduction of this apparently obvious simplification was delayed was that even with white light the screen exposure tended to be quite lengthy, so that screen-exposures made from masked transparencies using red, green, and blue exposures were very inconveniently long; this difficulty is aggravated by the fact that a size-change is nearly always required between the transparency and the screened negatives so that the exposure has to be made in an enlarger and not by contact. However, the high contrast black-and-white negative films necessary for producing satisfactory half-tone images became available with higher photographic speed, and condenser-type enlargers fitted with high-intensity pulsed-xenon lamps provided more light. Hence the exposure of screened negatives direct from masked colour transparencies, *direct-screening*, became feasible (Clapper, 1964). The availability of multi-layer colour masking films, such as Tri-Mask film, also facilitated direct-screening, by easing registration problems in the enlarger, and by providing non-scattering masks whose contrasts, unlike those of silver masks, are not dependent on the degree of specularity of the light in the enlarger.

The sequence of operations in one direct-screening system (Clapper, 1964) is as follows. First, a mask is exposed (with slight unsharpness) on Tri-Mask film by contact and, after processing, the mask is bound up in register with the colour transparency. The masked transparency is then placed in a suitable enlarger and a grey contact-screen placed upon a suitable high-contrast panchromatic black-and-white film on the enlarger easel (in order to obtain good contact between the contact-screen and the film being exposed, a vacuum printing frame is generally used). Exposures are then made through red, green, and blue filters on to three separate sheets of film; typical filters are Wratten 23A for the red, Wratten 58 for the green, and Wratten 47B for the blue. Contrast control is carried out by using an additional uniform exposure (*flashing*) made through the contact screen (in the case of the red separation a small additional exposure is also made from the transparency without the contact screen in position; this *no-screen* exposure increases the contrast of the red screened-negative and this is necessary to obtain a balanced grey scale in the final result (Pollak, 1955a)). The black-printer separation is made using a single exposure with a Wratten 85B filter, the exposure level being such that in the final reproduction black ink is only printed at reflection densities above about 0.8.

REFERENCES

Clapper, F. R., *J. Phot. Sci.*, **12,** 28 (1964).
Clark, W., *Penrose Annual*, **46,** 125 (1952).
Gresham, D. C., *Phot. J.*, **92B,** 91 (1952).
Gresham, D. C., *Penrose Annual*, **46,** 77 (1952) and **50,** 102 (1956).
Hardy, A. C., and Wurzburg, F. L., *J. Opt. Soc. Amer.*, **38,** 300 (1948).
Hepher, M., *Penrose Annual*, **47,** 116 (1953).
Kodak Graphic Arts Leaflet GA9, Kodak Ltd., London (1961).
Kodak Graphic Arts Leaflet GA5, Kodak Ltd., London (1964).
Maurer, R. E., *Penrose Annual*, **50,** 97 (1956).
Neugebauer, H. E. J., *Z. tech. Phys.*, **36,** 22 (1937).
Pollak, F., *J. Phot. Sci.*, **3,** 112 (1955a).
Pollak, F., *J. Phot. Sci.*, **3,** 180 (1955b).
Pollak, F., *J. Phot. Sci.*, **4,** 65 (1956).
Pollak, F., and Hepher, M., *Penrose Annual*, **50,** 106 (1956).
Preucil, F., *Tech. Assoc. Graphic Arts*, **5,** 102 (1953).
Staehle, H. C., *Tech. Assoc. Graphic Arts*, **4,** 143 (1952).
Yule, J. A. C., *Tech. Assoc. Graphic Arts*, **5,** 94 (1953).
Yule, J. A. C., and Clapper, F. R., *Tech. Assoc. Graphic Arts*, **7,** 1 (1955).
Yule, J. A. C., Johnston, F. B., and Murray, A., *J. Franklin Inst.*, **234,** 567 (1942).
Yule, J. A. C., and Maurer, R. E., *Penrose Annual*, **48,** 93 (1954).

GENERAL REFERENCES

Cartwright, H. M., *Ilford Graphic Arts Manual*, Ilford, London (Vol. 1, 1961; Vol. 2, 1966).
Gamble, C. W., *Modern Illustration Processes*, Pitman, London (1953).
Smith, W. J., Turner, E. L., and Hallam, C. D., *Photo Engraving in Relief*, Pitman, London (1932).
Yule, J. A. C., *Principles of Colour Reproduction*, Wiley, New York (1967).

CHAPTER 22

Colour Scanners

22.1 Introduction

THE facility with which electrical signals can be manipulated to correspond to a wide variety of algebraic equations has led to the use, in graphic arts processes, of a number of devices known as *scanners*; in these, either all or part of the picture information is converted point by point into electrical signals at some intermediate stage, and the picture then subsequently reconstituted in a more conventional form. During the electrical stage the equivalent of tone-correction and masking procedures are carried out, with almost limitless flexibility. In order to obtain the picture in the form of convenient electrical signals it is necessary, as in television, to convert the picture from a two-dimensional array, to a one-dimensional array, and this, as in television, is most conveniently done by scanning it in successive lines.

In graphic arts it is not necessary to scan pictures with the same rapidity as is required in television, but it is necessary to scan in such a way as to provide much better definition. Scanning times between a few minutes and an hour are therefore customary, and the number of lines in the scanned picture is usually either 250, 500, or 1000 per inch. The first two scanners to be constructed were those invented by Hardy and Wurzburg (Hardy and Wurzburg, 1948) and by Murray and Morse (Murray and Morse, 1941). The Hardy and Wurzburg scanner was developed initially by the Interchemical Corporation and subsequently by the Radio Corporation of America; the Murray and Morse scanner was developed in its early stages by the Eastman Kodak Company and subsequently by Time Incorporated and its subsidiary Printing Developments Incorporated (P.D.I.). These two scanners will now be described, after which various modified methods derived from them will be outlined.

22.2 The Hardy and Wurzburg scanners

As originally conceived, the Hardy and Wurzburg scanner resulted in the direct production of half-tone photographic plates, from which the printing surfaces were obtained. Later, however, the emphasis swung to the production of continuous-tone photographic plates from which the printing surfaces were obtained in the conventional way; but the photographic plates made full correction for all distortions of tone and colour introduced by the characteristics of the printing surfaces and of the inks so that no handwork or individual treatment of the printing plates was required.

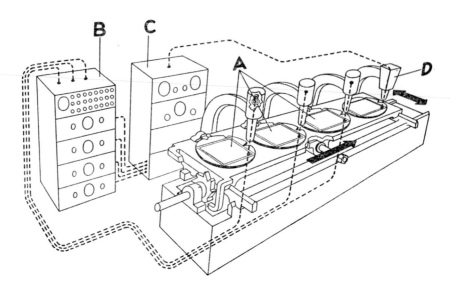

Fig. 22.1. The Interchemical version of the Hardy and Wurzburg method of producing colour-corrected dot-images or continuous-tone separations on a flat-bed mechanical type of scanner.

The Interchemical implementation of the Hardy and Wurzburg method is illustrated in Fig. 22.1. On a single carriage were mounted four separate photographic plates. One of these was an unexposed plate on which a fully corrected continuous-tone image was exposed; the other three plates were separation positives (or negatives), A, of the original scene which it was desired to reproduce. The carriage oscillated from side to side with an amplitude equal to the width of the separations and slowly progressed a distance equal to the length of the separations, thus enabling the whole area of the separations to be covered by an array of parallel lines.

Above the three separations were rigidly fixed three projectors which focussed sharp points of light on to them. The projectors and separations were so located, of course, that corresponding parts of the picture were illuminated on each of the three separations. If the three separations were obtained from the original scene using plates having effective spectral sensitivity curves equal to the colour-matching functions, $\bar{x}_\lambda$, $\bar{y}_\lambda$, $\bar{z}_\lambda$, the transmission of the separations at each point would be proportional to the tristimulus values X_P, Y_P, Z_P of the original colour at each point. Hence, by allowing the light transmitted by the separations to fall on three photo-cells, three signals were obtained, proportional to X_P, Y_P, and Z_P. The three signals were fed into an electric circuit network, B, in which were stored the tristimulus values X_1, Y_1, Z_1; X_2, Y_2, Z_2, etc., of the eight printing colours (produced by the eight different ways in which the dot images can overlap); the amounts of ink necessary to produce colours having the tristimulus values X_P, Y_P, Z_P, were continuously evaluated by electronic computing circuits, in terms of the corresponding values of c, m, and y in the Neugebauer equations described in Section 21.7.

The three images were exposed one at a time, and when it was required to expose the cyan image, for instance, the continuously evaluated value of c was fed into another electronic circuit network, C, which resulted in the exposing light being modulated in such a way as to produce the required image on the unexposed plate, above which the exposing light, D, was rigidly fixed.

The actual operations involved in making a colour reproduction by this means were as follows:

(1) The original scene was photographed on plates having effective spectral sensitivities equal to the $\bar{x}_\lambda$, $\bar{y}_\lambda$, $\bar{z}_\lambda$ curves (or any linear combination of them, since the electronic networks can solve the extra equations which result).

(2) The plates were developed, and from the three separation negatives thus obtained, three separation positives were usually made, an operation which had to be carried out without any distortion of the tones.

(3) The three separation positives were mounted in register on the scanning machine and the continuously evaluated value of c fed into the electronic network so that the required image was exposed.

(4) Similarly the image corresponding to m was exposed.

(5) Similarly the image corresponding to y was exposed.

(6) The three negatives were developed.

(7) Three half-tone printing surfaces were made.

(8) The three printing surfaces were inked and finally printed.

The conditions which have to be fulfilled, in order that exact colour reproduction is achieved with this system, are as follows:

(1) The three separation positives must at all points have transmissions proportional to the tristimulus values X_P, Y_P, Z_P, of the original (or to linear combinations of them). This is generally practicable to within the required accuracy.

(2) The final coloured dot mosaic must contain the eight colours in the required amounts. Owing to the non-linearities of the etching processes this is not easily achieved, but can be fairly well approximated to if special compensations are introduced in the electronic stages.

(3) Only the eight expected colours must be present in the final dot mosaic. Clapper and Yule (Clapper and Yule, 1953) have pointed out that inter-reflections of light, within the layers of ink and the paper fibres, introduce other colours which upset the simple eight-colour theory.

(4) The paper and inks used must be capable of reproducing all the tristimulus values for which the electronic networks call. Of course, some colours will be too saturated to be reproduced, but in addition there is the limitation common to all reflection print systems, as mentioned in Section 11.9, that the range of tones ordinarily visible is limited to about 55 to 1 in intensity, that is, a density range of about 1.75 (with some inks the density range is only just over 1.0).

In the Radio Corporation of America (R.C.A.) version of the Hardy and Wurzburg method, the separations and the plate being exposed were stationary, and the scanning was achieved by focussing on to them images of spots on cathode-ray tubes which were scanned in a suitable raster pattern (Rydz and Marquart, 1954).

Consideration was also given, in the various forms of the Hardy and Wurzburg method, to the need for producing four corrected separations for printing with a black ink, as well as with cyan, magenta, and yellow inks (Rydz and Marquart, 1955).

These scanners, although not now in commercial use, are important for their historical and theoretical interest. In spite of their limitations, as enumerated under the four headings given above, colour reproduction by means of their scanning method is capable of producing results of very high quality (Haynes, 1952; Ohler, 1955).

22.3 The P.D.I. scanner

The P.D.I. (Printing Developments Incorporated) scanner (known also at one time as the Time-Life Springdale scanner) is similar to the Hardy and Wurzburg scanner in that it breaks the image into a series of lines, converts it into electrical signals, carries out correction operations with them, and then exposes fully-corrected separations; but in almost all other respects

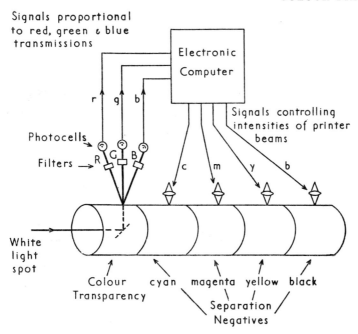

Signals proportional
to red, green & blue
transmissions

Electronic Computer

Signals controlling
intensities of printer
beams

r g b

Photocells

Filters

R G B

c m y b

White
light
spot

Colour   cyan   magenta yellow black
Transparency

Separation
Negatives

Fig. 22.2. Diagrammatic representation of the P.D.I. scanner. Fully corrected continuous-tone separations are made from colour transparencies wrapped round a rotating drum.

there are fundamental and important differences. Thus the P.D.I. scanner scans a colour transparency instead of three black-and-white separations, it scans cylindrically instead of on a flat-bed, its correcting functions depend on masking theory and not on the Neugebauer equations, and it exposes all three corrected-separations simultaneously (Bishop, 1951). The main features of the P.D.I. scanner are shown diagrammatically in Fig. 22.2.

A long cylinder, which has a transparent section at one end, is slowly rotated on its axis. The colour transparency to be reproduced is wrapped round the transparent section of the cylinder, while round the rest of the cylinder four unexposed sheets of film are wrapped. A small spot of light is focussed on to the colour transparency from the inside of the cylinder and, after passing through the transparency, the light is split into three beams and falls on to three separate photo-cells, after passing through red, green, and blue filters. As the cylinder rotates it also travels longitudinally by means of a fine screw-thread and by this means the small spot of light eventually scans the entire area of the colour transparency, at either 250, 500, or 1000 lines per inch, taking proportionately longer for the finer scans.

The three photo-cells give rise to three electrical signals which, for each point of the transparency, are proportional to its red, green, and blue transmittances. By means of an electronic computer these signals are transformed into four related signals which, by modulating the intensities of four spots of light focussed on the four unexposed films, result in fully-masked continuous-tone separation negatives being exposed. From these separation negatives, cyan, magenta, yellow, and black printing surfaces are made by orthodox methods.

One interesting feature of this scanner is that it can be arranged that, of the three coloured inks, only two are printed heavily at the same point in the reproduction, any required darkening of the colour being achieved mainly by means of the black image and not by means of the third colour, a technique known as *under-colour removal*. This means that parts of the picture which are neutral in colour are rendered mainly by the black printer, so that the correct rendering of a grey scale is greatly facilitated. Moreover, the variations in luminance in the reproduction are controlled in large measure by the black printer, and since impressions of sharpness and resolving power are dependent almost entirely on differences in luminance, rather than colour, some improvement in these respects arises from the fact that most of the luminance differences stem from a single-image, rather than from four superimposed images. It is interesting to note that, in colour television, luminance is transmitted as a separate high-definition signal for much the same reasons. (See Section 16.8.) Under-colour removal is illustrated in Plate 12 (page 466).

An electronic computing stage makes possible refinements in masking which in the ordinary way are often omitted. One refinement incorporated in the P.D.I. scanner is known as *undercolour correction* (Smith, 1954). In wet Letterpress printing, succeeding images are applied before the previous images are dry, and the wetness of the ink already printed prevents the next ink from transferring to the paper in the proper amount. The effect of this obviously depends on the order in which the inks are printed, but once this order has been established allowance can be made for it. This, the P.D.I. scanner can do.

It is clear that the P.D.I. scanner must work from a colour transparency, and, if the original consists of reflection copy, a colour transparency of it has to be made. The colour transparency can be of any size up to 11 in. × 14 in. The final reproduction can be the same size as the separation negatives, or it can be enlarged about 1½ times if 250-line scanning is used, about 3 times if 500-line scanning is used, or about 6 times if 1000-line scanning is used.

P.D.I. scanners also have facilities for scanning 2¼ in. square and 35 mm. transparencies and producing from them corrected separations, enlarged up to 14 times; for this work the transparencies are mounted in special frames off the drum, and oscillated mechanically in such a way that a spot of light scans their area in synchronization with the movement of the exposing light-spots on the films, but with all movements reduced by the chosen magnification factor.

P.D.I. scanners offer a service for providing separations from colour transparencies at special scanning studios in various parts of the world.

22.4 Other drum scanners

Working on principles similar to those used in the P.D.I. scanner is the Fairchild Scan-a-color (Sigler, 1964); but this scanner also has the facility of handling flexible reflection, as well as transmission, originals.

Less complicated, and smaller, drum scanners can be made if the separations are made one at a time instead of all four together; in this way it has been possible for scanners to be manufactured at a price low enough for it to be economic for many printing works to have their own equipment on the premises. Scanners of this type include the K.S. Paul Scanner, the Crosfield Diascan, and the Hell Chromagraph (Nash, 1965), all of which produce fully-corrected continuous-tone separations one at a time from originals consisting of transparencies wrapped round the drum.

A disadvantage of drum scanners is that they can only handle flexible originals, but most subjects can be copied on to colour transparency film so that the limitation is not too severe; moreover, such a copying step provides an opportunity of adjusting the sizes of the originals and this is useful when, as is common practice, a number of individual pictures are mounted together for common scanning so as to produce several scenes together on the same separations. The changes in tone and colour reproduction introduced by the copying step may have to be allowed for in the correcting circuits, however.

22.5 Other flat-bed mechanical scanners

Flat-bed scanners, such as the Hardy and Wurzburg machine described in Section 22.2, are not restricted to the use of flexible originals, and a number have been developed. The Hell Colorgraph (Allen, 1958a), produces continuous-tone separations, all four at the same time, from either separations, colour transparencies, or flat copy, according to the particular model. The models using separations as originals carry all seven plates (three originals and four being exposed) on the same reciprocating bed, which moves under three light-beams illuminating photo-cells, and four light-beams exposing the plates.

Some flat-bed mechanical scanners such as the Hell Vario-Klischograph (Hell, 1954 and 1957) are designed to produce Letterpress plates by arranging for the output signal from the correction circuits to cause a tool to engrave a printing plate physically with a dot structure (the size of the dots varying as a suitable function of the signal strength), instead of varying the intensity of a beam of light falling on to a photographic material; the dots can be formed by the tool at rates of up to about 1000 dots per second. In this way, these scanners can produce the actual letterpress printing plates directly. By using the tool to remove appropriate proportions of an opaque layer coated on a transparent support, half-tone images suitable for making conventional printing surfaces by screened photographic intermediates can be obtained, so that this type of scanner can be used for making litho plates, for instance, as well as letterpress plates. Changes in size between the original and the corrected printing surfaces are possible on the Hell Vario-Klischograph by means of a pantographic linkage, and either transparent or reflection originals can be used.

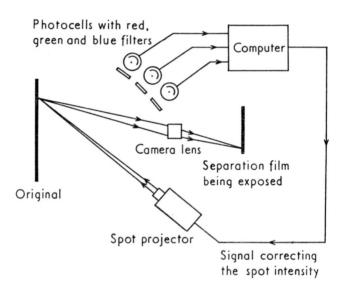

Fig. 22.3. The principle of the Hunter-Penrose Autoscan type of optical feed-back scanner.

22.6 Optical feed-back scanners

One of the disadvantages of scanners which convert the whole of the picture into electrical information is that to provide adequate definition a very fine line-structure has to be used, and this calls for very high precision in the scanning mechanism. Some scanners have therefore been developed in which separations are made optically, and only the corrections from the normal optical result are passed through the electronic stages. One such device is the Hunter-Penrose Autoscan (Kilminster, 1956), which is shown diagrammatically in Fig. 22.3. In this device the original, which is usually reflection material, and which need not be flexible, is scanned by a beam of light (from a spot projector), which is moved either by optical or mechanical (or a combination of both) means over the picture area. A camera lens forms an image on to a photographic plate in the usual way, but the definition is not limited by the size of the spot or by the number of lines in the scan so long as the lens can resolve any smaller detail. The corrections are applied by arranging that three photo-cells 'look' at the original through red, green, and blue filters while it is being scanned: the tubes therefore pick up signals proportional to the red, green, and blue reflectances of each spot of the original. Then,

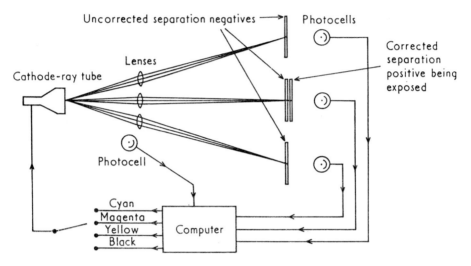

Fig. 22.4. The principle of the Crosfield Scanatron type of optical feed-back scanner.

with a red filter over the camera lens, the circuitry compares the red signal with what is required in order to give the correct exposure to the red separation at that point, taking into account the magnitudes of the green and blue signals at the same point: it then alters the luminance of the spot of light until it is such as to give the correct exposure, the electrical circuits thus applying a 'feed-back' control to the light. Of course the adjustment of the luminance of the spot of light has to be made so fast that the correction applies substantially to the spot scanned and not to some subsequent area, but with modern electronic techniques this can be done. In the same way, corrected green, blue, and black separations are made by using different constants in the circuits and putting green, blue or 'neutral' filters over the camera lens respectively.

Another scanner which achieves similar results, but by rather different means, is the Crosfield-Scanatron (Allen, 1958a and b), which is depicted in Fig. 22.4. In this equipment, the moving spot of light is obtained by having a suitable raster on a cathode-ray tube, and this is imaged by three lenses simultaneously on to three separation negatives mounted very carefully in optical registration relative to their images of the raster. These separation negatives are uncorrected, and are obtained by conventional means. Three photo-cells then measure the transmittances of the three separation negatives and provide a correction signal to the cathode-ray tube so that the light it emits, when transmitted by the centre separation negative, leads to the production of a corrected separation positive when it falls on a photographic material situated in contact with it. The corrected separation positives are made one at a time, the constants of the correction circuits being switched so as to be appropriate for production of the cyan positive (from the cyan negative), the magenta positive (from the magenta negative), the yellow positive from (the yellow negative), or the black positive (from whichever of the three negatives is most convenient to use for this purpose, or from a special fourth negative).

It is, of course, necessary in this equipment for the intensity of the spot on the cathode-ray tube to be modified fast enough to avoid any appreciable exposure of the separation positive material by the uncorrected intensity, but this can be accomplished. A fourth photo-cell picks up light direct from the cathode-ray tube, without it passing through any of the separation negatives, and this is used in the computer to supply a signal which can be subtracted from the other three signals, so that the calculations can be based on the uncorrected separation transmittances.

The Log-Etronic Color Separator is similar to the Scanatron but prints corrected separations one at a time through a colour transparency instead of through separations (Craig and Street, 1960).

22.7 Logic circuits in scanners

In photographic masking procedures, the degree of masking provided is usually represented by a single set of equations, which are regarded as applying to all colours. In practice, the actual effects usually vary somewhat from one colour to another, but such variations occur gradually throughout the distribution of colours. In scanners, however, it is possible to use logic types of circuit which will apply one set of masks to colours in one domain, and a different set to colours in a different domain, with a discontinuity in the masking equations at the boundary between the two domains. Thus yellowish colours might be treated in one way and bluish colours in a different way, with the transition taking place across the grey scale. The ability to incorporate such effects can provide useful degrees of freedom in adjusting the colour reproduction characteristics.

22.8 Unsharp masking in scanners

The enhancement of fine detail by the use of masks which are unsharp (see Section 13.2) is easily achieved in the optical feed-back type of scanners

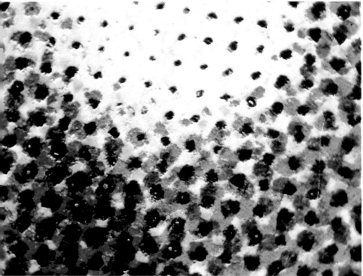

Plate 11
Photomicrographs
Photomicrographs of small areas of a Letterpress (*top*), a Lithographic (*centre*), and a Gravure (*bottom*), four-colour reproduction. (See Chapter 21)

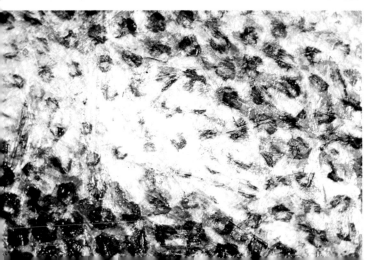

Plate 12
Under-colour removal

Each black image has been used with the combination of cyan, magenta, and yellow images shown on its left, to provide the final result shown on its right. Under-colour removal is absent in the top row, partially present in the middle row, and present to its maximum extent in the bottom row. The advantages of under-colour removal can include sharper rendering of fine detail, better consistency in the grey scale, and savings in ink costs. Maximum under-colour removal can increase registration problems, so that a partial level is usually preferred.

Reproduced from continuous-tone negatives exposed on a K.S. Paul scanner from an Ektachrome transparency.
(See Section 22.3)

Plate 13. Unsharp masking

Reproductions from continuous-tone negatives exposed on a K.S. Paul scanner: (*above*) without unsharp masking; (*below*) with unsharp masking.

From an Ektachrome transparency.
(See Sections 13.2 and 22.8)

simply by making the size of the scanning spot larger than that representative of the finest detail in the image obtained optically. But in the fully electronic scanners it is not quite so easy: if scanning is carried out with a large spot the whole image simply becomes unsharp. The effects of unsharp masking *along* each line can be simulated by suitably designing the frequency response of the electronic circuits; but the effect *across* the lines can only be simulated if the scanner has a memory from one line to the next at each point along each line. The only other way to simulate unsharp masking is to scan the image both with a small spot from which the image is derived, and with a large spot (about three times the diameter), from which the unsharp mask is derived (Hall and Yule, 1956; Nash, August, 1965). An example of unsharp masking obtained on a scanner is given in Plate 13 (page 468).

22.9 Differential masking in scanners

If the image is also scanned with a spot of very much larger size, something can be done to lighten areas of the pictures which are generally rather dark, and darken those which are rather light (Hall and Yule, 1964). This can be very useful when transparencies contain important parts of a scene illuminated at different levels, and corresponds to the individual shading, or *dodging*, of different parts of an image during photographic enlarging, a procedure which can be carried out by hand or electronically as in the Log-Etronic type of equipment (Cox, 1959).

22.10 Typical scanner signal sequences

The electrical input to the computer in a scanner generally consists of three d.c. currents proportional to the red, green, and blue transmittances (or reflectances) of the original material. It is usual, before scanning commences, to set into the computer the levels of the signals which correspond to the white level on each original, and sometimes the black level also. It is convenient to convert the signals from d.c. to a.c. either by chopping the light with a sector, or by electrical means, so that they can be amplified more easily. The signals may then be passed through a circuit which converts them from a linear to a logarithmic form so that they become proportional to density instead of to transmittance, and it may be necessary to compress the range of the signals so as to make them easier to handle in the circuits and more suitable for the final result which will be on a reflection support with its limited luminance range.

Masking is carried out by circuits, corresponding to three simultaneous equations, which add and subtract different proportions of the logarithmic signals; the circuits may also perform operations equivalent to two-stage masking and the use of non-linear masks (see Section 13.11); and logic circuits may be used to switch the computer from one mode to another as the colour being scanned varies. Partial or nearly complete under-colour removal and any necessary under-colour correction (see Section 22.3), and the computation of the signals needed for the black printer, may be carried out next; then each of the four signals may be passed through 'curve-shaping' circuits which ensure that the final logarithmic signals have the required gradation of tones: it is sometimes necessary to reproduce both highlights and shadows at fairly high contrast, in order to retain good visibility of detail in these areas, and middle-tones then have to be reduced in contrast; scanner circuits can usually produce the high-low-high contrast characteristic necessary to achieve this. Finally the signal may go through an anti-logging circuit prior to being used to control the intensity of the exposing light (or lights) or the depth of a cutting tool.

REFERENCES

Allen, G. S., *J. Phot. Sci.*, **6**, 125 (1958a).
Allen, G. S., *Penrose Annual*, **52**, 123 (1958b).
Bishop, N., *Penrose Annual*, **45**, 92 (1951).
Clapper, F. R., and Yule, J. A. C., *J. Opt. Soc. Amer.*, **43**, 600 (1953).
Cox, H. W., *Penrose Annual*, **53**, 88 (1959).
Craig, D. R., and Street, J. N., *Tech. Assoc. Graphic Arts*, **12**, 175 (1960).
Hall, V. C., and Yule, J. A. C., *U.S. Patent* 2,744,950 (1956).
Hall, V. C., and Yule, J. A. C., *U.S. Patent* 3,153,698 (1964).
Hardy, A. C., and Wurzburg, F. L., *J. Opt. Soc. Amer.*, **38**, 300 (1948).
Haynes, H. E., *Penrose Annual*, **46**, 83 (1952).
Hell, R., *Penrose Annual*, **48**, 101 (1954).
Hell, R., *Penrose Annual*, **51**, 117 (1957).
Kilminster, R., *Penrose Annual*, **50**, 111 (1956).
Murray, A., and Morse, R. S., *U.S. Patent* 2,253,086 (1941).
Nash, C. F., *Litho Printer*, **8**, 33 (August, 1965).
Nash, C. F., *Litho Printer*, **8**, 43 (September, 1965).
Ohler, A. E., *Penrose Annual*, **49**, 80 (1955).
Rydz, J. S., and Marquart, V. L., *Tech. Assoc. Graphic Arts*, **6**, 139 (1954).
Rydz, J. S., and Marquart, V. L., *Tech. Assoc. Graphic Arts*, **7**, 15 (1955).
Sigler, H., *Tech. Assoc. Graphic Arts*, **16**, 192 (1964).
Smith, F. H., *Penrose Annual*, **48**, 131 (1954).

GENERAL REFERENCES

Allen, G. S., *J. Phot. Sci.*, **6**, 125 (1958).
Nash, C. F., *Litho Printer*, **8**, 33 (August, 1965).
Nash, C. F., *Litho Printer*, **8**, 43 (September, 1965).
Yule, J. A. C., *Principles of Colour Reproduction*, Chapter 12, Wiley, New York (1967).

APPENDICES

APPENDIX I

Matrix algebra

MATRIX algebra is useful in colorimetric calculations, in the evaluation of colour correcting masks, and in the formulation of colour reproduction theory. In this Appendix, therefore, a short explanation of matrix algebra is given, together with an example of its application to a common colorimetric problem. A matrix is an array of numbers or symbols; thus

$$\begin{pmatrix} 271 & 18 \\ 671 & 12 \end{pmatrix} \text{ and } \begin{pmatrix} x_1 & x_2 & x_3 \\ x_4 & x_5 & x_6 \end{pmatrix}$$

are both matrices. If two matrices are equal, each term of the first matrix is equal to the corresponding term of the second. Thus the single matrix equation:

$$\begin{pmatrix} x_1 & x_2+b \\ y_1+c & y_2 \end{pmatrix} = \begin{pmatrix} 61 & d+3e \\ 12 & 6f \end{pmatrix}$$

represents the four equations:

$$x_1 = 61 \qquad x_2+b = d+3e$$
$$y_1+c = 12 \qquad y_2 = 6f$$

By adopting a set of rules for multiplying matrices, sets of simultaneous equations, when written as single matrix equations, can be simplified by factorizing. For example, the equations:

$$a_1x+a_2y = a_5$$
$$a_3x+a_4y = a_6$$

when written in matrix algebra take the form:

$$\begin{pmatrix} a_1x+a_2y \\ a_3x+a_4y \end{pmatrix} = \begin{pmatrix} a_5 \\ a_6 \end{pmatrix}$$

or after factorizing:

$$\begin{pmatrix} a_1 & a_2 \\ a_3 & a_4 \end{pmatrix} \begin{pmatrix} x \\ y \end{pmatrix} = \begin{pmatrix} a_5 \\ a_6 \end{pmatrix}$$

The multiplication rule in this case is therefore that the terms of the first row of the first matrix are multiplied successively by the terms of the column of the second matrix and summed, to give the term for the first row of the product matrix; the term for the second row of the product matrix is similarly

473

derived from the second row of the first matrix. The rule can be stated quite generally as follows: the term in the pth row and qth column of the product matrix, is given by the sum of the successive products of the terms of the pth row of the first matrix and the qth column of the second. Thus:

$$\begin{pmatrix} a_1 & a_2 \\ a_3 & a_4 \end{pmatrix} \begin{pmatrix} b_1 & b_3 \\ b_2 & b_4 \end{pmatrix} = \begin{pmatrix} a_1b_1+a_2b_2 & a_1b_3+a_2b_4 \\ a_3b_1+a_4b_2 & a_3b_3+a_4b_4 \end{pmatrix}$$

Two of the most important uses of matrix algebra occur when variables have to be changed in equations and when equations have to be solved. Thus if

$$a_1x+a_2y = a_5$$
$$a_3x+a_4y = a_6$$
$$b_1x'+b_3y' = x$$
$$b_2x'+b_4y' = y$$

Then in matrix algebra we have:

$$\begin{pmatrix} a_1 & a_2 \\ a_3 & a_4 \end{pmatrix} \begin{pmatrix} x \\ y \end{pmatrix} = \begin{pmatrix} a_5 \\ a_6 \end{pmatrix}$$

$$\begin{pmatrix} b_1 & b_3 \\ b_2 & b_4 \end{pmatrix} \begin{pmatrix} x' \\ y' \end{pmatrix} = \begin{pmatrix} x \\ y \end{pmatrix}$$

Therefore
$$\begin{pmatrix} a_1 & a_2 \\ a_3 & a_4 \end{pmatrix} \begin{pmatrix} b_1 & b_3 \\ b_2 & b_4 \end{pmatrix} \begin{pmatrix} x' \\ y' \end{pmatrix} = \begin{pmatrix} a_5 \\ a_6 \end{pmatrix}$$

That this substitution is valid is easily checked by multiplying out this triple matrix product and comparing the two equations obtained with the results of ordinary algebra. It should be noted, however, that the order of the matrices is important, and must not be changed. Thus if two matrices are represented by A and B, then

$$A.B \text{ is not equal to } B.A$$

Matrix algebra is often very useful when sets of simultaneous equations have to be solved, as is sometimes the case in colorimetric calculations. In order to simplify the solution of equations two derived matrices are used, as follows:

$A' =$ the *transpose* of A, obtained by writing the rows as columns and the columns as rows.

adj. $A =$ the *adjugate* of A, obtained by replacing each term of the matrix by the determinant formed by all the rows and columns of the matrix not containing that term, and transposing the result, a negative sign being prefixed to all terms situated an odd number of non-diagonal moves from the first term.

Thus if
$$A = \begin{pmatrix} a_1 & a_2 & a_3 \\ a_4 & a_5 & a_6 \\ a_7 & a_8 & a_9 \end{pmatrix}$$

$$A' = \begin{pmatrix} a_1 & a_4 & a_7 \\ a_2 & a_5 & a_8 \\ a_3 & a_6 & a_9 \end{pmatrix}$$

$$\text{adj. } A = \begin{pmatrix} |A_1| & -|A_4| & |A_7| \\ -|A_2| & |A_5| & -|A_8| \\ |A_3| & -|A_6| & |A_9| \end{pmatrix} \qquad \begin{aligned} \text{where } |A_1| &= a_5 a_9 - a_6 a_8, \\ |A_2| &= a_4 a_9 - a_6 a_7, \\ &\text{etc.} \end{aligned}$$

The *inverse* or *reciprocal* matrix A^{-1} is the matrix that expresses solution equations. Thus if

$$\begin{pmatrix} x \\ y \\ z \end{pmatrix} = A \begin{pmatrix} x' \\ y' \\ z' \end{pmatrix} \quad \text{then} \quad \begin{pmatrix} x' \\ y' \\ z' \end{pmatrix} = A^{-1} \begin{pmatrix} x \\ y \\ z \end{pmatrix}$$

It may be shown by simple algebra that the reciprocal matrix is given by:

$$A^{-1} = \frac{\text{adj. } A}{|A|}$$

where $|A|$ is the determinant corresponding to the matrix A. Hence if

$$A = \begin{pmatrix} a_1 & a_2 & a_3 \\ a_4 & a_5 & a_6 \\ a_7 & a_8 & a_9 \end{pmatrix} \qquad |A| = \begin{vmatrix} a_1 & a_2 & a_3 \\ a_4 & a_5 & a_6 \\ a_7 & a_8 & a_9 \end{vmatrix}$$

thus
$$|A| = a_1(a_5 a_9 - a_6 a_8) - a_2(a_4 a_9 - a_6 a_7) + a_3(a_4 a_8 - a_5 a_7).$$

A common problem in colorimetry is as follows: given the position of three stimuli R, G, and B in some colour triangle, for instance the XYZ triangle, it is required to find the transformation equations necessary to transfer to that triangle results obtained using R, G, and B as matching stimuli, using units such that equal quantities are required to match some white stimulus W. The basic data therefore consist of equations of the type:

$$\begin{aligned} (R) &\propto a_1(X) + a_2(Y) + a_3(Z) \\ (G) &\propto a_4(X) + a_5(Y) + a_6(Z) \\ (B) &\propto a_7(X) + a_8(Y) + a_9(Z) \\ (W) &\propto h_1(R) + h_2(G) + h_3(B) \\ (W) &\propto j_1(X) + j_2(Y) + j_3(Z) \end{aligned}$$

where in each equation the coefficients sum to unity ($a_1 + a_2 + a_3 = 1$ etc.).

It is convenient to insert constants k_1, k_2, k_3, k_4, and k_5 so as to avoid the proportional signs, thus:

$$k_1(R) \equiv a_1(X) + a_2(Y) + a_3(Z)$$
$$k_2(G) \equiv a_4(X) + a_5(Y) + a_6(Z)$$
$$k_3(B) \equiv a_7(X) + a_8(Y) + a_9(Z)$$
$$k_4(W) \equiv h_1(R) + h_2(G) + h_3(B)$$
$$k_5(W) \equiv j_1(X) + j_2(Y) + j_3(Z)$$

It is now required to evaluate k_1, k_2, and k_3, and in order to do this it is necessary to solve the above equations for (X), (Y), and (Z).

A convenient systematic way of doing this is by means of matrix algebra. It is required to find the reciprocal of the matrix,

$$\begin{pmatrix} a_1 & a_2 & a_3 \\ a_4 & a_5 & a_6 \\ a_7 & a_8 & a_9 \end{pmatrix}$$

If this matrix is represented by A, then:

$$A^{-1} = \frac{1}{|A|} \begin{pmatrix} a_5 a_9 - a_6 a_8 & -(a_4 a_9 - a_6 a_7) & a_4 a_8 - a_5 a_7 \\ -(a_2 a_9 - a_3 a_8) & a_1 a_9 - a_3 a_7 & -(a_1 a_8 - a_2 a_7) \\ a_2 a_6 - a_3 a_5 & -(a_1 a_6 - a_3 a_4) & a_1 a_5 - a_2 a_4 \end{pmatrix}'$$

$$= \frac{1}{|A|} \begin{pmatrix} b_1 & b_2 & b_3 \\ b_4 & b_5 & b_6 \\ b_7 & b_8 & b_9 \end{pmatrix}' = \frac{1}{|A|} \begin{pmatrix} b_1 & b_4 & b_7 \\ b_2 & b_5 & b_8 \\ b_3 & b_6 & b_9 \end{pmatrix}$$

When, as is usually the case, $a_1 + a_2 + a_3 = a_4 + a_5 + a_6 = a_7 + a_8 + a_9 = 1$, then:

$$|A| = b_1 + b_4 + b_7 = b_2 + b_5 + b_8 = b_3 + b_6 + b_9$$

which, as well as evaluating $|A|$ very simply, provides a check on every term of the matrix.

Dividing each term of the matrix by $|A|$, we obtain:

$$A^{-1} = \begin{pmatrix} c_1 & c_2 & c_3 \\ c_4 & c_5 & c_6 \\ c_7 & c_8 & c_9 \end{pmatrix}$$

and as a final check: $c_1 + c_2 + c_3 = c_4 + c_5 + c_6 = c_7 + c_8 + c_9 = 1$ should be true.

We can now write:

$$1.0(X) \equiv c_1 k_1(R) + c_2 k_2(G) + c_3 k_3(B)$$
$$1.0(Y) \equiv c_4 k_1(R) + c_5 k_2(G) + c_6 k_3(B)$$
$$1.0(Z) \equiv c_7 k_1(R) + c_8 k_2(G) + c_9 k_3(B)$$

and substituting for (X), (Y), and (Z) in the equation:

$$k_5(W) \equiv j_1(X) + j_2(Y) + j_3(Z)$$

and comparing the result with the equation:

$$k_4(W) \equiv h_1(R) + h_2(G) + h_3(B)$$

we obtain:

$$k_1 = k_5h_1/k_4(j_1c_1+j_2c_4+j_3c_7)$$
$$k_2 = k_5h_2/k_4(j_1c_2+j_2c_5+j_3c_8)$$
$$k_3 = k_5h_3/k_4(j_1c_3+j_2c_6+j_3c_9)$$

The value of k_5/k_4 depends upon the relation between the average magnitude of the XYZ units and that of the RGB units; but as far as the position of points in the colour triangles is concerned it can be arbitrarily set at 1.0. Hence k_1, k_2, k_3 are evaluated and the transformation equations are given by:

$$1.0(R) \equiv (a_1/k_1)(X)+(a_2/k_1)(Y)+(a_3/k_1)(Z)$$
$$1.0(G) \equiv (a_4/k_2)(X)+(a_5/k_2)(Y)+(a_6/k_2)(Z)$$
$$1.0(B) \equiv (a_7/k_3)(X)+(a_8/k_3)(Y)+(a_9/k_3)(Z)$$

and the reciprocal transformation equations by:

$$1.0(X) \equiv c_1k_1(R)+c_2k_2(G)+c_3k_3(B)$$
$$1.0(Y) \equiv c_4k_1(R)+c_5k_2(G)+c_6k_3(B)$$
$$1.0(Z) \equiv c_7k_1(R)+c_8k_2(G)+c_9k_3(B)$$

In general, the coefficients of these equations will not sum to unity.

APPENDIX 2

PHOTOMETRIC UNITS

1. RELATIONS BETWEEN UNITS OF LUMINANCE

	candelas per sq. foot	candelas per sq. inch	candelas per sq. metre	candelas per sq. cm. (stilbs)	foot-lamberts (equivalent foot-candles, or e.f.c.)	lamberts	millilamberts
candela per sq. foot =	1	1/144	3.281^2	$10.76/100^2$	π	$\pi/929$	$\pi/0.929$
		0.00694	10.76	0.001076	3.142	0.003382	3.382
candela per sq. inch =	12^2	1	144×10.76	$1550/100^2$	144π	$\dfrac{144\pi}{929}$	$\dfrac{144\pi}{0.929}$
	144		1550	0.1550	452.5	0.4871	487.1
candela per sq. metre =	0.3048^2	$\dfrac{0.3048^2}{144}$	1	1/10000	0.0929π	$\dfrac{\pi}{10000}$	$\dfrac{\pi}{10}$
	0.0929	0.0006451		0.0001	0.2918	0.0003142	0.3142
candela per sq. cm. (stilb) =	929	929/144	10000	1	929π	π	1000π
		6.451			2918	3.142	3142
foot-lambert (equivalent foot-candle, or e.f.c.) =	$1/\pi$	$1/144\pi$	$10.76/\pi$	$\dfrac{0.001076}{\pi}$	1	1/929	1/0.929
	0.3183	0.002210	3.426	0.0003246		0.001076	1.076
lambert =	$929/\pi$	$929/144\pi$	$\dfrac{10000}{\pi}$	$1/\pi$	929	1	1000
	295.7	2.053	3183	0.3183			
millilambert = 10 apostilbs =	$0.929/\pi$	$0.929/144\pi$	$10/\pi$	0.0003183	0.929	1/1000	1
	0.2957	0.002053	3.183			0.001	

2. RELATIONS BETWEEN UNITS OF LUMINANCE AND ILLUMINATION

A surface of luminance factor β under an illumination E has a luminance:

$L = E.\beta/\pi$ candelas per sq. metre when E is measured in lux (lumens per sq. metre).

$L = E.\beta/\pi$ candelas per sq. foot when E is measured in lumens per sq. foot (foot-candles).

$L = E.\beta$ foot-lamberts when E is measured in lumens per sq. foot (foot-candles).

$L = E.\beta/10$ millilamberts when E is measured in lux (lumens per sq. metre.)

APPENDIX 3

Colorimetric Tables

In this Appendix sufficient information is given to enable colorimetric specifications to be evaluated from spectrophotometric data. The data may be in one of two forms: either the amount of light (in photometric units) at each wavelength may be known; or the amount of energy or power (in radiometric units) at each wavelength may be known.

In the first case the calculation proceeds by applying the Centre of Gravity Law of colour mixture as described in Sections 6.6, 7.5, and 7.6. If the amounts of light at successive wavelengths, λ_1, λ_2, λ_3, etc. are L_1, L_2, L_3, etc., then the chromaticity of the resultant mixture is given by calculating the centre of gravity of weights:

$$L_1/v_1 \text{ at } u_1, v_1$$
$$L_2/v_2 \text{ at } u_2, v_2$$
$$L_3/v_3 \text{ at } u_3, v_3 \text{ etc.}$$

where u_1, v_1, etc., are the chromaticity co-ordinates in the UVW system of the wavelengths λ_1, λ_2, λ_3, etc. The co-ordinates u_m, v_m, of the centre of gravity of such a system of weights is given by:

$$u_m = \frac{u_1 L_1/v_1 + u_2 L_2/v_2 + u_3 L_3/v_3 + \ldots}{L_1/v_1 + L_2/v_2 + L_3/v_3 + \ldots}$$

$$v_m = \frac{v_1 L_1/v_1 + v_2 L_2/v_2 + v_3 L_3/v_3 + \ldots}{L_1/v_1 + L_2/v_2 + L_3/v_3 + \ldots}$$

$$= \frac{L_1 + L_2 + L_3 + \ldots}{L_1/v_1 + L_2/v_2 + L_3/v_3 + \ldots}$$

In the tables, values of u and v (for the 2° Standard Observer) are given at 10 nm intervals from 380 to 770 nm so that the above type of calculation can be made. The values of w are also given, and by calculating

$$w_m = \frac{w_1 L_1/v_1 + w_2 L_2/v_2 + w_3 L_3/v_3 + \ldots}{L_1/v_1 + L_2/v_2 + L_3/v_3 + \ldots}$$

and checking that $u_m + v_m + w_m = 1$, the whole computation is checked.

481

In the second case, where the amount of power or energy, e_λ, at each wavelength is known (in radiometric units), we could convert this to the amount of light at each wavelength by multiplying each value of e_λ by the appropriate value of the spectral luminous efficiency function $\bar{v}_\lambda$ (or $\bar{y}_\lambda$ or V_λ which are the same, see Sections 7.5 and 7.6); and the calculation would then proceed as above:

$$u_m = \frac{u_1 e_1 \bar{v}_1/v_1 + u_2 e_2 \bar{v}_2/v_2 + u_3 e_3 \bar{v}_3/v_3 + \ldots}{e_1 \bar{v}_1/v_1 + e_2 \bar{v}_2/v_2 + e_3 \bar{v}_3/v_3 + \ldots}$$

$$v_m = \frac{e_1 \bar{v}_1 + e_2 \bar{v}_2 + e_3 \bar{v}_3 + \ldots}{e_1 \bar{v}_1/v_1 + e_2 \bar{v}_2/v_2 + e_3 \bar{v}_3/v_3 + \ldots}$$

But because the chromaticity co-ordinates u, v, w of spectral colours are related to the colour-matching functions $\bar{u}_\lambda$, $\bar{v}_\lambda$, $\bar{w}_\lambda$, by expressions of the type $u_1 = \bar{u}_1/(\bar{u}_1 + \bar{v}_1 + \bar{w}_1)$, $v_1 = \bar{v}_1/(\bar{u}_1 + \bar{v}_1 + \bar{w}_1)$, and $w_1 = \bar{w}_1/(\bar{u}_1 + \bar{v}_1 + \bar{w}_1)$, it follows that $u_1/v_1 = \bar{u}_1/\bar{v}_1$; similarly $u_2/v_2 = \bar{u}_2/\bar{v}_2$ etc; and $w_1/v_1 = \bar{w}_1/\bar{v}_1$, etc. Hence the summations simplify to:

$$S_m u_m = e_1 \bar{u}_1 + e_2 \bar{u}_2 + e_3 \bar{u}_3 + \ldots = U_m$$
$$S_m v_m = e_1 \bar{v}_1 + e_2 \bar{v}_2 + e_3 \bar{v}_3 + \ldots = V_m$$
$$S_m w_m = e_1 \bar{w}_1 + e_2 \bar{w}_2 + e_3 \bar{w}_3 + \ldots = W_m$$

where $S_m = e_1 \bar{v}_1/v_1 + e_2 \bar{v}_2/v_2 + e_3 \bar{v}_3/v_3 + \ldots$

It is therefore more convenient, when the data is in radiometric units, to use the tabulated values of $\bar{u}_\lambda$, $\bar{v}_\lambda$, $\bar{w}_\lambda$; these are therefore also given in the tables (for the 2° Standard Observer), at every 10 nm from 380 to 770 nm. If U_m, V_m, W_m and S_m are all evaluated, u_m, v_m, w_m can be obtained, and the computation can again be checked by making sure that $u_m + v_m + w_m = 1$. (Individual entries in the computation can also be checked by seeing whether at each wavelength $U_1 + V_1 + W_1 = S_1$ etc.) Alternatively, the more usual procedure is to ignore S_m altogether and to obtain u_m, v_m and w_m from:

$$u_m = U_m/(U_m + V_m + W_m)$$
$$v_m = V_m/(U_m + V_m + W_m)$$
$$w_m = W_m/(U_m + V_m + W_m)$$

When the spectrophotometric data is in radiometric units, it often takes the form of spectral reflectance or transmittance readings, t_λ, and the spectral energy distribution, E_λ, of an illuminant. The calculation then proceeds as follows:

$$U_m = E_1 t_1 \bar{u}_1 + E_2 t_2 \bar{u}_2 + E_3 t_3 \bar{u}_3 + \ldots$$
$$V_m = E_1 t_1 \bar{v}_1 + E_2 t_2 \bar{v}_2 + E_3 t_3 \bar{v}_3 + \ldots$$
$$W_m = E_1 t_1 \bar{w}_1 + E_2 t_2 \bar{w}_2 + E_3 t_3 \bar{w}_3 + \ldots$$

The corresponding values of u_m, v_m, w_m are then evaluated as before. The total spectral reflectance (or transmittance), V or Y, is given by

$$Y = V = \frac{V_m}{V_o} = \frac{E_1 t_1 \bar{v}_1 + E_2 t_2 \bar{v}_2 + E_3 t_3 \bar{v}_3 + \ldots}{E_1 \bar{v}_1 + E_2 \bar{v}_2 + E_3 \bar{v}_3 + \ldots}$$

so that to obtain this result $V_o = E_1 \bar{v}_1 + E_2 \bar{v}_2 + E_3 \bar{v}_3 + \ldots$ must also be evaluated.

To facilitate the above type of calculation, values of the spectral energy distributions, E_λ, are given in the tables for the standard sources S_A, S_B, S_C, and D_{6500}, together with those of a full radiator of colour temperature $3250° K$ (which is representative of the light emitted by tungsten-filament projector lamps), and of D_{5500} (which is representative of sunlight and skylight as often used for outdoor pictures).

For reflecting samples it is often also required to evaluate

$$U^* = 13W^*(u - u_o)$$
$$V^* = 13W^*(v - v_o)$$
$$W^* = 25Y^{\frac{1}{3}} - 17$$

To facilitate this evaluation, the chromaticity co-ordinates u_o, v_o of various illuminants are given in the tables, and also values of W^* corresponding to various values of Y. The difference between two reflecting samples having values U_1^*, V_1^*, W_1^* and U_2^*, V_2^*, W_2^* can then be evaluated as

$$[(U_1^* - U_2^*)^2 + (V_1^* - V_2^*)^2 + (W_1^* - W_2^*)^2]^{\frac{1}{2}}.$$

A worked example is included to clarify the actual procedures involved: the values of U^*, V^*, W^* are found corresponding to a reflecting sample whose spectral reflectance, t_λ, is known, when it is illuminated by standard illuminant A. (A desk calculating machine greatly facilitates this type of work, or of course a computer can be used.) From the table of results for the worked example (page 485) we have:

$$U_m = 19701$$
$$V_m = 38934$$
$$W_m = 57596$$
$$S_m = 116225$$

Hence:

$$u_m = U_m/S_m = 19701/116225 = 0.1695$$
$$v_m = V_m/S_m = 38934/116225 = 0.3350$$
$$w_m = W_m/S_m = 57596/116225 = 0.4956$$

The values of u_m, v_m, w_m sum to 1 (actually 1.0001) thus checking the whole computation. The total percentage reflectance is obtained thus:

$$Y = V = \frac{\Sigma t_\lambda E_\lambda \bar{v}_\lambda}{\Sigma 100 E_\lambda \bar{v}_\lambda} = \frac{38934}{107896} = 36.1$$

Hence using the table of values of W^*, we obtain $W^* = 65.62$. The values of u, v for standard illuminant A are $u_o = 0.2560$, $v_o = 0.3495$ and hence

$$U^* = (13)65.62(0.1695-0.2560) = -73.79$$
$$V^* = (13)65.62(0.3350-0.3495) = -12.37$$
$$W^* = 65.62$$

If another sample, having a slightly different spectral reflectance curve, resulted in values for illuminant A as follows:

$$U^* = -75.13$$
$$V^* = -11.04$$
$$W^* = 62.31$$

then the difference between the two samples would be given by:

$$[(-73.79+75.13)^2+(-12.37+11.04)^2+(65.62-62.31)^2]^{\frac{1}{2}}$$
$$= [(1.34)^2+(-1.33)^2+(3.31)^2]^{\frac{1}{2}}$$
$$= (1.80+1.76+10.96)^{\frac{1}{2}}$$
$$= (14.52)^{\frac{1}{2}} = 3.81$$

It will be seen that in the above example the difference in lightness, W^*, contributes most to the total colour difference; however, if the two samples are not seen side by side across a narrow dividing line, less weight should be given to the lightness difference. In this case a difference formula of the type

$$[(U_1^*-U_2^*)^2+(V_1^*-V_2^*)^2+k(W_1^*-W_2^*)^2]^{\frac{1}{2}}$$

should be used, where k is chosen appropriately for the particular case. Thus if k is put equal to $\frac{1}{4}$, then in the above example the difference becomes:

$$[(1.34)^2+(-1.33)^2+\tfrac{1}{4}(3.31)^2]^{\frac{1}{2}}$$
$$= (1.80+1.76+2.74)^{\frac{1}{2}}$$
$$= (6.30)^{\frac{1}{2}} = 2.51.$$

Worked Example

λ	t_λ	E_λ	$t_\lambda E_\lambda \bar{u}_\lambda$	$t_\lambda E_\lambda \bar{v}_\lambda$	$t_\lambda E_\lambda \bar{w}_\lambda$	$t_\lambda E_\lambda \bar{v}_\lambda / v_\lambda$	$100 E_\lambda \bar{v}_\lambda$
380	51.3	9.79	0	0	1	0	0
390	56.2	12.09	2	0	6	7	0
400	60.5	14.71	8	0	24	33	1
410	66.5	17.68	34	1	98	134	2
420	72.5	21.00	136	6	398	539	8
430	75.3	24.67	352	22	1056	1427	29
440	76.2	28.70	508	50	1605	2159	66
450	75.9	33.09	563	95	1946	2608	126
460	74.8	37.82	549	170	2204	2921	227
470	73.4	42.87	410	286	2148	2844	390
480	71.6	48.25	220	480	1960	2660	671
490	69.5	53.91	80	779	1981	2840	1121
500	66.7	59.86	13	1290	2467	3770	1933
510	63.9	66.06	26	2123	3500	5649	3323
520	60.8	72.50	186	3130	4727	8043	5148
530	57.0	79.13	498	3888	5554	9939	6821
540	52.6	85.95	876	4313	5859	11048	8200
550	48.0	92.91	1289	4437	5709	11437	9245
560	42.8	100.00	1697	4259	5124	11079	9950
570	37.0	107.18	2016	3775	4156	9948	10204
580	30.6	114.44	2140	3047	2969	8155	9956
590	25.5	121.73	2125	2350	1934	6408	9215
600	20.9	129.04	1911	1702	1121	4734	8142
610	16.8	136.34	1532	1152	580	3264	6858
620	12.9	143.62	1056	706	268	2030	5472
630	10.0	150.83	646	400	115	1161	3997
640	7.8	157.98	368	216	47	631	2765
650	6.7	165.03	209	118	21	348	1766
660	6.2	171.96	117	65	10	192	1049
670	5.9	178.77	61	34	5	100	572
680	5.4	185.43	31	17	2	50	315
690	4.9	191.93	14	8	1	23	157
700	5.0	198.26	8	4	0	12	81
710	6.2	204.41	5	3	0	8	43
720	9.3	210.36	4	2	0	6	21
730	17.4	216.12	3	2	0	6	11
740	27.5	221.66	3	2	0	5	7
750	42.7	227.00	2	1	0	3	2
760	56.2	232.11	1	1	0	4	2
770	66.1	237.01	2	0	0	0	0
Totals			19701	38934	57596	116225	107896

485

18

RELATIONSHIP BETWEEN THE XYZ AND UVW SYSTEMS

$$x = 1.5u/(u-4v+2)$$
$$y = v/(u-4v+2)$$
$$u = 2x/(6y-x+1.5)$$
$$v = 3y/(6y-x+1.5)$$
$$X = 1\tfrac{1}{2}U$$
$$Y = V$$
$$Z = 1\tfrac{1}{2}U-3V+2W$$

$$U = \tfrac{2}{3}X$$
$$V = Y$$
$$W = -\tfrac{1}{2}X+1\tfrac{1}{2}Y+\tfrac{1}{2}Z$$

CHROMATICITY CO-ORDINATES OF VARIOUS ILLUMINANTS

Illuminant	x	y	u	v
S_A	0.4476	0.4075	0.2560	0.3495
3,250° K	0.4196	0.3974	0.2422	0.3440
S_B	0.3484	0.3516	0.2137	0.3235
S_C	0.3101	0.3162	0.2009	0.3073
D_{5500}	0.3324	0.3475	0.2043	0.3205
D_{6500}	0.3127	0.3291	0.1977	0.3122
S_E	0.3333	0.3333	0.2105	0.3158

THE U*V*W* SYSTEM

$$U^* = 13W^*(u-u_0)$$
$$V^* = 13W^*(v-v_0)$$
$$W^* = 25Y^{\frac{1}{3}}-17$$

u_0, v_0 are the chromaticity co-ordinates of the nominally achromatic colour, usually the illuminant for reflection samples. Colour differences are expressed as

$$[(U_1^*-U_2^*)^2+(V_1^*-V_2^*)^2+k(W_1^*-W_2^*)^2]^{\frac{1}{2}}$$

where $k = 1$ for samples in close proximity, but may have a lower value for other situations.

COLOUR MATCHING FUNCTIONS AND CHROMATICITY CO-ORDINATES

λ (nm)	$\bar{u}$	$\bar{v}$	$\bar{w}$	u	v	w
380	0.0009	0.0000	0.0025	0.2647	0.0000	0.7353
390	0.0028	0.0001	0.0081	0.2545	0.0091	0.7364
400	0.0095	0.0004	0.0274	0.2547	0.0107	0.7346
410	0.0290	0.0012	0.0837	0.2546	0.0105	0.7349
420	0.0896	0.0040	0.2616	0.2523	0.0113	0.7365
430	0.1894	0.0116	0.5682	0.2462	0.0151	0.7387
440	0.2323	0.0230	0.7339	0.2348	0.0233	0.7419
450	0.2242	0.0380	0.7749	0.2162	0.0366	0.7472
460	0.1940	0.0600	0.7792	0.1878	0.0581	0.7542
470	0.1303	0.0910	0.6826	0.1442	0.1007	0.7552
480	0.0638	0.1390	0.5672	0.0829	0.1805	0.7366
490	0.0213	0.2080	0.5286	0.0281	0.2744	0.6975
500	0.0033	0.3230	0.6180	0.0035	0.3421	0.6545
510	0.0062	0.5030	0.8289	0.0046	0.3759	0.6195
520	0.0422	0.7100	1.0724	0.0231	0.3891	0.5877
530	0.1104	0.8620	1.2313	0.0501	0.3912	0.5587
540	0.1937	0.9540	1.2959	0.0793	0.3904	0.5303
550	0.2891	0.9950	1.2801	0.1127	0.3880	0.4992
560	0.3965	0.9950	1.1972	0.1532	0.3844	0.4625
570	0.5083	0.9520	1.0480	0.2026	0.3795	0.4178
580	0.6112	0.8700	0.8477	0.2624	0.3736	0.3640
590	0.6845	0.7570	0.6229	0.3316	0.3667	0.3017
600	0.7085	0.6310	0.4158	0.4036	0.3595	0.2369
610	0.6687	0.5030	0.2533	0.4693	0.3530	0.1778
620	0.5699	0.3810	0.1444	0.5203	0.3478	0.1318
630	0.4285	0.2650	0.0763	0.5566	0.3442	0.0991
640	0.2987	0.1750	0.0385	0.5832	0.3417	0.0752
650	0.1891	0.1070	0.0187	0.6007	0.3399	0.0594
660	0.1100	0.0610	0.0090	0.6111	0.3389	0.0500
670	0.0583	0.0320	0.0043	0.6163	0.3383	0.0455
680	0.0312	0.0170	0.0021	0.6203	0.3380	0.0417
690	0.0151	0.0082	0.0009	0.6240	0.3388	0.0372
700	0.0076	0.0041	0.0004	0.6281	0.3388	0.0331
710	0.0039	0.0021	0.0002	0.6281	0.3388	0.0331
720	0.0019	0.0010	0.0000	0.6281	0.3388	0.0331
730	0.0009	0.0005	0.0000	0.6281	0.3388	0.0331
740	0.0005	0.0003	0.0000	0.6281	0.3388	0.0331
750	0.0002	0.0001	0.0000	0 6281	0.3388	0.0331
760	0.0001	0.0001	0.0000	0.6281	0.3388	0.0331
770	0.0001	0.0000	0.0000	0.6281	0.3388	0.0331

W* FOR VARIOUS VALUES OF Y

Y	0	0.1	0.2	0.3	0.4	0.5	0.6	0.7	0.8	0.9
100	99.05	99.09	99.13	99.16	99.18	99.23	99.28	99.32	99.35	99.38
99	98.65	98.69	98.73	98.77	98.80	98.84	98.88	98.93	98.98	99.02
98	98.25	98.30	98.35	98.39	98.43	98.47	98.50	98.54	98.58	98.62
97	97.88	97.92	97.95	97.99	98.03	98.07	98.10	98.14	98.18	98.22
96	97.48	97.52	97.55	97.59	97.63	97.67	97.70	97.75	97.80	97.84
95	97.08	97.12	97.15	97.19	97.23	97.28	97.33	97.37	97.40	97.44
94	96.68	96.72	96.75	96.79	96.83	96.88	96.93	96.97	97.00	97.04
93	96.28	96.32	96.35	96.39	96.43	96.47	96.50	96.55	96.60	96.64
92	95.85	95.90	95.95	95.99	96.03	96.07	96.10	96.14	96.18	96.23
91	95.45	95.49	95.53	95.58	95.63	95.67	95.70	95.74	95.78	95.82
90	95.03	95.08	95.13	95.17	95.20	95.24	95.28	95 32	95.38	95.42
89	94.63	94.67	94.70	94.74	94.78	94.83	94.88	94.92	94.95	94.99
88	94.20	94.24	94.28	94.33	94.38	94.42	94.45	94.49	94.53	94.58
87	93.78	93.82	93.85	93.90	93.95	93.99	94.03	94.08	94.13	94.17
86	93.35	93.39	93.43	93.48	93.53	93.57	93.60	93.65	93.70	93.74
85	92.93	92.97	93.00	93.05	93.10	93.14	93.18	93.23	93.28	93.31
84	92.50	92.54	92.58	92.63	92.68	92.72	92.75	92.79	92.83	92.88
83	92.05	92.10	92.15	92.19	92.23	91.28	92.33	92.37	92.40	92.45
82	91.63	91.67	91.70	91.75	91.80	91.84	91.88	91.93	91.98	92.02
81	91.18	91.22	91.25	91.30	91.35	91.39	91.43	91.48	91.53	91.58
80	90.73	90.78	90.83	90.87	90.90	90.95	91.00	91.04	91.08	91.13
79	90.28	90.33	90.38	90.42	90.45	90.50	90.55	90.59	90.63	90.68
78	89.83	89.87	89.90	89.95	90.00	90.05	90.10	90.14	90.18	90.23
77	89.35	89.40	89.45	89.50	89.55	89.59	89.63	89.68	89.73	89.78
76	88.90	88.95	89.00	89.04	89.08	89.13	89.18	89.23	89.28	89.32
75	88.43	88.48	88.53	88.58	88.63	88.67	88.70	88.75	88.80	88.85
74	87.95	88.01	88.05	88.10	88.15	88.20	88.25	88.29	88.33	88.38
73	87.48	87.53	87.58	87.63	87.68	87.72	87.78	87.82	87.88	87.91
72	87.00	87.05	87.10	87.15	87.20	87.25	87.30	87.34	87.40	87.44
71	86.53	86.57	86.63	86.67	86.73	86.76	86.80	86.86	86.90	86.96
70	86.03	86.08	86.13	86.18	86.23	86.28	86.33	86.38	86.43	86.47
69	85.55	85.59	85.65	85.69	85.75	85.79	85.83	85.89	85.93	85.98
68	85.05	85.09	85.15	85.19	85.25	85.29	85.35	85.39	85.45	85.49
67	84.55	84.59	84.65	84.69	84.75	84.79	84.85	84.89	84.95	84.99
66	84.03	84.08	84.13	84.19	84.23	84.29	84.35	84.39	84.45	84.49
65	83.53	83.57	83.63	83.67	83.73	83.78	83.83	83.88	83.93	83.98
64	83.00	83.05	83.10	83.16	83.20	83.26	83.33	83.36	83.43	83.47
63	82.48	82.53	82.58	82.64	82.70	82.74	82.80	82.84	82.90	82.95
62	81.95	82.00	82.05	82.11	82.15	82.21	82.28	82.32	82.38	82.43
61	81.43	81.47	81.53	81.57	81.63	81.68	81.73	81.79	81.85	81.90
60	80.88	80.93	80.98	81.04	91.10	81.14	81.20	81.25	81.30	81.36
59	80.33	80.38	80.43	80.49	80.55	80.60	80.65	80.71	80.78	80.82
58	79.78	79.83	79.88	79.94	80.00	80.05	80.10	80.16	80.23	80.27
57	79.23	79.27	79.33	79.38	79.45	79.49	79.55	79.61	79.65	79.72
56	78.65	78.70	78.75	78.82	78.88	78.93	79.00	79.04	79.10	79.16
55	78.08	78.13	78.20	78.25	78.30	78.36	78.43	78.48	78.53	78.59
54	77.50	77.55	77.60	77.67	77.73	77.79	77.85	77.90	77.95	78.02
53	76.90	76.97	77.03	77.09	77.15	77.20	77.25	77.32	77.38	77.44
52	76.33	76.37	76.43	76.49	76.55	76.61	76.68	76.73	76.80	76.85
51	75.70	75.77	75.83	75.89	75.95	76.01	76.08	76.13	76.20	76.25

W^* FOR VARIOUS VALUES OF Y

Y	0	0.1	0.2	0.3	0.4	0.5	0.6	0.7	0.8	0.9
50	75.10	75.16	75.23	75.29	75.35	75.41	75.48	75.53	75.60	75.65
49	74.48	74.55	74.60	74.67	74.73	74.79	74.85	74.92	74.98	75.04
48	73.85	73.92	73.98	74.05	74.10	74.17	74.23	74.30	74.35	74.42
47	73.23	73.29	73.35	73.41	73.48	73.54	73.60	73.67	73.73	73.79
46	72.58	72.64	72.70	72.77	72.83	72.90	72.98	73.03	73.10	73.16
45	71.93	71.99	72.05	72.12	72.18	72.25	72.33	72.38	72.45	72.51
44	71.25	71.33	71.40	71.46	71.53	71.59	71.65	71.73	71.80	71.86
43	70.58	70.65	70.73	70.79	70.85	70.92	71.00	71.06	71.13	71.19
42	69.90	69.97	70.05	70.11	70.18	70.25	70.33	70.38	70.45	70.52
41	69.20	69.28	69.35	69.42	69.48	69.56	69.63	69.69	69.78	69.83
40	68.50	68.57	68.65	68.71	68.78	68.85	68.93	69.00	69.08	69.14
39	67.78	67.85	67.93	68.00	68.08	68.14	68.21	68.29	68.35	68.43
38	67.05	67.12	67.20	67.27	67.35	67.42	67.50	67.56	67.63	67.71
37	66.30	66.38	66.45	66.53	66.60	66.68	66.75	66.83	66.90	66.98
36	65.55	65.62	65.70	65.78	65.85	65.93	66.00	66.08	66.15	66.23
35	64.78	64.86	64.93	65.01	65.10	65.17	65.25	65.32	65.40	65.47
34	64.00	64.07	64.15	64.23	64.30	64.39	64.48	64.54	64.63	64.70
33	63.20	63.27	63.35	63.43	63.50	63.59	63.68	63.75	63.83	63.91
32	62.38	62.45	62.53	62.62	62.70	62.78	62.88	62.95	63.03	63.11
31	61.53	61.62	61.70	61.79	61.88	61.96	62.05	62.12	62.20	62.29
30	60.68	60.77	60.85	60.94	61.03	61.11	61.20	61.28	61.38	61.45
29	59.80	59.90	59.98	60.07	60.15	60.25	60.33	60.42	60.50	60.60
28	58.93	59.01	59.10	59.19	59.28	59.37	59.45	59.54	59.63	59.72
27	58.00	58.09	58.18	58.28	58.38	58.46	58.55	58.64	58.73	58.83
26	57.08	57.16	57.25	57.35	57.45	57.54	57.63	57.72	57.83	57.91
25	56.10	56.20	56.30	56.39	56.50	56.59	56.68	56.78	56.88	56.97
24	55.11	55.21	55.33	55.41	55.50	55.61	55.70	55.81	55.90	56.00
23	54.10	54.20	54.30	54.41	54.50	54.61	54.70	54.81	54.93	55.01
22	53.05	53.16	53.28	53.37	53.48	53.58	53.68	53.79	53.90	53.99
21	51.97	52.08	52.20	52.30	52.40	52.52	52.63	52.73	52.85	52.95
20	50.86	50.97	51.08	51.20	51.30	51.42	51.53	51.64	51.75	51.86
19	49.71	49.83	49.95	50.06	50.18	50.29	50.40	50.52	50.63	50.75
18	48.52	48.64	48.75	48.88	49.00	49.12	49.25	49.36	49.48	49.59
17	47.28	47.41	47.53	47.66	47.78	47.91	48.03	48.15	48.28	48.40
16	46.00	46.13	46.25	46.39	46.53	46.65	46.78	46.90	47.03	47.16
15	44.66	44.79	44.93	45.06	45.20	45.33	45.48	45.60	45.73	45.87
14	43.25	43.40	43.55	43.68	43.83	43.96	44.10	44.24	44.38	44.52
13	41.78	41.93	42.08	42.23	42.38	42.53	42.68	42.82	42.98	43.11
12	40.24	40.40	40.55	40.71	40.88	41.02	41.18	41.33	41.48	41.63
11	38.60	38.77	38.93	39.10	39.28	39.43	39.60	39.76	39.93	40.08
10	36.86	37.04	37.23	37.39	37.58	37.75	37.93	38.09	38.25	38.43
9	35.00	35.19	35.38	35.57	35.78	35.95	36.13	36.32	36.50	36.68
8	33.00	33.21	33.43	33.62	33.83	34.02	34.23	34.42	34.63	34.81
7	30.82	31.05	31.28	31.50	31.73	31.94	32.15	32.37	32.58	32.79
6	28.43	28.68	28.93	29.17	29.43	29.66	29.90	30.13	30.38	30.60
5	25.75	26.03	26.33	26.59	26.85	27.13	27.40	27.66	27.93	28.18
4	22.69	23.01	23.33	23.65	23.96	24.28	24.58	24.88	25.18	25.46
3	19.06	19.45	19.85	20.22	20.60	20.96	21.33	21.67	22.03	22.35
2	14.50	15.02	15.53	16.00	16.48	16.93	17.38	17.81	18.25	18.65
1	8.00	8.81	9.58	10.29	10.98	11.62	12.25	12.84	13.40	13.97

SPECTRAL ENERGY DISTRIBUTIONS

λ (nm)	S_A	3,250° K	S_B	S_C	D_5500	D_6500
300	0.93				0.02	0.03
310	1.36				2.1	3.3
320	1.93		0.02	0.01	11.2	20.2
330	2.66		0.50	0.40	20.6	37.1
340	3.59		2.40	2.70	23.9	39.9
350	4.74		5.60	7.00	27.8	44.9
360	6.15		9.60	12.90	30.6	46.6
370	7.82		15.20	21.40	34.3	52.1
380	9.79	16.59	22.40	33.00	32.6	50.0
390	12.09	19.63	31.30	47.40	38.1	54.6
400	14.71	22.95	41.30	63.30	60.9	82.8
410	17.68	26.55	52.10	80.60	68.6	91.5
420	21.00	30.42	63.20	98.10	71.6	93.4
430	24.67	34.53	73.10	112.40	67.9	86.7
440	28.70	38.87	80.80	121.50	85.6	104.9
450	33.09	43.42	85.40	124.00	98.0	117.0
460	37.82	48.15	88.30	123.10	100.5	117.8
470	42.87	53.04	92.00	123.80	99.9	114.9
480	48.25	58.06	95.20	123.90	102.7	115.9
490	53.91	63.19	96.50	120.70	98.1	108.8
500	59.86	68.40	94.20	112.10	100.7	109.4
510	66.06	73.67	90.70	102.30	100.7	107.8
520	72.50	78.97	89.50	96.90	100.0	104.8
530	79.13	84.27	92.20	98.00	104.2	107.7
540	85.95	89.56	96.90	102.10	102.1	104.4
550	92.91	94.81	101.00	105.20	103.0	104.0
560	100.00	100.00	102.80	105.30	100.0	100.0
570	107.18	105.12	102.60	102.30	97.2	96.3
580	114.44	110.14	101.00	97.80	97.7	95.8
590	121.73	115.05	99.20	93.20	91.4	88.7
600	129.04	119.83	98.00	89.70	94.4	90.0
610	136.34	124.48	98.50	88.40	95.1	89.6
620	143.62	128.99	99.70	88.10	94.2	87.7
630	150.83	133.33	101.00	88.00	90.4	83.3
640	157.98	137.51	102.20	87.80	92.3	83.7
650	165.03	141.52	103.90	88.20	88.9	80.0
660	171.96	145.35	105.00	87.90	90.3	80.2
670	178.77	149.00	104.90	86.30	93.9	82.3
680	185.43	152.46	103.90	84.00	90.0	78.3
690	191.93	155.74	101.60	80.20	79.7	69.7
700	198.26	158.83	99.10	76.30	82.8	71.6
710	204.41	161.73	96.20	72.40	84.8	74.3
720	210.36	164.44	92.90	68.30	70.2	61.6
730	216.12	166.96	89.40	64.40	79.3	69.9
740	221.66	169.30	86.90	61.50	85.0	75.1
750	227.00	171.46	85.20	59.20	71.9	63.6
760	232.11	173.43	84.70	58.10	52.8	46.4
770	237.01	175.23	85.40	58.20	75.9	66.8
780	241.67				71.8	63.4
790	246.11				72.9	64.3
800	250.32				67.3	59.5
810	254.30				58.7	52.0
820	258.06				65.0	57.4
830	261.59				68.3	60.3

INDEX

491